ARTISTIC METALWORK

ARTISTIC METALWORK

A. F. BICK

Instructor, Public Schools, Milwaukee, Wisconsin, and Shorewood
Opportunity School, Shorewood, Wisconsin; Special Instructor,
Milwaukee Downer College; Summer School Instructor, Colorado
State College, Fort Collins

THE BRUCE PUBLISHING COMPANY
MILWAUKEE

INTRODUCTION

This book is the outgrowth of years of experience as an instructor of boys and adults in day and evening classes. It was designed for classes and home shops with very limited equipment, and for those who are seeking for projects that are artistic and yet low in cost.

To make this work as rich as possible, every effort was made to embody in each project both the historical and the artistic. For this reason the projects offered were adapted from historical sources: French Empire, Renaissance, and modern thin metalwork; medieval and Early American ironwork; and classic and Renaissance cast work. An iron modeling process was introduced to replace most forging. Altogether, the projects were selected for their simplicity, their color and interest, and their adaptability to the conditions already mentioned.

The projects are arranged in the following groups:

1. Thin metals, tin, pewter, copper, brass.
2. Wrought and modeled iron.
3. Cast metals.
4. One tool-steel project.

Those marked with the letter *A* in the index of projects are suitable for beginners; those with *B* are for intermediate work and generally require some previous related experience; those marked with *C* are for experienced students.

The time given is estimated on the basis of continuous work with tools and fixtures available. Adjustments can be made to fit conditions.

The following is a typical selection of work:

Plate 1. Colonial Tin Candlestick
4 hours
Plate 14. Modern Copper Bowl
9 hours
Plate 27. Medieval Iron Hook
4 hours
Plate 46. Eighteenth-Century Iron Lamp
14 hours
Plate 59. Classic Bronze Paperweight
4 hours
Plate 60. Wood-Carving Chisel
3 hours

While this book offers projects which may be copied just as they are, nevertheless, the ideal, that the student or home-crafter should be given opportunity to embody his own design in the projects which he makes, must not be lost sight of. For this purpose, the subject may best be presented to classes on the basis of group achievement and learning; that is, the group selects the type, a candlestick for example, and each individual designs his own piece from source materials made available. This permits the introduction of a period of exploration and design to precede the actual work.

The material embodied in this book embraces an outline of construction, in which, for the sake of compactness, resort is taken to a system of cross references to items in the process section, where the methods are dealt with at length. The illustrations include the project and also one or two supplementary items, similar in construction, and, where space permits, these are included in the scale drawings.

Lastly, an acknowledgment of deep appreciation to all whose encouragement, even though indirectly, served to build up the structure upon which this book is written. Thanks are due particularly to the Industrial-Arts Departments of the Milwaukee schools and to the Shorewood Opportunity School, whose leaders, art-metal staff, and students, past and present, encouraged the author to continue in his search for the material embraced by this book.

CONTENTS

SECTION I
EQUIPMENT AND MATERIALS

Fig. 1. A bright room is essential for artistic metalwork.

CHAPTER I

EQUIPMENT AND MATERIALS

EQUIPMENT

A bright room is essential. The ideal room is on the ground level with windows the full length of the wall, on as many sides as possible. Good artificial lighting should be arranged for on dark days and awnings to keep out the glare of the sun on bright days. One section of the room should be set aside for exhibits and photographs. Tools should be displayed on neatly arranged and varnished tool boards rather than hidden away. Another part of the room should be set aside for chairs and drawing tables, where lectures may be held and layouts made.

TOOLS

To purchase quality in tools, rather than quantity, is old but good advice. It is no doubt true that a fine tool is a strong in-centive to man's best efforts. If fine tools are hung within sight on equally fine tool boards, their value is considerably enhanced.

The following list is given in two sections: *A,* the least necessary to produce the work here outlined, and *B,* additional tools that more efficiently accomplish the same end. However, with the first three items in list *A* — hammers, hand shears, and files — one may construct a surprising number of the projects. It is assumed, of course, that the devices described in Chapter III as well as a wood vise and some heat source, such as an alcohol or gas flame, be utilized with list *A.* The figure preceding each tool is an estimate of the number of tools required for classes of 24 students. Good work may be done with fewer tools if groups are properly alternated. This policy, however, is not recommended.

3

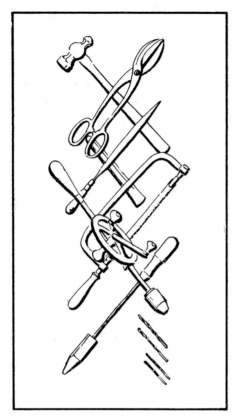

Fig. 2. Good tools facilitate good work.

A. Minimum Requirements

No. of
Tools

8   Ball-peen hammers — 10- or 12-oz. This all-purpose hammer must have an oval face with rounded edges. The ball is best ground and finished to bun shape as in Figure 61. Hammers listed further on are preferred for some processes

8   Hand shears. These should have a 2½- to 3-in. cutting edge, unless the hand is too small. A small shears is limited in use

10   Files, 8-in., half-round bastard cut
8   Files, 6-in., half-round second cut
4   Files, 6-in., mill file bastard cut
2   Files, 6-in., round file bastard cut
    Files are discussed further and listed under "Filing"

3   Cold chisels, ¾-in. cutting edge
1   Cold chisel, ½-in. cutting edge
2   Cold chisels, ¼-in. cutting edge
4   Hack saws. A nonadjusting frame for 8-in. saws is suggested for simplicity

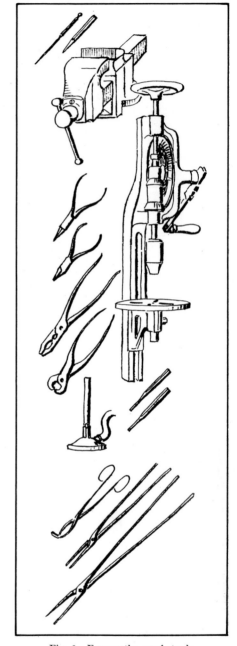

Fig. 3. Frequently used tools.

No. of
Tools

24 8-in. blades of 18 point for iron
12 8-in. blades of 24 point for thin sections
12 8-in. blades of 32 point for tubing
1 Hand drill, 3/8-in. capacity is recommended. A small tool is difficult to handle
   Twist drills: 3/32nds to 17/64ths by 64ths (2 sets); 3/16ths to 3/8ths
   by 32nds (1 set)
4 Soldering bits of at least 1 lb. each. These are cold forged (see Soldering 6)

B. Additional Tools

The following tools may be added to the foregoing in about the order given:

8 Scribers
4 Center punches
8 Bench vises of at least 3¼-in. jaw, having a stationary base
1 Bench drill, ½-in. capacity
2 Pliers, 6-in. round nose for hot and cold bending of thin metal
2 Pliers, 5-in. flat nose
1 Pliers, 8-in. pipe
1 Pliers, 7- or 8-in. end-cutting nippers
2 Pin punches, 3/16 and ¼ in.
2 Bunsen burners or some other heat source
1 Tongs, 12-in. crucible
1 Tongs, 8½-in. soldering
1 Tongs, 16-in. annealing
1 Heating furnace of at least Johnson 3-jet standard
1 Anvil, 100-lb. tool-steel face
1 Adjustable wrench
2 Raising hammers
2 Planishing hammers (light claw hammers will answer the same purpose if the
   faces are perfect)
1 Rawhide mallet — 6-oz.
1 Blacksmith cross-peen hammer, 24-oz., rounded off at the ends
1 Riveting hammer, also rounded off at the ends
2 Dividers, 6-in. spring
1 Caliper, 4-in. spring outside
1 Stake, broad oval anvil head
1 Stake, round anvil head
1 Stake, flat anvil head
   Others will be suggested as the work proceeds
1 Set taps and dies with wrenches: 6 — 32, 8 — 32, 10 — 24 machine screw
1 Set taps and dies with wrenches: ¼ — 20, 5/16 — 18, U. S. Standard
1 Set taps and dies with wrenches: ⅛-in. pipe (straight tap)
1 Pipe cutter
6 C clamps, 2- and 4-in.
2 Jeweler's saw frames with No. 2/0 and No. 1 blades
1 Drill-press vise
1 V block and clamp
1 Drill gauge
1 Wire gauge
1 Drill-and-tap sizes reference table
6 Steel scales, 12-in.
1 Combination square with center head
1 Pipe vise
1 Surface gauge
1 Bench grinder

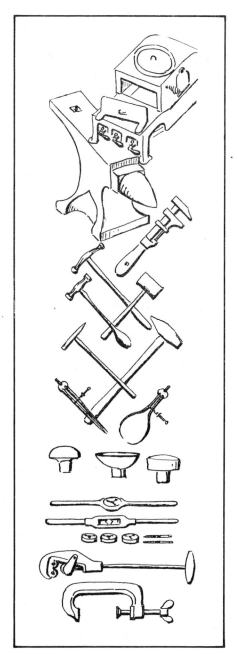

Fig. 4. These tools are desirable.

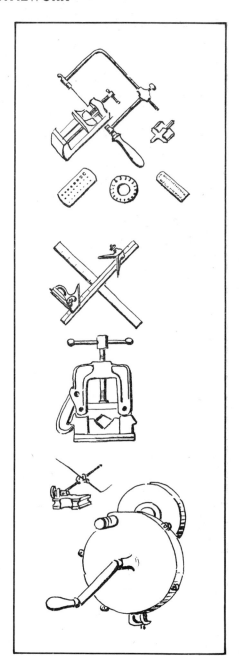

Fig. 5.

Further additions are left to experience. It must be remembered that the given list covers only minimum requirements. To thoroughly equip a shop is a matter necessitating at the outset a knowledge of metal-work preference. Some shops are adequately equipped with the foregoing list except for a larger assortment of files, especially of the needle variety, and stakes. Other shops supply each student with a vise, several

files, round-nose and flat-nose pliers, a   in addition to the general tools that have
hammer, shears, saw, and Bunsen burner,   been listed.

MATERIALS AND SUPPLIES

A. Materials

Tin cans, used, 2-in., 3⅝-in., and 4-in. diameters
Tin can, used 1-lb. coffee can
Tin plate, I.C., bright coke sheets, 20 x 28 in. (Imperial No. 3 grade)
Type metal or white metal — order by weight
Britannia metal, 18-gauge disks, up to 7 in. in diameter
Britannia metal, 16-gauge disks, up to 12 in. in diameter, and 14-gauge up to
  18 in. in diameter
Britannia metal, 18- and 16-gauge sheets up to 24 x 24 in.
Bronze, commercial, 24-gauge sheets 10, 14, and 18 in. wide, any length
Bronze castings (cast from patterns)
Copper, cold-rolled, annealed, 12-oz. (26 B. & S. gauge) sheet 30 x 96 in.
Copper, cold-rolled, annealed, 24-oz. (20 B. & S. gauge) sheet 30 x 96 in.
Copper, cold-rolled, annealed, 32-oz. (18 B. & S. gauge) sheet 30 x 96 in.
Copper sheet of any gauge may also be purchased in rolls 12 in. wide — order by
  length or weight
Copper tubing, half hard, ½-in. O.D. — order by length or weight
Copper tubing, half hard, ¼-in. O.D. — order by length or weight
Copper rod, hard drawn round, 3/16-in. diameter, length or weight
Copper wire, half hard, 3/32-in. diameter, length or weight
Copper wire, half hard, ⅛-in. diameter, length or weight
Brass sheets, soft spinning brass, 28 gauge, 12 in. wide, any length
Brass sheets, soft spinning, 20 gauge, 12 in. wide, any length
Brass sheets, soft spinning, 22 gauge, 12 in. wide, any length
Brass sheets, soft spinning, 18 gauge, 12 in. wide, any length
Brass tubing, half-hard seamless, 1¼-in. O.D., 20 gauge, any length
Brass bars, half hard, 1/16 x ½ in. — order by length or weight
Brass rods, half hard, ⅛-in. round — order by length or weight
Brass rods, half hard, 3/16-in. round — order by length or weight
Brass rods, half hard, ¼-in. round — order by length or weight
Brass rods, half hard, ⅜-in. round — order by length or weight
Brass wire, half hard, 16 gauge — order by length or weight
Brass wire, half hard, 14 gauge — order by length or weight
Black iron nut, ⅝ in., ¾ in.
Black iron washers, ½ in., ⅜ in.
Sheet iron, box annealed, one pass CR, 18-gauge B. & S., sheet 30 x 96 in., cut
  into 2½-, 3-, 3½-, 4-, and 5-in. strips for lamp bases, drip cups, etc.
Mild steel hoops, 14 gauge x ½ in., 12-ft. lengths
Mild steel hoops, 14 gauge x ¾ in., 12-ft. lengths
Mild steel hoops, 14 gauge x 1 in., 12-ft. lengths
Mild steel hoops, 14 gauge x 1¼ in., 12-ft. lengths
Mild steel hoops, 14 gauge x 1½ in., 12-ft. lengths
Mild steel hoops, 14 gauge x 1¾ in., 12-ft. lengths
Mild steel hoops, 14 gauge x 2 in., 12-ft. lengths
Mild steel hoops, 14 gauge x 2½ in., 12-ft. lengths
Mild steel bands, 12 gauge x ½ in., 12-ft. lengths
Mild steel bands, 12 gauge x ¾ in., 12-ft. lengths
Mild steel bands, 12 gauge x 1 in., 12-ft. lengths
Mild steel bands, 12 gauge x 1½ in., 12-ft. lengths
Mild steel bands, 12 gauge x 2½ in., 12-ft. lengths
Mild steel bands, 3/16 x ½ in., 12-ft. lengths

Mild steel bands, 3/16 x ¾ in., 12-ft. lengths
Mild steel bands, 3/16 x 2 in., 12-ft. lengths
Mild steel bars, ¼ x ½ in., 12-ft. lengths
Mild steel bars, square ¼ in., 12-ft. lengths
Mild steel bars, square ⅜ in., 12-ft. lengths
Mild steel bars, square ½ in., 12-ft. lengths
Mild steel bars, round 3/16 in., 12-ft. lengths
Mild steel bars, round ¼ in., 12-ft. lengths
Mild steel bars, round 5/16 in., 12-ft. lengths
Black iron pipe, ⅛ in., 20-ft. lengths
Black iron pipe, ¼ in., 20-ft. lengths
Black iron pipe, ⅜ in., 20-ft. lengths
Black iron pipe, ½, ¾, and 1 in., short lengths
Black iron wire, 16, 14, and 12 gauge, small amount
Tool steel, ⅛ x ½-in. carbon, "Sanderson Extra" Crucible Steel Co., or its
    equivalent

B. Supplies

Soldering

Soldering salts, 1-lb. tins, Kester, Nokorode, Snowflake, or equivalent brands
Solder, 50-50 wire, plain, order by weight
Solder, 60-40 wire, or pewter solder obtained from pewter distributors
Black iron wire, annealed, 30 gauge, 1-oz. spools

Miscellaneous Fastenings

Copper rivets, ⅛ x ¼ in., roundhead, 1 lb.
Iron rivets, ⅛ x ¼ in., roundhead — order by weight
Iron rivets, ⅛ x ⅜ in., roundhead — order by weight
Iron rivets, ⅛ by ½ in., roundhead — order by weight
Iron rivets, ⅛ by ¾ in., roundhead — order by weight
Iron rivets, 3/16 x 1¼ in., roundhead — order by weight
Iron rivets, ¼ by 1 in., roundhead — order by weight

Finishing

Steel wool, No. 4/0 1-lb. packages
Pumice powder
Rottenstone
Abrasive cloth, 240, Metalite or equivalent
Abrasive cloth, 180, Metalite or equivalent
Tripoli polishing compound, brick
Rouge polishing compound, brick
Abrasive grit, 120, for cloth abrasive wheels
Animal glue, flake, for cloth abrasive wheels
Cloth buffing wheels, 6 in., ½-in. hole, sewed
Sulphuric acid, commercial, order from bulk in any quantity needed
Nitric acid, commercial
Hydrochloric acid, commercial
Barium sulphide (crystal), pound bottles
Potassium sulphide (lump) — order small quantity as needed
Copper sulphate (lump) — order small quantity as needed
Ammonium chloride (crystal) — order small quantity as needed
Floor wax (paste), pound tins
Lacquer (clear)
Spray can, insecticide pump type
Quick-drying enamel, cans — oriental yellow, white, Nile green, turquoise blue
Gold or silver gummed paper in small rolls
Chinese silver paper, sheets

Vegetable glue, bottle, Higgins or equivalent
Tube oil colors, raw umber
Linseed oil, bulk
Turpentine, bulk
Varnish
Asphaltum (stovepipe enamel)
Pipe nipples, iron, $\frac{1}{8}$ x $\frac{3}{4}$ in., box of 100
Pipe couplings, brass, $\frac{1}{8}$ x $\frac{1}{2}$ in., dozen or box of 100
Pipe nipples, brass, $\frac{1}{8}$ x $\frac{3}{4}$ in., box of 100
Running threaded iron pipe, $\frac{1}{8}$ in., 3-ft. lengths
Lock nuts, brass or iron, $\frac{1}{8}$-in. hex., box of 100
Candle sockets, 2 in.
Candle sockets, 4 in.
Fiber candle covering, $1\frac{1}{4}$-in. O.D., 3-ft. lengths
Silk- or rubber-covered cord, gold or silver, 250- and 500-ft. rolls
Plugs
Tape
Light switch

SECTION II

METHODS AND DEVICES

The material in this section was developed on the basis of low initial and maintenance costs, and is presented in the hope that elementary and secondary schools in need of expansion in the creative arts may be encouraged to adopt art metalwork.

CHAPTER II

MARKING

A. *Rough marking* is done with soapstone, aluminum pencil, or slate pencil on iron and with colored crayon pencil on other metals.

B. *Accurate marking* is invariably done with a scriber or divider point.

C. *Laying out.* 1. In general, measuring and laying out are done with dividers, scriber, scale, and square, as in drafting,

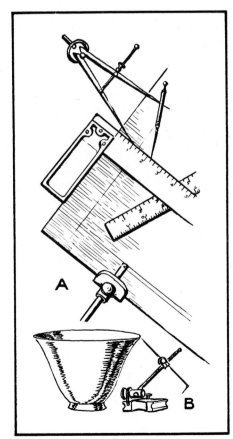

Fig. 6. Marking tools.

the scriber taking the place of a pencil. This work proceeds from a straight edge or a center line.

2. Economy and often convenience require the rough cutting of metal out of stock from measurements taken from a paper pattern, after which the foregoing procedure follows.

3. Irregular designs are drawn on metal around cut patterns or templates preferably made of metal.

4. Lines parallel to a convenient edge are scribed with a marking gauge or dividers. The latter is used on edges that are too irregular for a marking gauge (*A*, Fig. 6).

5. Lines parallel to the table, such as bowl rims, or to edges which may easily be clamped to the object, are scribed by means of a surface gauge (*B*, Fig. 6).

6. Metal to be bent hot is marked with a center punch at the bending point. This is distinguishable on the red-hot metal.

D. *Decorative design to be transferred to metal.* 1. Cut or uncut paper patterns are glued to the metal with one part of cold fish glue diluted with two parts of water. This method is recommended for all ironwork in this book.

2. A design often is transferred by means of carbon paper, the design being scratched over with a scriber.

3. The following method also may be used on small work: A thin coat of wax is melted over the surface of light-colored metals. The pencil-drawn design then is reversed and rubbed into the wax with a

smooth metal tool. These lines are finally scratched in as directed in the preceding step.

4. A design, identical on both sides, is transferred to its second side by being drawn with a soft pencil on one side of a folded center line, after which the paper is folded, rubbed, opened, and retouched where necessary. Transfer the design to the metal; then proceed as explained.

CHAPTER III

METAL SHAPING

Metal is hand shaped by cutting with a shears, a chisel, or a saw, depending upon the thickness and size of the metal, and by forming with a file, a hammer, a wrench, or an equivalent tool.

CUTTING

Thin metal up to 18-gauge copper and 20-gauge brass and iron is cut with a hand shears.

1. For economy, all rectangular forms are cut out of the corners of stock, and all circular and irregular forms are cut first as rectangular blanks large enough to enclose the pattern, and then are laid out and cut to shape.

2. Light should be reflected so as to throw the line into sharp contrast. The metal should be fed into the slowly closing shears, both on straight and curved cuts. This is preferred to snipping a succession of straight trimmings off curved edges and then filing to the line. Heavy metal, however, often is snipped.

3. Cutting with the back of the blade is most efficient (Fig. 7, *A*).

4. The point of the blade is useful when cutting up to a line or into a corner (Fig. 7, *B*).

5. A seamed and joined tin can or a bowl may be cut only in one direction, that is, from the right to the left when the bottom is turned away from the operator (Fig. 8). This is required for clearance.

6. Scallops are cut as follows: With the point of the shears, cut into each intersecting corner, then again at 45 deg. on a line tangent to the scallop line, first all right- and second, all left-hand cuts. The remaining corners are trimmed and filed (Fig. 9).

Metal of medium thickness, 18 to 12 gauge, is cut with a cold chisel by the

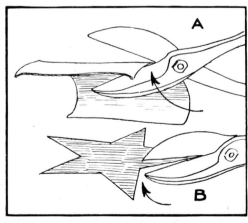

Fig. 7. Cutting with hand shears.

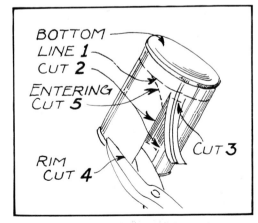

Fig. 8. Cutting up a tin can.

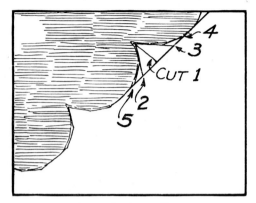

Fig. 9. Cutting scallops.

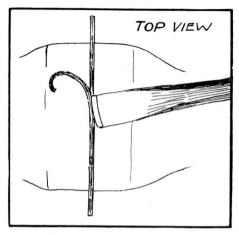

Fig. 11. Shearing narrow strips.

shearing method if space and size permit. Otherwise, it is sawed or drilled, depending upon the design.

1. Long, narrow strips of band or hoop iron, such as are used in the crown of projects in Plates 40 and 46, are sheared in the vise as explained in the following (Figs. 10 and 11).

2. These and small irregular pieces convenient for vise cutting are sheared as follows. Cutting may follow the line, or, if the latter is too deeply curved, the cut should come as close as possible to the line (Fig. 12). It may also proceed from saw cuts at each end of the shearing as described in the following paragraphs.

The chisel is held with its lower bevel flat on the front jaw of the vise (Fig. 10), and is turned about 10 deg. to the side (as seen from the top, Fig. 11). Then, beginning at the right end, heavy blows break the metal and force it over the rear vise jaw. The chisel and the vise jaw constitute the shears. By cutting low the chisel may injure the vise, or, by cutting higher than the line of the vise, the metal will be torn rather than cut. The speed of cut, which may be about $\frac{1}{4}$ in. to the blow, depends upon the weight of the blow. Heavy tools, therefore, are used; a chisel with a $\frac{3}{4}$-in. edge and a 20-oz. hammer are recommended.

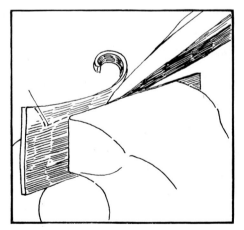

Fig. 10. Shearing narrow strips.

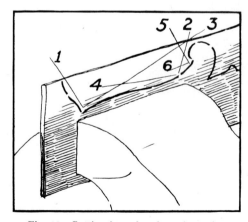

Fig. 12. Cutting irregular shape in a vise.

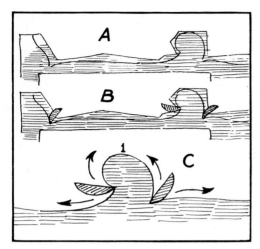

Fig. 13. Finishing cut edges.

Rough cutting away of waste material in a design such as is shown in Figure 12 then is best done by: (*a*) sawing down into the corners of the design (cuts 1 and 5), and (*b*) shearing along the pattern line with a cold chisel (Fig. 10). Curves may be sheared with a chisel if the metal is turned to the line as the chiseling proceeds.

3. Irregular edge cuts, too short between vertical cuts to shear, are roughed out of material up to ¼ in. in thickness with a hack saw (Figs. 12 and 13). They are then filed to the line.

4. The same shapes in very thin metals may be cut with a coping saw, equipped with metal cutting blade. This process is slow on metals of over 14-gauge thickness and is recommended only for small irregular corners difficult to file.

5. Metal up to 3/16 in. in thickness may be removed with a nibbler if this tool is a part of the shop equipment.

6. Pieces too large for vise cutting, whether iron, copper, or brass, are cut on cast-iron or mild-steel blocks with heavy cold chisels. For example: (*a*) The entering cut is made just outside the line (Fig. 14). (*b*) The chisel is tipped backward, its edge being drawn forward in the cut about one fourth of the width of the chisel. It is then straightened and hit, tipped back and moved forward in its cut, and so on around (Fig. 14). The first time around usually is not a through cut.

7. Open work not easily sawed in thin metal (Fig. 15) is cut on a cast-iron or mild-steel cutting block with a cold chisel. For such work in soft metals like copper, the chisel bevel is ground long, the cutting edge is rounded (Fig. 14) to facilitate cutting along curved pattern lines, and the cutting proceeds as in step 6. Corners are drilled out, or, on very thin sheet, they are punched as indicated by the arrow in Figure 14. This minimizes the danger of tearing the metal.

8. Open work in heavy material is cut out by drilling holes as shown in Figure 15.

9. To conserve material when working a

Fig. 14. Cutting with chisel.

Fig. 15. Cutting open work.

large hole into a narrow iron bar, a row of small holes is drilled. The bar is heated red, the holes are slit with a cold chisel, and then stretched to shape with a taper pin. To avoid tearing the metal, the cold chisel must be ground sharp on its side edges as shown.

10. To cut *bar metal* 3/16 in. thick and heavier, a hack saw is used. This is held with one hand on the handle and the other on the front of the frame. An 18-tooth blade is recommended. The saw must be held in a constant right-angle position to avoid arrest and breakage. Sawing in any but a straight-down direction is to be avoided. Pressure and long strokes are efficient while quick strokes are not.

11. *Pipe* is best cut with a pipe cutter without which a hack saw with a blade of 24 teeth to the inch is used. Pressure on the blade is varied according to the thickness of the pipe wall.

12. *Tubing* is cut by the use of a fine-toothed hack saw, 32 teeth to the inch. It is held in the vise between protecting wood or metal so as not to destroy its shape (*A,* Fig. 16). Tubing and pipe are marked for sawing by wrapping paper around them and cutting along the edge of the paper. To cut accurately, sawing proceeds from three or more sides, the tubing being revolved in the vise.

Vises used for holding fine work, whether for sawing or any other purpose, are lined with sheet lead or copper (*B,* Fig. 16). The latter on becoming hard by use may be annealed. Softwood and leather jaws, especially if shaped somewhat to the work, are best for quantity cutting of tubing and other oddly shaped pieces.

13. The cutting of *plate and heavy bar,* machine sawing, bench shearing, lathe cutting, oxygen cutting, and hot chisel cutting do not come within the scope of this book.

14. The cutting of *tool steel* requires good judgment. Theoretically, steel is cut by another steel of harder quality. If the hardness varies by a wide enough margin, and the steel is uniform throughout, the

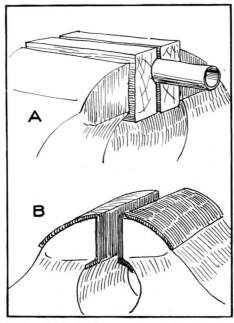

Fig. 16. *A.* Cutting a tube. *B.* Vise lined for fine work.

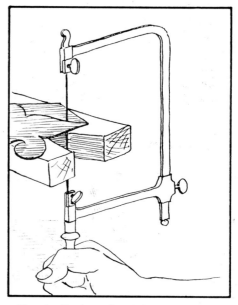

Fig. 17. Cutting a fine design on a V block.

theory is of practical use. A hack-saw blade of tungsten steel, then, should cut anything to within a number of points of its hardness.

a) Hardened alloy steel is not cut. It is cracked off by a shear blow on a notched line if a chisel or an abrasive wheel groove is possible. The practice is to anneal and cut by the ordinary processes.

b) Annealed steel bar, rod, or wire is notched either with a saw or cold chisel and broken. It also may be sheared with a chisel and vise, or sawed, depending upon its size.

c) Spring-steel wire is cut with a chisel and not with pliers or shears. In fact, no wire should be sheared and only mild steel and soft metal wires are plier cut.

15. Cutting into *pewter and silver sheet* is customarily done with a jeweler's saw. The advantage of this method lies in its economy; the waste is small and the metal remains flat and clean which it would not were it sheared or chiseled.

Small design work in copper and brass, especially if open work, may also be pierced, first by drill and then by saw to the line. Blades range from No. 8/0, the finest, to No. 14. Numbers 2/0 to 1 are recommended.

The process is as follows: The metal is held over a wood bench pin having a V cut on its front edge. The saw frame is provided with a No. 2/0 blade which is first inserted into a hole drilled within the design and tightened into the frame with a slight tension (Fig. 17).

The operator should sit at such a height that his forearm is on a horizontal plane holding the saw easily in a uniformly vertical position. As it moves up and down, the metal is guided into it.

FORMING

Forming in general is done with a file, a hammer, or a wrench. In the use of the latter two, more depends upon the form over which the metal is drawn than upon the tool itself. Therefore, much of the text under Bending, Folding, and so on, concerns itself with forms. Only in forging is the hammer of importance over a supplementary device.

ANNEALING

Annealing is a process of metal softening by heat treatment. Theoretically, its crystalline pattern is rearranged so that further working may proceed outside the range of easy fracture. As a rule, metal is fit for working only when it is uniformly soft, and it should be bought in this state (see Chapter I). However, if it is to be worked beyond its original elastic range, it is done in stages between frequent annealings. On the other hand, metal often is locally hardened by careless bending, hammering, or stretching, and may be returned to a workable condition only by proper annealing.

1. Iron or mild steel, as used in the projects here given, need not be annealed. It may be bent cold at right angles without danger of fracture. Further bending, however, and return bending or correcting may be safely done only by annealing both before and after the process. For this purpose, the iron is heated cherry red (1650 deg. F.) and cooled slowly, either under ash, pumice, or lime, or in warm air, the rule being, "the slower the cooling the softer the iron."

2. The same rule applies to carbon tool steel. Other steels are best heat treated according to the manufacturer's formula.

3. Copper, bronze, and particularly brass sheet and wire become hardened readily by working. The need for annealing is all but eliminated in the selection of the projects. Incorrect bending and working over parts longer than intended, however, will necessitate such annealing.

The process is as follows: The metal is heated to a bright red and quenched in a weak bath of sulphuric acid followed by rinsing and scouring (see Finishing, Metal Cleaning). In the absence of an acid bath, water or air cooling will do.

Thin sections of brass melt easily in a blue flame. They are moved through as quickly as the red heat is attained. Sheet is more readily annealed within an enclosed space. In the absence of proper equipment an efficient enclosure may be constructed around a burner with firebrick and sheet iron.

A gas torch is ideal for annealing, the metal being placed on a pan of coke or lump pumice during the process.

4. Brass and copper wire should be coiled for annealing.

5. Sheet tin and galvanized iron may not be annealed without destruction of the coating.

6. Pewter is so ductile that annealing is not necessary except in very high raising from the flat sheet. In the course of such raising, constant forcing hardens the metal and annealing becomes necessary after each stage of the process. This is done by covering its surface with a thin film of machine oil and rotating it over a flame until the oil smokes freely. It is then ready for cooling in water and further hammering.

7. Thin metals are held over the flame with light tongs. These absorb the least amount of heat.

HARDENING

Metals are hardened by pressure, alloying, and heat treating.

1. Pressure hardening of metals is accomplished by hammering, bending, rolling, and drawing. For example, copper, brass, bronze, or silver bowls are hard finished by planishing. Forged ironwork is hard finished by hammering. Such hardening, however, prior to shaping into scrolls and sim-

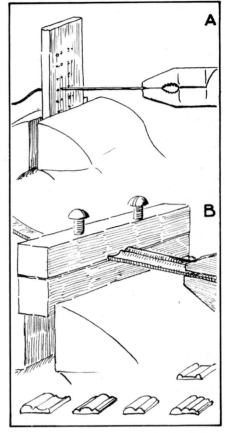

Fig. 18. *A*. Cold drawing wire. *B*. Cold drawing small moldings.

ilar bends, tends to make curves angular and other work difficult of manipulation. Purposeless peening of ironwork should be avoided. All metals are hardened at bending points through pressure toward the inside simultaneously with drawing on the outside of the bend. Sheet metal is hardened by cold rolling. Wire is hardened by cold drawing (Fig. 18, *A*).

2. Metals are commonly alloy hardened and heat treated as well. Formulas and laboratory data for these are available for every conceivable metal need. While this interesting and timely subject cannot be touched upon here, it is necessary to consider at least two phases of heat treating for those who need to make special tools

or fixtures with hardened points, edges, or wearing surfaces.

3. Hardening by heat treatment. (*a*) Mild steel may be used for wearing surfaces and tools (chasing tools, groovers, hammers, etc.), if hardened after forging and finishing by a process of casehardening. This consists of alloying carbon with the outer layer of iron by absorption at red heat. The following method is most simple.

The equipment necessary is a heat source and a casehardening compound. The finished metal part is heated cherry red and plunged into the compound which in turn melts and adheres to the metal. With this coating, the metal is again heated to cherry red and plunged into water. A thicker casing may be had by a repetition of this process.

Casehardening practice varies widely in industry where the carbon and other content of steels, the particular carbonizing material, and the temperatures and methods are carefully selected to fit its many applications. For general purpose steels, containing between .15 and .25 per cent carbon, the method given is adequate.

b) Mild steel also may be stiffened by heating cherry red and quenching in water. Drilling and bending, however, is done before such hardening. Sudden cooling of iron

after forging necessitates an annealing before further cold working.

c) Wrought iron is stiffened to some extent by heating and quenching.

d) Tool steel (carbon) is hardened by heating cherry red (1652 deg.) and quenching in oil or water. This extreme hardness, however, being impractical for the majority of tools, the steel is tempered or relieved of some of its hardness by drawing out in low heat. This may be done in an open flame for general work. The metal temperature is determined by color, or more correctly, by an oxide film over the heated metal which registers as color, depending upon film thickness, as for example:

Color	Deg. F.	Color	Deg. F.
Pale yellow	430	Brown yellow	500
Light yellow	440	Red brown	510
Pale straw	450	Brown purple	520
Straw	460	Light purple	530
Deep straw	470	Purple	540
Deep yellow	480	Dark purple	550

Useful hardness disappears at higher temperatures.

The tool to be tempered is brightened with emery cloth, held in the flame at a point away from its cutting edge until color forms at the hottest area and runs into the desired shade at the cutting edge (Fig. 19). It is then quenched in water or oil. For example, chasing tools are quenched at 440 deg., drills at 450 deg., dies at 500 deg., and cold chisels at 530 deg., that is, if their carbon content is correct.

Water quenching is adequate for most shopwork and gives a harder surface than the more gentle oil bath. The latter is used, however, for thin or irregular pieces which are likely to crack with sudden cooling.

The chief hardening agent in steel is carbon, which changes from pearlite, its normal form, to martensite, its hard form, during the process of sudden cooling from just above the critical temperature (1652 deg. or cherry red). In slow cooling, as in

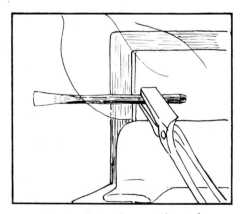

Fig. 19. Tempering a cutting tool.

annealing, it changes back to pearlite. However, the steel must be brought fully up to the critical point or a trifle above (cherry red or 1652 deg.) before it may benefit from this change, and it must be quenched before dropping to the critical point.

Tempering, on the other hand, is a compromise between great tensile strength and practical shock resistance. The martensitic steel, on being reheated, begins to change to troostite, the degree of mixture of the two giving us our range of practical tempers. For further treatment of this subject, metallurgical works should be consulted. More specific heat-treating schedules may be obtained from steel-supply companies.

STRAIGHTENING

Metals must be uniformly straight, as well as soft, prior to and during the forming process. Sheet-metal dents and folds are hard to remove. With this in mind, it is handled and worked with great care over forms and surfaces with tools especially adapted for it.

1. Sheet metal. (*a*) Soft or annealed sheet, slightly bent, is straightened over a polished metal surface with a leather-covered wood mallet, or, if the sheet is half hard or stiff because of its thickness, with a rawhide mallet. Pewter comes under the former rule (Fig. 20). In no case is a metal hammer or an uncovered wood mallet used to straighten metal except as noted in the following.

b) Hardened metal sheet, such as cold-rolled copper, brass, or iron, is flattened by alternate annealing and tapping as mentioned in the foregoing. For example, a folded edge, to be straightened, is annealed, bent back and flattened, and then annealed again.

c) Assembled, soldered, and coated work, such as tin which may not be annealed, is straightened with a soft mallet over polished forms, or by planishing. It must be remembered, however, that metal is stretched in the area of a dent and therefore is harder than its surrounding areas. Rather than straighten such an area, hammering will tend to stretch it more and harden it, forming a bulge. This can be avoided by equalizing the stretching across the sheet. The weight and place of hammer work is indicated by the size and place of circles (Fig. 21).

2. Bar iron. (*a*) To be straightened from a right angle, bar iron is placed angle down over the horn of the anvil and is hammered while red hot. It also may be annealed, bent cold, and reannealed.

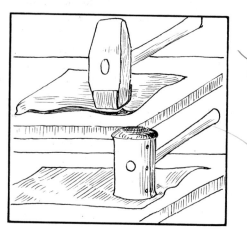

Fig. 20. Straightening sheet metal.

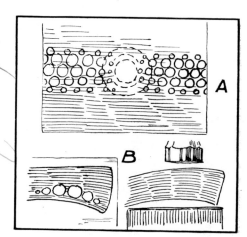

Fig. 21. Straightening a dent.

b) Bar iron out of alignment, whether in the long or in the curled state, is straightened in a vise with a wrench, the part being corrected protruding beyond the holding point, and the wrench straightening a small section at a time (Fig. 22).

c) Volutes are corrected or opened with a forked wrench (Fig. 23).

d) Flat bar, bent sidewise in forging, is straightened by hammering on the short side (*B, Fig. 21*). Otherwise it is set upon its side and hammered down, set flat and smoothed out alternately until aligned.

e) The alignment of a bar or a rod is tested during and after forging by lifting it so that the eye may sight along its edge. On the anvil, it is tapped with a well-calculated blow on the high point of each arch as it appears.

3. Wire is straightened by tightening one end in a vise, grasping the other with pliers, and stretching. If it is too hard, it is annealed prior to stretching. This process reduces its size and hardens it slightly. If the slight waves still remaining are an objection, these and all other faults may be removed by drawing through a draw plate, Figure 18, finishing one point smaller than the original size.

FILING

1. Files found most useful for the projects in the text are: For roughing on heavy gauge metals — 8-in. half-round bastard*

---

* Files marked with an asterisk are included in the minimum list.

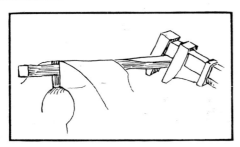

Fig. 22. Straightening bar iron.

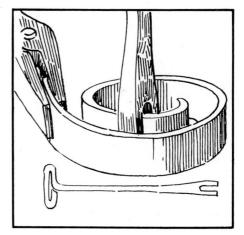

Fig. 23. Bending a volute with a forked wrench.

and 6-in. round bastard*; for finishing heavy gauge and for filing thin metals — 8-in. half-round second cut, 6-in. half-round second cut,* and 6-in. square bastard; for drawfiling — 6-in. mill bastard*; and for corners — 6-in. handsmooth.

Inaccessible corners are filed by using the blade of a metal coping saw. Small corners may be reached with 6-in. swiss-style files, round, half round, or square, which come with ends tapered to sharp points.

Jeweler's needle files may be used for the same purpose, though they are not necessary for the work laid out. They are used for fine open work and modeling in silver and bronze.

Filing surfaces on bronze castings inside an angle is done with a handsmooth file. This tool has one safe edge which is held facing one of the filed surfaces while the second is being worked upon.

2. General procedure. (*a*) Lines should be accurately followed, for it is astonishing what little change will alter the character of a curve. To produce satisfactory curves, however, the thought must be focused upon both the line and the general flow of the contour.

b) Work is placed in a copper-lined vise

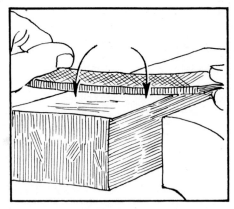

Fig. 24. Filing a wide flat surface.

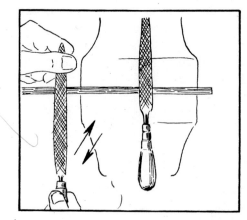

Fig. 25. Direction of filing stroke.

for all but rough iron filing (*B*, Fig. 16).

c) Work is held on a level with the elbow, and the body is braced to throw the weight on the file.

d) On wide, flat surfaces, the bowed side of the flat file is held to the work in order to produce more easily and to maintain the center surface on a flat plane with its outer edges and corners (Fig. 24).

e) The handle of the file is held in one hand and the tip in the other.

f) The file is held at right angles to the work and is worked obliquely forward (Fig. 25), with adequate pressure and a deliberate stroke rather than a quick one. It is brought back lightly except on cast iron when it is lifted back.

3. Filing irregular edges of thin metal (Fig. 13). (*a*) The sharp edge of a half-round file is worked into the first corner of the design (*B*, Fig. 13).

b) The metal is filed nearly to the line in each direction away from the corner (*C*, Fig. 13), the file moving obliquely in either direction while being held in a straight position (Fig. 25).

c) The second and remaining corners and intervening curves are filed similarly.

d) A second-cut file is used to finish the work to the line in the order given above. During these processes the file is rolled in the hand and fingers around curvatures, and

rocked in others while being held at right angles to the work (*C*, Fig. 13).

4. Thin metal edges are held with the thumb against a hardwood block fastened in a vise, and are filed close to the wood (*B*, Fig. 26). If held otherwise, they are filed in the direction of the edges or diagonally in order to reduce chatter (*A*, Fig. 26). A 6-in. second-cut file is used for this work.

5. Pewter and other soft metals are filed most satisfactorily by means of coarse files, such as 8-in. bastard or 8-in. cabinet files, held lightly. Such metal should be held in leather-lined vises. A hand vise, shown in Figure 27, is very convenient for holding

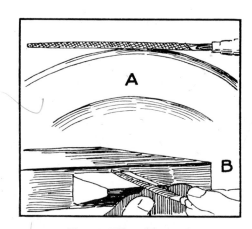

Fig. 26. Filing thin metal.

small, odd-shaped pieces. Fine files clog too easily, although they may be filled with chalk to facilitate cleaning.

6. Hard metals are annealed before filing. Even then, considerable pressure must be applied to carbon steels. The file must not be allowed to glaze.

7. Cast iron, due to the hardness of its chilled surface — if not first ground, chipped, or pickled — is filed with considerable pressure by means of used bastard files, the purpose being to cut beneath the hardened outer layer. The file is lifted on the back stroke. Finishing may be done with a good second-cut file. Files should not be used interchangeably on iron and brass or bronze.

8. Roughly filed surfaces and edges may be smoothed by drawfiling (Fig. 28). This is a process of sidewise filing with a 6-in. mill bastard file which, if continued until all marks from previous work are cut down, will produce highly finished surfaces.

9. Modeling. This method of surface decoration by filing is applied principally to 14- and 12-gauge ironwork of the type represented here by toasting forks, handles of letter openers, book ends, and back plates of plant and light brackets. The

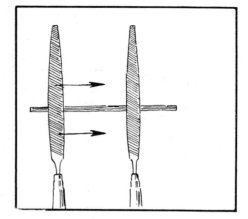

Fig. 28. Drawfiling.

essence of low relief carving as that on a coin is rounding in the flat. In other words, it is effecting depth and the third dimension on a plane surface by the use of slightly oval contours in place of round. Applied to ironwork, it involves carrying up over the top surface the forms (usually of floral origin) previously cut and filed into the outer edge. Success depends not alone upon filing but also upon the ability to interpret living form. The process is as follows:

a) The metal is clamped to the top of a piece of wood held in a vise (Fig. 29).

b) It is then chamfered with an 8-in. half-round bastard-cut file held at a constant approximate angle of 10 deg. This is

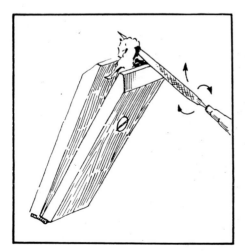

Fig. 27. Filing odd-shaped piece.

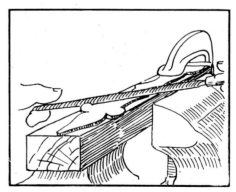

Fig. 29. Chamfering.

moved forward in a diagonal direction from sharp corners to either side much as was done on the edge (*C,* Fig. 13). The result will be sharp corner valleys and clearly defined ridges at pointed projections in the design. The chamfer should be ⅛ in. wide all around except at leaf and volute ends (*XX,* Fig. 30). These are left as they are.

c) The resulting ridge at *X* is now draw-filed (see Filing, step 8) within sections long enough to admit sidewise filing. It is otherwise filed round (scallops, volutes, and neck sections) with a 6-in. half-round sec-ond-cut file, the tools rocking in an arc within the shaded area (*B,* Fig. 30), thus blending all work into a unified whole. The top surface remaining somewhat flat may in certain instances be rounded by the method explained in Low Raising, 1, and Figure 61.

d) Finishing and coloring are explained under Finishing, Antique Iron.

10. Pipe and tubing ends are filed with sharp second-cut or smooth files. For test-ing they are set on end on a level surface and rotated against a square also set up vertically. Frequent testing requires that work be free of holding devices. Long pieces therefore are held in a V cut in wood, similar to the block shown in Fig-ure 17, and short ends and rings are set over dowels held vertically in the vise at a height just below that of the work to be filed.

11. Dull files. The life of files may be lengthened if they are kept hung in tool boards and otherwise free from contact with other hardened tools. The practice of carrying two or more files in the hand at once, or of sliding them over others in a storage drawer, is ruinous to their cutting edges. The use of fine files on soft metals and of heavy pressure on coarse files on the same metals also is expensive practice as has been mentioned. Choked and dull small files may be reclaimed by soaking in a

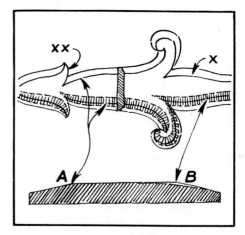

Fig. 30. Modeling.

furnace at red heat for five minutes and then plunging them vertically into water at room temperature. The loosened scale will expose new cutting edges.

BENDING

The following paragraphs are concerned with the shaping of thin metals over pre-pared forms. Shaping into forms is treated under Raising, and folding along straight edges is described under Folding.

1. Rims, bent vertically up or down, on covers, and vase bottoms of any shape — round, square, oval, half round, or those irregularly cut — are made as follows: The blank is set between two identical wood or metal forms cut to the inside dimension of the finished design. The edge extending beyond the forms then is bent over by degrees, first 30 deg. along a convenient section, then 60 deg., and last 90 deg. or tight to the form. The unit then is turned so that the operation may be continued on the next section (*A,* Figs. 31 and 32). The edge of the wood form may be beveled or molded to conform to the design, as in the base of the scuttle project (*B,* Fig. 31). The bending on straight sections is done with a mallet and a wood block. If the form is molded, a finishing tool may be curved to

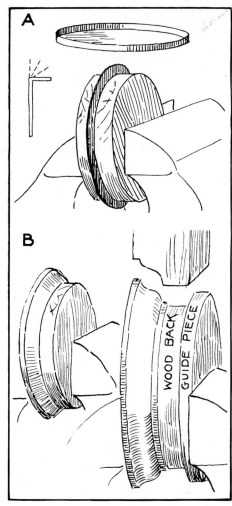

A

B

WOOD BACK

GUIDE PIECE

Fig. 31. Bending rims.

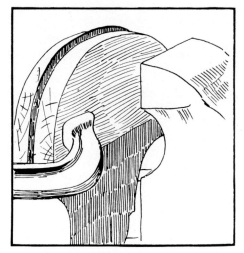

Fig. 32. Bending odd rims.

tion were they not so easily filed smooth. The tool is set over the edge of the plate, pressed in and down, while the edge is turned about 25 deg. upward. The tool then is moved 1/16 in. to the side and turned again, and so on around the plate. On the next rounds, the metal is bent to a 50-deg., to a 75-deg., and finally to a 90-deg. angle all around. If the plate is held in the hand, greater effort is required to produce a reasonably sharp bend, although adjustment is possible. A smooth result depends on a smoothened tool as shown, a constant, firm pressure inward, a gradual procedure upward, and no more than 1/16-in. progress to the side at a time. The process in step 3, below, then follows.

conform to its shape (*B,* Fig. 31). The ideal bending height is from ⅛ to 3/16 in. Wider rims and odd shapes are annealed between stages.

2. Plate rims, etc., may be bent up in the process of rolling (*a*) by similar means (Fig. 33).

b) The recommended and most simple and accurate method of plate- and bowl-edge bending, however, is that accomplished with the small bending tool shown in Figure 34. The roughened edges resulting from this method might be an objec-

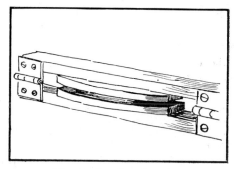

Fig. 33. Bending plate rims.

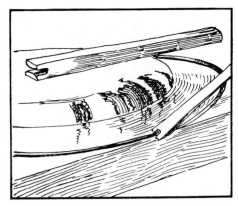

Fig. 34. Bending edge of rim with forked
tool.

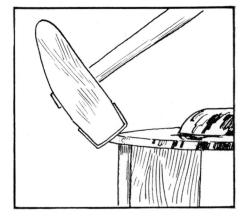

Fig. 35. Bending edge of plate over block.

c) The traditional method rarely needs to be resorted to. It consists of bending the metal rim over a sharp-edged block by mallet, the bend being held constant on a gauged line. If not so held, difficulties arise (Fig. 35). This method is not recommended for beginners.

3. Folding in. Plate- and tray-rim folds are bent over and down from the right-angle bend just described, in the following order:

a) Adjustment of the right-angle bend. (1) The rim is tapped lightly on its side with a hammer to correct irregularities. (2) It is then set on a polished surface. There its top edges are tapped squarely down to adjust differences in height and in the sharpness of the bend as well as to remove waves in the undersurface (*A*, Fig. 36). (3) The edge then is filed to uniform height.

b) It is next bent inward by a hammer over a polished surface, to within 45 deg. of the closed position (*B*, Fig. 36). Particular attention to the constant angle of the hammer will produce a uniform bend.

c) Grooving is the final step in the edge-rolling process. The project now is set on the end grain of a wood block, supported on its opposite side by a frame like the one shown in Figure 116.

Grooving tools are filed and polished to conform to the shape of the modeled edge, the outer side longer than the inner for better grip on the edge of the plate, and both the entering and leaving edges of the grooves rounded for smoothness of work (Fig. 37). One of these tools then is placed over the fold and tapped lightly while it

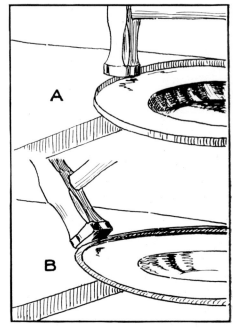

Fig. 36. *A*. Tapping bend to uniform height.
B. Folding in edge.

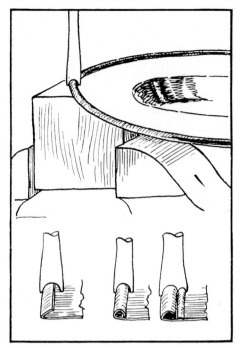

Fig. 37. Producing a high folded edge.

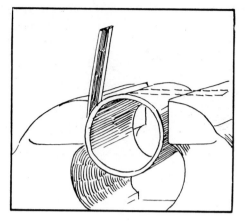

Fig. 38. Bending cylindrical form over pipe.

is drawn slowly toward the operator, his small finger holding the rim down tightly to the block in the process. The tool is held perpendicular to the rim and tipped slightly outward up to the last, the fourth or fifth round, when the edge is brought down tight. The operator's particular concern is to proceed downward uniformly by slow degrees.

An oversize tool tends to flatten the fold while one undersized cuts the edge. The former may, however, be used for the first round.

Tools may be filed to produce a high rounded edge, an oval edge, or one with a chased inner line or lines. Figure 37 shows how such edges are made.

The grooving of bowl edges requires a perfectly fitting wood form below the grooves, and since the slightest tipping of the bowl opens a space underneath for the groover to put an ugly dent into the edge, it is also important that the bowl be held

in a positive position by some support on its lower edge. Otherwise, the procedure is identical with that described for plate edges.

Filing of the outer surfaces of the molded edge from the flat of the back side around to the top proceeds as in *A*, Figure 26. (See Filing.) The inner surface is finished by means of abrasive cloth held tightly over a small square of brass bent to the curvature of the edge. Cuts on the inner edge are scraped prior to finishing. (See Finishing.)

4. Cylindrical forms and rings of thin metal (Pl. 4) are bent as directed in the following paragraphs:

a) A wood or metal form of approximate diameter, whether a pipe end, a mallet end, or vise handle, if its size is right, is set horizontally into a vise (Fig. 38).

b) A hemmed strip of metal is placed into the space between the form and the vise jaw and is bent over.

c) The form and the metal are removed from the vise and bending proceeds over the form by hand, the end being lightly tapped down by mallet.

d) A small diameter may be bent in the same manner. The end of the ring is held to the form with pliers while it is drawn partly around. The pliers then are shifted

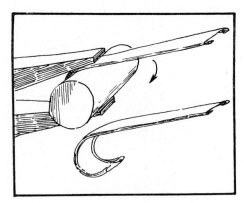

Fig. 39. Forming ring of small diameter.

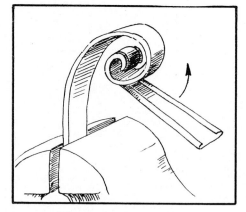

Fig. 41. Bending a volute.

over the bent portion and bending proceeds until the ring is formed (Fig. 39).

5. Cylinders (Pls. 1, 9, 18, and 19) are bent over rods or pipes by similar means. If the metal is thin, the following process is easier:

a) Set a pipe of proper diameter vertically into the vise, and hold the metal against it on its center line, and then bend it around by hand, with or without a leather or linoleum pad.

b) Tap the joining edges to the pipe with a mallet (Fig. 40). Spouts are made on tapered wood or metal bars.

6. Volutes like those used as handles on candlesticks (Pl. 1) are bent over forged iron forms (Fig. 41), or over forming blocks constructed of nails driven into

wood (Fig. 42). In each instance the volute is begun as follows:

a) A double-hemmed metal strip is grasped by flat-nosed pliers and held over a rod (Fig. 39).

b) It is drawn around by hand to the form of a hook.

c) This hook is placed into the forming scroll and is drawn around (Fig. 41).

d) Kinks, which appear around the edge unless the metal has been double hemmed, are removed over a conforming curvature with a soft mallet.

e) The end is cut off, leaving a finished handle.

7. Other similar pieces are bent over or into standardized forms which have a place

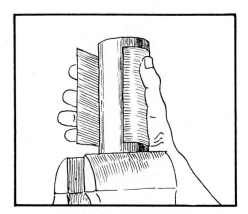

Fig. 40. Bending a cylinder.

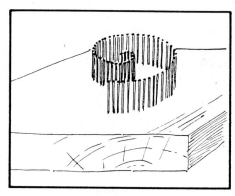

Fig. 42. A volute bending form made of nails.

in modern manufacture though their product, unless sincerely modern, is often stiff and without the feeling of hand work.

8. Lamp feet (Pls. 4 and 19) are made as follows:

a) A narrow strip of metal is held over a ¼-in. rod and bent as far as the pliers allow, as shown in Figure 39.

b) The pliers then are moved around ahead of each successive bend, each time drawing more and more metal into the scroll, until it is bent twice around.

9. Boxes, as well as square and angular lamp and vase bottoms are bent over full-sized wood forms, cut to correct inside dimension. The metal is set between two such forms and bent carefully over by block and mallet, the joining edges in the bent work having been mitered by file. End laps are not used in fine work. If solder joints are not of sufficient strength, which is seldom the case on small boxes, separate angle pieces are soldered into the inside corners in the usual manner after the box is bent and wired (Fig. 43).

A box and cover require two forms, one of which will serve as a backing piece for the other while the one part is bent, after which they are reversed for the bending of the second part. In other words, one

Fig. 43. Bending a box.

form is cut to the size of the inside of the cover while the other, a little less than a sixteenth smaller all around, is the form over which the box is bent, and that not in use is at that moment the backing piece.

FLARING

1. Candlestick and lamp-base rims of the tin-can type are flared by setting them over the rounded edge of a wood block, grooved to accommodate their bottom seam (*A,* Fig. 44). They are then worked over the curve by means of a rounded leather-covered mallet (Fig. 45), the blows being about ⅛ in. apart. Progress over the curved edge is by slow degrees in courses around the rim until the full flare is attained. The latter may vary within the limit of metal elasticity.

2. Vase, bowl, flowerpot, and lamp-shade rims are flared by similar means.

a) If flaring is to be slight, a block may be filed to the desired curvature, nails placed as gauges, and the rim gradually worked down from the inside by leather-covered mallet, two or three revolutions being sufficient to complete the operation (*A,* Fig. 70).

b) A more pronounced flaring, however, requires another technique:

(1) With a filed wood block form, nails, and mallet as before, unplanished copper, pewter, and other metal objects are flared by hammering in courses around the rim from as far back of the edge as the curve extends, to the edge, advancing from ⅛ to ¼ in. at each revolution (*B,* Fig. 44). This is repeated until the work is complete, copper being annealed after each operation. In the process the edge of the metal will crimp which is such an advantage that prior crimping or stretching over a groove in wood by a wedge-shaped mallet is often resorted to as a timesaving measure.

(2) Soldered seams in vase and flowerpot projects preclude any resort to anneal-

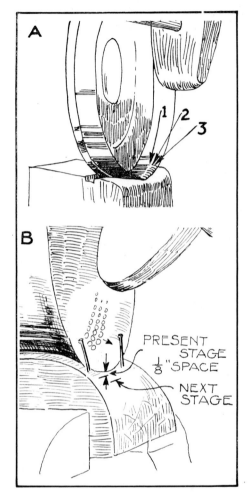

Fig. 44. *A*. Flaring on a grooved wood block.
B. Flaring on a curved wood block.

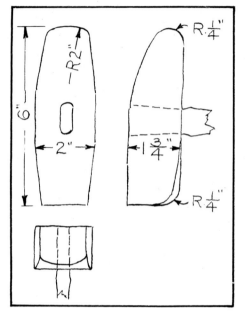

Fig. 45. Leather-covered mallet for
metal forming.

ing. These rims, therefore, are driven to the approximate elastic limit of the metal in one operation.

(3) Lap-seamed projects sometimes are cut with an allowance of metal for the flare, and are soldered in that area after the flare.

(4) Preplanished pewter and pewter not to be planished, together with other metal projects of the same type, demand a very gradual stretching not to injure the smoothness of the finish. This is done over filed wood forms, the procedure being almost the reverse of that just described. The project is placed over the wood form back of its final position to a point where the space under its edge is open ⅛ in. (*B*, Fig. 44). Nails are set there as gauges and the rim is worked gradually down with a leather-covered mallet, the blows being just heavy enough to make progress, and so close together that no perceptible ripple is produced. The work proceeds in courses from the edge *inward,* and is repeated until the metal is down. Then the nails are reset and the work is moved to a position toward the front of the wood form where the space is again opened to ⅛ in., when the operation proceeds as before. This entire process continues until the flare is worked down over the last position on the wood form. The procedure is shown in illustration *B*, Figure 44.

(5) Deep flaring necessitates reaching into the inside of the object with a rather longheaded mallet and striking from the end at an angle by a glancing blow. This type of contact is highly satisfactory and may be used to advantage throughout.

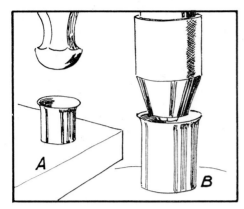

Fig. 46. Flaring a tube.

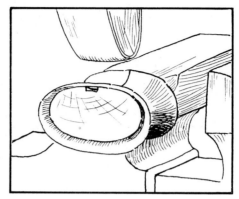

Fig. 47. Flaring an oval cylinder.

c) Flaring from the outside is in some instances permissible, but it must be borne in mind that movement of metal takes place principally at the point of contact with the mallet. The process, therefore, produces a lesser flare with a consequent shrinking of metal in the area under it which if not included in the original calculations, is undesirable. In either case, it is better not to exaggerate the flare, for a rim must not be conspicuous.

d) Flaring on welded and soldered pewter projects, if too pronounced or not carefully done, breaks the seam. As a precaution, welded joints should not be filed down until after the flaring operation. Even so, ambitious rims cannot be kept intact. Therefore, it is good practice to allow breakage and in addition cut into the rim at several equal intervals and insert triangular pieces by welding.

3. Tubing may be flared by ball-peen hammer (*A*, Fig. 46).

4. Cylinders for candle cups are flared on the bench drill by pressing the chuck into the cup, or by the process described in step 2.

5. Oval cylinders are flared as directed in step 2, or, if there is a considerable flare as shown in Plate 15, it is done in reverse. A hardwood block is filed to the oval and the flaring curvatures. The metal is slipped

over and slowly driven down into the curvature by a mallet, working around as often as necessary. If there is a seam, a groove is made to accommodate it (Fig. 47).

FLUTING

1. Fluting bowls. Fluting is done over hardwood forms filed to conform both to the curve of the bowl on its radiating line from center to rim, and to the sectional curves of two flutes in the center of which is a groove correctly filed to the depth and shape of the flute (Fig. 48). Lines then are drawn over the outer surface and these are placed, one at a time, over the grooved form, and (*a*) are driven in by a sharp, wedge-shaped, hardwood mallet, starting

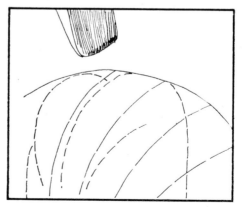

Fig. 48. Fluting a bowl.

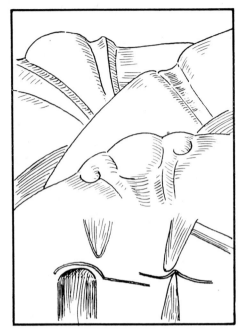

Fig. 49. Fluting forms for plate and
tray edges.

person, the first one holding the bowl over
the fluted wood form.

2. Certain popular forms of edge work
to be seen on bowls and plates, both modern and sixteenth century (Fig. 49), are
included under fluting. Such decorations
are worked over a variety of sharp-edged
and round-topped wood stakes with softwood mallets. (*a*) Knobs are made by setting the area to be worked over a wood or
metal stake of the desired shape, and striking around it with a mallet.

b) Ridges are made in the same manner
except for a change in the stakes. The stake
must be curved if curved ridges are to be
used. However, long curves may be worked
from short, straight stakes.

c) The three fluting processes, the flute,
the knob, or the ridge (reverse flute), may
be applied in combination. These and
other edge decorations cutting into rims,
create a feeling of disconnection and in-
terruption in the members meant to hold
their functional units within continuous
frames. Unless they are bound in by strong
molded edges, all such decorated rims are
discouraged.

3. Fluting of cylindrical forms will be
discussed under folding in the following
paragraphs.

lightly at the bottom of the flute and pro-
gressing slowly to the rim. This is repeated
until the metal is fully and evenly brought
in. The flute usually fades out three fifths
of the distance down from the rim.

A metal fluting hammer may be used on
hard metals if it is filed as shown in Figure
48. The important factor in successful fluting is the position of the operator. Since
the hammer must strike accurately and re-
peatedly, the body is braced against the
bench or vise, and the wrist is held against
the body so that the hammer will fall me-
chanically from a constant height. Not
enough emphasis can be placed upon the
importance of working metal down by
gradual stages and by light and quick
mallet blows in all thin metal processes.

b) Another method of greater accuracy,
recommended especially for work in soft
metals, is that of driving a wide wood tool
of wedge shape, curved slightly to the contour of the bowl into the flute by a second

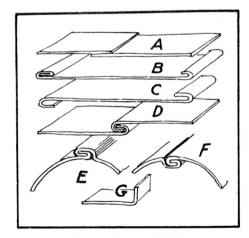

Fig. 50. Laps and folds.

Fig. 51. Folding in vise jaw.

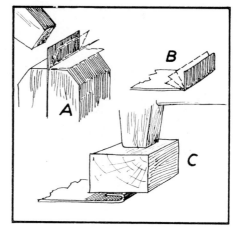

Fig. 52. Steps in folding edges.

FOLDING

The following directions are confined to the bending of straight edges, as for example: single- and double-hemmed edges (*B*, Fig. 50); right-angle folds for laps and rims (*G*, Fig. 50); folds for seams (*C* and *D*, Fig. 50); and the same, but grooved outside and inside (*E* and *F*, Fig. 50).

1. Folding by vise and mallet is satisfactory providing the vise does not mark the metal and the vise edges are sharp. Copper-lined vise jaws, as shown in *B*, Figure 16, have round edges and, therefore, are not satisfactory for this process.

2. The simple wood vise jaws shown in Figure 51 are preferable. (*a*) Two hardwood blocks with vertical grain are cut as shown.

b) A ⅛-in. strip of wood is nailed along the inside on the bottom of one piece.

c) The pieces are hinged by leather or metal.

d) Rubber bumpers 3/16 in. thick are made from pieces of inner tube and fastened inside above the strip, their purpose being to spread the jaws as the vise opens.

e) A strip on the wood vise level is nailed to the back piece, as shown at *X* in Figure 51.

These jaws, used in standard wood or metal vises, bring metalwork within the scope of shops that are handicapped in metal equipment. The jaws also may be bolted to a table and closed by means of clamp or bolt and wrench.

3. Smooth folding by mallet is an art. (*a*) The metal is folded over lightly to about 30 deg. along the entire edge, then to about 60 deg., and again to 90 deg. (*A*, Fig. 52).

b) It is removed from the vise, placed on the bench, and folded down by degrees (*B*, Fig. 52). The fold is left open if used as a seam, and closed, though not driven down flat, if used as a hem.

4. The recommended method, however, will complete a bend more quickly and smoothly: a wooden block is held against the fold and is struck by mallet (Fig. 51 and *C*, Fig. 52).

5. If a great deal of folding is to be done, the following devices are recommended: (*a*) A simple contrivance is shown in Figures 53 and 54. It is made of 1¼ by 12-in. stock, constructed as shown in Figure 51, except that the grain runs horizontally and the tops are flat.

b) Make a third piece for folding as shown in Figure 53.

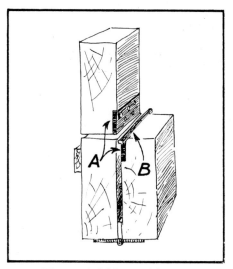

Fig. 53. A folding contrivance.

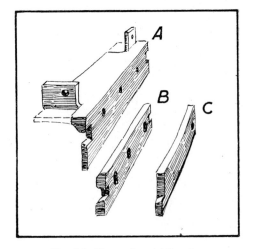

Fig. 55. Three-piece folding jig.

c) A piece of band iron is set into rabbeted cuts along the wearing edges at *A*, and a 3/16-in. rounded lug is left standing at *B*.

d) Two hooks are laid out on the ends of a piece of iron so that the center of the ⅜-in. hole strikes the center of the folding point (Fig. 54). The iron is bent around the block and screwed to its ends. It is then hooked over the lugs.

6. The three-piece metal folding jig by the slide method, in its simple form, is very efficient for the projects of this course. Figure 55 shows the angle-iron frame piece *A*, with bent-up guides for the bar clamping piece *C*, having holes and a handle slot for the bending iron *B*. The assembled end view (*D*, Fig. 56) shows the slots and leverage points for raising the bending iron. It also shows the round bending edge at *E*.

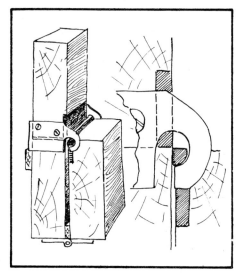

Fig. 54. A hinged folding bar.

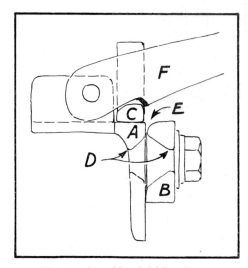

Fig. 56. Assembly of folding jig.

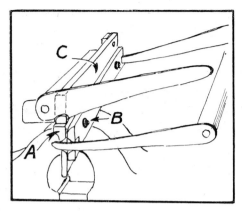

Fig. 57. Folding jig with handles in place.

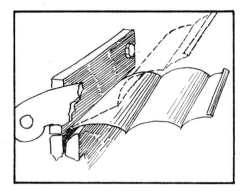

Fig. 59. Fluting with folding jig.

Figure 57 shows the assembly with the handles in place. Note that the bar *C*, Figure 55, is sprung straight over the metal by the clamping lever. The slide bar *B*, Figure 55, has three vertically elongated bolt holes, and is held by a washer, a lock nut, and a cap screw, with enough tension to allow for the thickness of the metal at the end of the bend (Fig. 57). The free space should be at least 10 in. long. Soap is used as a lubricant on the bending edge.

7. Folding the sides of small boxes or trays (Pls. 12 and 21) is done quite efficiently in a large hinge, cut to length and held in large pliers. The work is pressed against the edge of a bench (Fig. 58).

8. Heavy iron (18 gauge and over) is folded in the metalworking vise, no protection from jaw marks being practical.

9. Fluting of cylindrical objects, such as flowerpots (Pls. 6 and 8), is done over previously scribed lines in a metal-folding device as shown in Figure 59.

a) The upper seam is folded first (Fig. 59).

b) Next, the first flute fold nearest the seam is bent up 45 deg., and while still held in the jig, it is carefully curved down by the fingers. Each succeeding fold is treated in the same manner as those preceding.

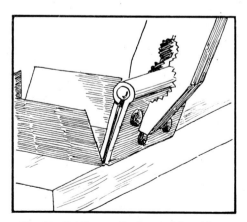

Fig. 58. Folding small pieces with a hinge.

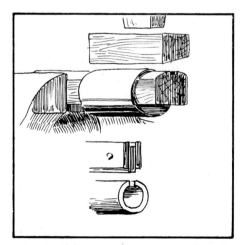

Fig. 60. Inside grooving over grooved wood.

c) When all folds are complete and the last seam is bent, the whole is drawn carefully around a large round form and locked.

GROOVING

Grooving is the process of locking a seam by pressing into a groove. Inside grooving, the purpose of which is to hide the seam, may be done over a built-up metal form, a grooved bar of wood, or a split pipe (Fig. 60). The metal is driven into a sharp-edged groove by block and mallet.

The use of grooving tools over metal seams held on flat surfaces is also practical, though the foregoing method insures a smooth seam and is recommended for beginners.

Plate-edge grooving is described under Bending, step 3, *c*.

LOW RAISING AND SHAPING

The following paragraphs are concerned with the pressing or driving of thin metals into hollow forms.

1. Iron may be raised hot or cold though the former method is not necessary for the projects offered (Pls. 27, 28, etc.). The cold raising of iron cups, bracket plates, and knobs on lamp feet, may be done by ball-peen hammer over hollow lead or wood blocks, iron shaping blocks, or rounded pipe ends (Figs. 61 and 62).

2. Pewter, copper, or aluminum plates are raised in the following manner. The use of turned hardwood plate forms is not favored because they limit the worker and are expensive. The following recommended method has been used successfully for years in large pewter classes. (*a*) A wide birch or maple block is cut as shown in Figure 63, the end grain being used for working surfaces. Two blocks may be glued to meet the same requirement. The plate depth is controlled by that of the step in the block, and the plate rim by the position of nails. If the rim is to be hemmed, the nails are set back accordingly.

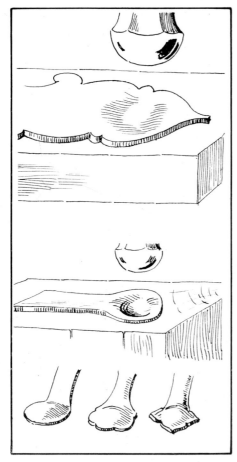

Fig. 61. Low raising of iron parts.

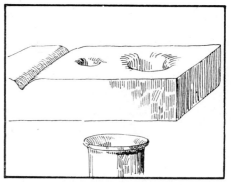

Fig. 62. Devices for low raising.

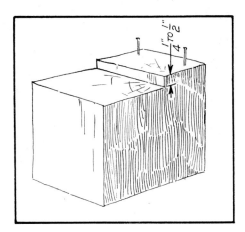

Fig. 63. Block for raising plates.

b) The curvature of the plate below the rim is provided for by that of the mallet shown in Figure 45. This tool is made of hardwood covered by leather, rounded and wedge shaped at one end and flat on the other, except for the inner edge which also is rounded.

If the plate is to be planished, its raised curvature should conform to that of the stake. The mallet therefore is rounded slightly less than the radius of the stake.

c) An adjustable holding frame is fastened to the side of the block to support the back of the pewter plate while it is being raised (Fig. 64). The block and frame are set into the vise so that they may be held

(Fig. 65) at an angle aligned with a point slightly below the elbow.

d) It is important that the disk of pewter remains in contact with both nails on the wood forming block throughout the raising operation (Fig. 66).

e) To begin work, the body and the wrist assume fixed positions, the body against the bench and the wrist against the body. The hand holds the mallet flat side down so that it may strike directly down between the nails and just beyond the bending edge as in *A*, Figures 65 and 66.

f) The work is then slowly revolved under repeated mallet blows. It has been found advantageous to hold the plate at a reasonable distance back, and feed it slowly to the right with conscious pressure on the nails during the placing of a

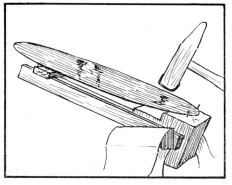

Fig. 64. Raising a pewter plate.

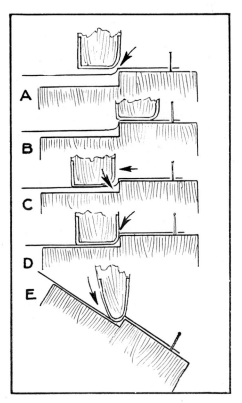

Fig. 65. Steps in raising a plate.

continuous line of mallet blows, the eye watching for uniformity of reflection in the curvature just driven down. At the completion of the first feeding, work momentarily stops until the thumb moves back to a fresh position, and so on around. The traditional method based on a rhythmic movement at intervals between three mallet blows is recommended.

g) After two or three rounds of work immediately inside the edge, raising should have progressed about 3/16 in. down all around. If this were to continue, the edge might stretch to the point of breaking.

(1) The better plan is to feed enough metal into the curvature from the inner surface so that the reduction of thickness by stretching is negligible. Therefore, a round of mallet blows are delivered inside, ⅛ in. beyond the edge (*C*, Fig. 65), to be followed by a round in the original position (*D*, Fig. 65), and so on alternately to the depth.

(2) To flatten the rim and sharpen the edge, a round may be made in the position of *B*, Figure 65.

(3) The final round or rounds are those during which faults are removed by stretching the bottom. Deep depressions, however, may not be eliminated by any process short of planishing, which see.

In this step the mallet is held back at the moment of contact, as if one tried to prevent its slipping forward in the curvature. The effect of such drawing in is to reduce the curvature and stretch the bottom surface.

Thus the raising process may be reduced to machinelike precision with the mind concentrated upon smoothness of work, the essence of which is slow progress to the side as well as down.

3. The raising of trays. Not until the beginner has made two or three plates is he ready for tray work.

a) Oval trays with rims of uniform

Fig. 66. Final steps in raising a plate.

width are made in the same manner as plates in the foregoing procedure.

b) A cut rimmed tray with an oval center may be made likewise, the rim being cut after the center has been raised.

c) A tray with an irregular center, as for example an elongated clover pattern, is beaten down into a frame of the proper depth cut to the design from hardwood on a band or jig saw, and nailed to a board. The work of beating down proceeds as explained for the plate (*A*, Fig. 67).

d) Trays with unusual rims that curve from sharp-cornered flat bottoms like pie tins, are raised by being clamped between two identical wood forms, or, if too large, sectional forms over which the metal is worked by round mallet. The rim is then trued, top down, over a flat surface (*B*, Fig. 67).

4. Low raising of bowls. Candle drip cups, dished vase bottoms, etc., are in this group.

a) Diameters of 7 in. and under are raised as follows: The metal disk is placed over a shallow depression on the end grain of a hardwood block (Fig. 68). With a ball-peen or raising hammer the center of the metal is brought down just deep enough to be within a safe stretching range. From that point the hammer blows are directed in close formation, three at a time, in concentric circles up to within ¼ in. of the outer edge, the traditional practice here followed, being to feed the bowl at measured intervals from left to right by a slight movement of the thumb. This is done by the help of the fingers which at once maintain the proper angle of contact and sense the position of the area of operation through pressure on the block below, the latter be-

ing hidden from the eye for most of the time. In the interval between thumb movements, three blows are directed on the slowly moving bowl, the last remaining until the thumb slides back for a new hold, and so on. Such rhythmic practice is known to have been familiarly audible in the narrow streets of the middle ages, coppersmiths, silversmiths, pewterers, and armorers having used it.

Depth is obtained by repeating the process as many times as is necessary.

Copper, bronze, and brass bowls stiffen to the point of fracture when hammered more than two rounds. Such work is annealed and cleaned when hard. (See Annealing.)

Pewter bowls may be brought up almost to the height of a half sphere without annealing. They may be worked to advantage with leather-covered mallets having faces of low crown (Fig. 69). These do relatively smooth work with little strain to the metal. For the same reason, ball-peen and raising

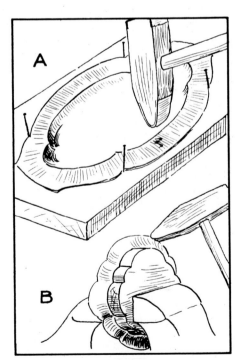

Fig. 67. Raising trays.

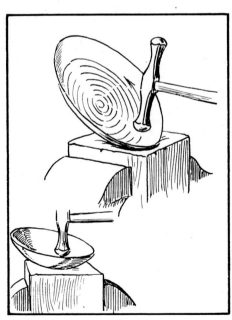

Fig. 68. Raising low bowls.

hammers used in this process should be ground and polished to bun shape.

b) Bowls of larger diameter and those of more than ordinary depth in any diameter require a technique that conserves bottom metal. This is accomplished by working or moving the metal toward the center or into any area which is to be deep. Therefore, work may begin near the outer edge and end near the center when a bowl is uniform in curvature, or it may begin one third down and progress in both directions from that course if the bowl is to be straight from bottom to rim (Fig. 69), or the order may be reversed for bowls of great depth on their sides.

Depth is obtained by repetition of the first stage. Smoothness is not an object in the raising process. Later steps correct irregularities.

Large bowls are raised with greater facility on hard-packed sandbags (Fig. 69). For the same reason corrections may be made in the lap or in the palm of the hand.

c) For beginners, it is recommended that all bowls be held to the simple contours of the perfect arc so that planishing may be done on a single stake of similar arc. Further shaping is explained in the following paragraphs.

Planishing is then so simple that at no

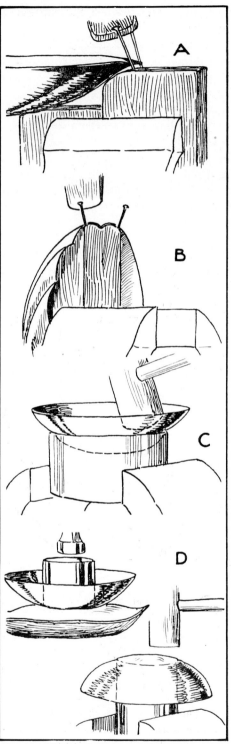

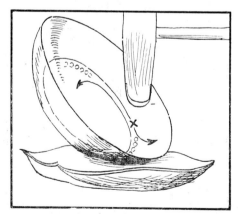

Fig. 69. Raising a pewter bowl.

Fig. 70. Flaring, fluting, and stepping a bowl.

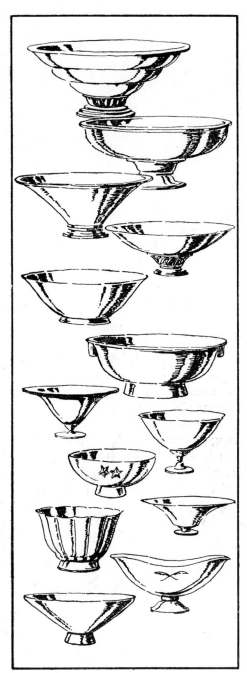

Fig. 71. Typical shapes for bowls.

time should one be tempted to turn out the crude work that often hides under the title of "primitive," "rustic," or "antique."

Fig. 72. Forming a step in a large bowl.

If the truth were known, one would find that primitives rarely do crude work, to say nothing of the high perfection of middle-age work, and, after all, we are not primitives.

d) Correcting. Uniformity of contour is obtained by confining the last hammer work to flat areas. Testing is by eye. On large bowls cardboard templates are useful. It has been found most advantageous, however, to cut a wood template of fair thickness into which the bowl is trued by hammer. Further smoothing is seldom necessary, and when it is, the flat surface of a wood block serves well (Fig. 68).

e) Further shaping of bowls, etc.

(1) Edge flaring (*A*, Fig. 70), explained under Flaring, 2.

(2) Edge bending is accomplished by the same means and consists merely of bending the edge straight out over a sharp edge or driving it by slow degrees into a molded edge over variously formed wood blocks.

(3) Body fluting (*B*, Fig. 70) is explained under Fluting, 1.

(4) Body shaping into stratified sections, as shown in the first illustration in Figure 71. This is done by soft mallet into short sections of large dimensioned pipe (*C*, Fig. 70), into wood forms, or into wood segments reinforced by wire (Fig. 72). When the design calls for two or three steps, the top one is done first. Still an-

Fig. 73. Forming a bottom step or base.

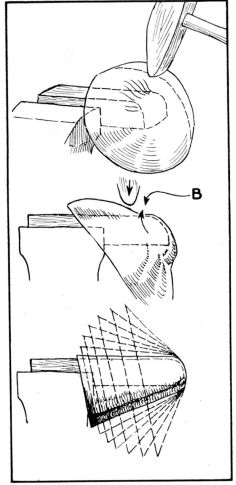

Fig. 74. Steps in high raising a bowl.

other method is explained under High Raising by Seaming, Figure 77.

(5) Rim shaping of plates and trays as shown in *B* and *C*, Figure 175. The rim is set over the end grain of a block of wood much like that in *A*, Figure 70, filed to the desired depth and curvature, nails being used for purposes of guiding. Into this the rim is slowly driven by leather-covered mallet, the body of the plate being maintained at an even angle by means of some holding device.

f) Flat bottoms (*D*, Fig. 70). The planished bowl is set into a sandbag while a round stake of the bottom diameter is carefully centered on it and struck a heavy hammer blow. The purpose of this procedure is to mark the bowl just deeply enough so that when it is reversed over the stake, it may be easily held in place. The bowl now is held down firmly on the metal stake with the left hand while the bottom area is flattened by soft leather-covered mallet proceeding in concentric circles from the outside to the center. Replanishing will be necessary in several places (*D*, Fig. 70).

The bottom step or shoulder is made over the same stake (Fig. 73) by a sharp-edged wooden mallet used very lightly, the blow falling just beyond the stake edge.

To flatten bottoms is not the best solution of the base problem. Too often the bowl then resembles a common article. The bases conforming most to those of fine period work are built up, the process necessary thereto being given in the text for Plates 13 and 14.

5. High raising. Under this heading is included high raising by driving metal up from a flat sheet, and building it up of welded and soldered parts. Neither of these processes concerns the projects of the book, but they are included for comparison and perspective. For the sake of simplicity, we shall consider pewter raising.

a) High raising from the sheet.

(1) A disk is hammered up into bowl form in stages as described under paragraph 4, Low Raising.

(2) This is annealed (see Pewter Annealing).

(3) The bowl is hung over a metal stake set horizontally into the vise, with the line of the vase bottom resting on the projecting end of the stake (Fig. 74).

(4) The metal is held at an angle approximating the amount to be drawn in for the first stage while a wedge-shaped wood mallet, or better, a cross-headed metal-raising hammer begins driving the metal ahead of the corner down to the stake. The left hand rotates the bowl, keeping the bottom close to the end of the stake and the driving distance constant.

After the first round, the hammering moves ⅛ in. up and proceeds around again, and so on, until enough metal has been driven down to provide bearing surface (*B*, Fig. 74) against which the driving blow is exerted. Several warnings are in order:

(*a*) If, after many rounds, the driving distance increases, it is safer to reduce it by half and work to the end returning to the same point to resume on the old level. Unreasonable crowding of metal, even though soft, will fracture it. Cracks may not appear at once but they will open during subsequent work.

(*b*) More care is required near the top, for the tendency of the metal will be to flatten out unless procedure is by ⅛-in. advances for each round. Blows should be delivered straight down.

(*c*) Even then, it will be found that crimps develop at the edge to take up the shrinkage of the body. To gain time crimps are often purposely made over grooved wood blocks by wedge-shaped mallets. These must be carefully drawn down. If they are allowed to fold, trouble ensues. If they are beaten down hard, nothing is gained, for the process is one of shrinkage, and hard hammering is a stretching process.

(5) Annealing is necessary after each stage.

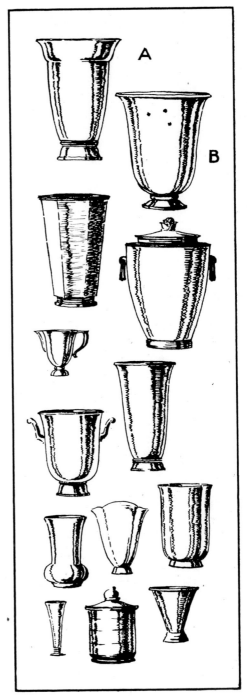

Fig. 75. Typical shapes of vases.

(6) Since the greatest shrinking is at the rim, the stages of work must conform

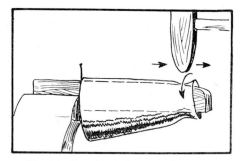

Fig. 76. Drawing in bottom of a high-
raised bowl.

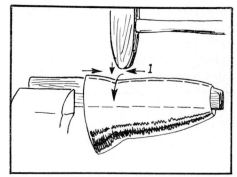

Fig. 77. Forming a vase body.

to the need, some beginning at the upper half of the body rather than at the base line. If the vase were to be barrel shaped, this would particularly apply (Fig. 75, Vase 4).

(7) When the vase is raised almost to its intended contour, a template is used to correct its irregularities. (See Low Raising, 4, *d*.) It is then planished.

(8) Bases and rims are provided as explained in the text under Plates 13 and 14.

(9) If cracks appear, they are immediately welded and scraped down to metal thickness (see Pewter Welding).

b) High raising by seaming.

(1) Most of the objects discussed in this section are constructed by combining two or more distinct processes, as for example, parts may be shaped by low raising and others in the same object may be welded or seamed and shaped. To illustrate, the vase in *A*, Figure 75, is made as follows:

(*a*) A tapered cylinder of pewter is seamed by welding. The weld is filed and scraped to proper thickness.

(*b*) It is carefully planished.

(*c*) It is drawn in at the bottom (Fig. 76).

i. The cylinder is hung over a horizontal wood bar, previously filed to the exact intended curvature of the vase both in its length and cross section.

ii. It is set back over the curve until the distance from its bottom edge is ⅛ in.

from the wood. This is carefully driven down to the wood during slow rotation.

iii. The vase cylinder is now moved sufficiently so that it extends another ⅛ in. off the wood. This is again driven slowly down, starting above the area at first worked down and proceeding to the end.

iv. The same is repeated to the completion of the drawing. A leather-covered wood mallet is used. Nails are inserted as guides. Work gradually drawn in will need no further planishing.

(*d*) The cylinder is now drawn in at the section line near the top over a wood form filed to its intended contour. A wedge-shaped, softwood mallet is used in the process and, particularly if drawing is deep, procedure is similar from both sides to that described in the preceding steps (*c*), ii, iii, and iv (Fig. 77).

(*e*) The top flare is made as described in step 2 under Flaring (*A*, Fig. 70).

(*f*) A base is formed as described in step 1 under Bending.

(*g*) This is soldered to the body as in Pewter Soldering.

Many types of vases, bowls, and lamp sections may be shaped in the same manner.

(2) The vase in *B*, Figure 75, is made as follows:

(*a*) A tapered cylinder is welded, cleaned (Fig. 144), and carefully planished as directed under Planishing.

(*b*) The bottom is slightly drawn in as in step (*c*) under High Raising by Seaming, and the top is flared as described in step 2 under Flaring (*A,* Fig. 70).

(*c*) A dish is made to fit the bottom of the cylinder. It is of sufficient curvature to run smoothly into the body curve (see step *a*, under 4, Low Raising of Bowls). This is planished and filed.

(*d*) It is next welded to the body, a folded cloth being held under the seam to confine the melted metal. The weld is cleaned by scraping as in Finishing 3, and Figure 144.

(*e*) A stem is cast (see Casting), turned, and burnished in a lathe (see Burnishing). Turning may be done on a grinder adapted by simple means to turning processes (see Finishing). The stem then is soldered to the body (see Pewter Soldering).

(*f*) A base is made in two pieces as described in step 1 under Bending.

(*g*) The top piece is spot welded to the stem (see Welding). The lower piece is soldered.

6. Raising by pressure. (*a*) Black iron lamp-base plates and drip cups are raised between two pieces of pipe of different diameters, being forced into each other in a heavy metal vise, as shown in Figure 78. If pressure is exerted unevenly the pieces are shifted and pressed over several areas until the raising is uniform.

b) Vase and bowl-base unit raising by pressure. These parts, usually of copper, bronze, or pewter, having had their rims bent as in Bending, 1, are often raised between the rim and the point of contact with the next unit above. See Figures 176, 178, and 180. Such raising is done by pressure. The unit is set over a circular hole in wood, held in position by nails, and pressed down by vise, hammer, or press (a drill press will do) through an intermediate form of smaller diameter (Fig. 177), approximating the size of the contact surface of the next unit above. The hole in the lower form should support the edge or that part not to be bent. Its edges may be left round or sharp as the design may indicate.

COLD FORMING OF IRON

Cold forming of iron over and into prepared forms will be discussed in the following paragraphs. Hot forming will be discussed under forging.

1. Cold forming of scrolls or volutes. (*a*) In form volutes follow the unwinding curve of a snail shell. Merely bending a hook for the beginning of such a curve is incorrect; the end of the hook must de-

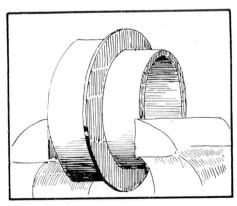

Fig. 78. Raising iron plate between pipes.

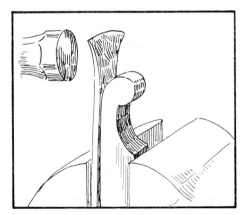

Fig. 79. Form for bending volute.

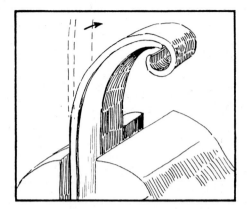

Fig. 80. Bending a volute over iron bar.

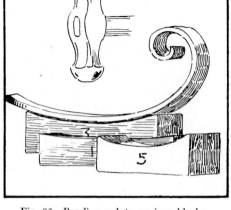

Fig. 82. Bending volute on iron blocks.

crease in radius to its very tip. With this in view, a form of bar iron is filed (Fig. 79).

b) The iron is flared or tapered at its tip and is placed in the vise back of the form as shown. It is then bent to shape by hammer.

c) The secondary, or continuing bend, may be made in various ways.

(1) Over a bar-iron form (Fig. 80) held in a vise and used the same as the form in Figure 79, or

(2) Over a forged iron-bar form on whose end the iron to be bent is hooked by means of the primary curve (Fig. 81). By this process the volute may be completed.

d) If the volute is to be continued, the final curving may be done as explained

in the following paragraphs:

(1) It may be bent over a form similar to the one shown in Figure 80.

(2) It also may be driven into graduated sets of blocks of varying radii (Fig. 82).

If the pieces are marked and placed exactly into such forms, either of the preceding methods will produce identical curves in any number of pieces.

(3) The secondary curve also may be made in a U jig (Fig. 83), by making repeated bends in close succession in the manner shown. Making identical curves by this process requires skill. The processes illustrated in Figures 79, 80, and 82 are recommended for their simplicity.

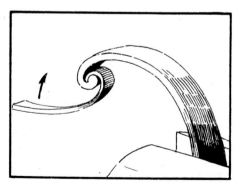

Fig. 81. Iron bar for bending volute.

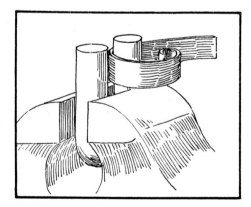

Fig. 83. U jig for bending volute.

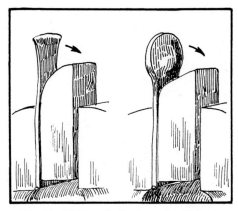

Fig. 84. Making duplications of cold bent forms.

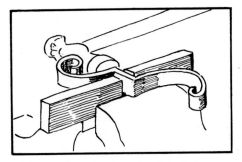

Fig. 86. Forming sharp bends in S form.

2. Duplications of bent cold forms are made over filed or forged irons like those shown in Figures 84 and 85. (*a*) A foot in S form, as shown in Plates 45–47, and 50–53, is first bent over an iron form by hammer (Fig. 84).

b) The bar is turned around and raised to a second mark, and bent over by means of a bar and hammer as shown in Figure 85. The hammer alone is not practical.

3. Sharp angle bends and S bends in hemmed bands as on the bracket in Plate 11, and in the iron crown members of the lamp in Plate 46, are made by placing the piece of metal to be bent into a slotted bar of iron of the thickness of the offset to be bent, and bending one end to the right and

the other to the left (Fig. 86). The 180-deg. bend in the bow (Pl. 38) is made in the same slotted bar. This method is found to be the most satisfactory also for all angle bending of brass bar and sheet of limited widths used on projects in Plates 23 and 24, of iron band 14 gauge and thinner, and of small rod (Pls. 38 to 43).

4. Forming in multiple by means of dies of sharply bent pieces such as are used in the lamp base in Plate 49, or on the open-work lamp socket in Plate 46, the bracket in Plate 45, the bend in the lower arm in Plate 51, the arms in Plates 50 and 53, as well as all lamp feet, may be done as follows. Wood patterns are made according to the exact curvatures of the pieces to be bent, making allowance for the back spring of the metal and enough for clear-

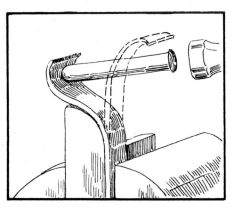

Fig. 85. Making an S-form foot.

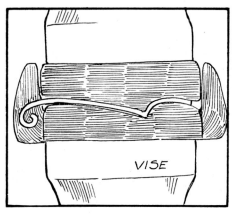

Fig. 87. Forming piece in a die.

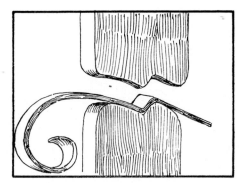

Fig. 88. Using wood or metal dies for forming hemmed tin parts.

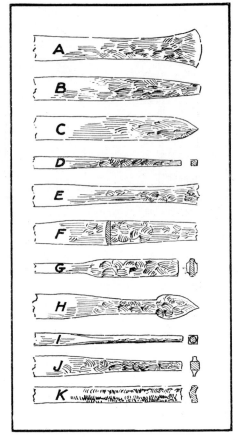

Fig. 89. Forged and hot formed pieces.

ance. They are then shellacked and sent to a foundry for casting. The final castings are finished off (see Fig. 87) and used as follows:

a) The upper scrolls are bent over a form similar to the one shown in Figure 79.

b) The lengths are checked and the location of the sharp bend is marked.

c) The piece is laid into the die, on its mark, and pressed into shape in a vise (Fig. 87).

A like result may be obtained by cutting dies of mild steel, and forcing the metal into one with the other by cross-peen hammer. Sheet-metal forms also may be pressed into wood or metal dies (Fig. 88).

5. Wire forming, as shown in Plate 25, is done over wood patterns as explained in the text. Forms whose bending areas are constructed of closely driven nails also are useful.

FORGING AND HOT FORMING

Forging is an ancient form of sculpture or modeling, its final result being an expression of rugged beauty. This may also be obtained by file and cold bending.

Much of the ironwork in this book is done by cold bending. Some of it is designed for light forging, and a few pieces require a small bench furnace. Almost all of the latter, however, with minor design changes, may be forged cold or filed.

1. Texture. Hot forging has a twofold purpose: One is the shaping of metal, and the other is the development of texture (modeling). On fine work, texture is a natural effect of drawing out and working the metal. If texture becomes conspicuous, one feels it is there to hide poor work. All-over peening of iron is of this class and should be avoided.

Commercial iron appears cold and raw. It needs texture, and an effort should be made to apply it. For example:

a) In the course of drawing out, the ends may be forged; in fact, they should never be used unforged.

b) Intentional application of occasional oval-face hammer marks may be made on the surface and the edge of metal prior to shaping.

c) In the process of width reduction during tapering, and so on, when the metal is compressed by edge hammering, textures may be applied hot or cold (Fig. 89). These are simple but very effective ways to treat band stock for feet, scrolls, and rings.

d) In surface modeling, edge forging may be applied to produce the effects explained in step 9 under Filing.

e) An unusual texture is given iron by the removal of a heavy scale formed in *soaking* at a red heat (see Antique Iron in the chapter on Finishing).

f) A mild steel hammer with a pitted and marked oval face may be used conservatively on surfaces.

2. General forge practice. Iron resists the effort to change its form. To make it plastic under a hammer, it is brought up to a bright red heat (about 1800 deg. F.) in a clean fire. Unless the piece has a long end, it must be handled by tongs or other holding device.

a) The tongs must close to parallel position and fit the piece well.

b) They may be held in this position by a spanning ring, round or oval, slipped back over the handles or reins. Such rings may be bent cold of 3/16-in. rod (Fig. 90).

c) Special holders are made of pipe or bar, if the quantity to be made warrants it. An example is shown in Figure 90.

For most purposes the iron is laid across the anvil at right angles, the horn to the left. A rather heavy hammer is held firmly toward the end of the handle. The body and arm are aligned with the work, and the arm motion is free so that the hammer may strike effectually. Practice will develop a certain arm and wrist control by which a calculated force is delivered on a point with accuracy. Eye appraisal and quick judgment precede each hammer blow.

3. Forming of stock. The object of the

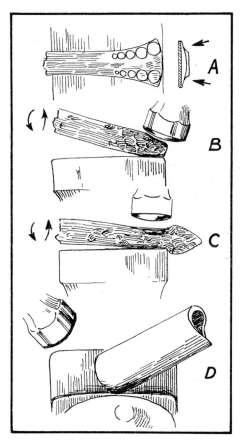

Fig. 91. Flaring, pointing, and shouldering.

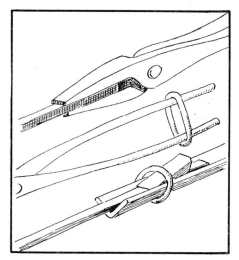

Fig. 90. Using spanning rings.

following paragraphs is to outline a means
by which character may be applied to raw
commercial flat stock. To do so, iron is
drawn backward and forward in one or a
combination of the following processes
(Fig. 89): For example, lamp feet are
drawn in and flared, or they may be pointed
and shouldered, and hooks are drawn out to
a taper on the neck after being shouldered.
Almost all of the following operations may
be worked cold by a hammer and file if
fire is not available; in fact, 40 of the 47
iron projects offered may be made without
a forge fire, if necessary.

a) Flared ends used as lamp feet and
scroll terminals. The iron is heated bright
red, laid across the anvil to the far side,
and hammered from a point back on the
bar to the end, first on one side, then on
the other to the tip, and so on, from side
to side until the flare is drawn. The hammer is tipped slightly outward. The flare
is usually short and if made as above, is
crowned in the center and well balanced
(*A*, Fig. 91, also see Straightening). The
hammering begins lightly as indicated.

b) Drawing narrower in the flat (*B*,
Fig. 89) as used on lamp feet, scroll ends,
etc. The heated iron is set upon its side
and the hammer proceeds from a point well
back, working gradually to the tip, increasing the weight of the blow as it advances.
During the procedure the iron will tend to
buckle. It is therefore revolved to its flat
side, hammered lightly from the same point
to the end, turned up again and hammered
as at first and back, and so on, until it is
drawn. It is checked by sighting and
straightened if necessary by hammering.

c) Drawing to a point (*C*, Fig. 89) as
used in lamp feet. The heated iron is set
at an angle, edge up, on its point at the
farther side of the anvil (*B*, Fig. 91), and
the hammer is tipped at twice the angle,
as it drives the corner down just hard
enough not to buckle the iron. The metal

then is turned flat and tapped smooth, and
turned back to be driven down still farther;
in fact, it is turned back and forth in the
above manner until pointed, the working
angle being changed as the need demands.

d) Drawing a taper (*D*, Fig. 89) as used
on hooks, lamps, stems, etc. All tapers,
from the flat, square, or round, and to the
square, octagon, or round, are begun by
drawing the square, and are rounded from
the square through the octagon. To draw
a square taper from a flat bar, therefore, is
the first problem.

Cold reducing tends to split the iron; a
constant red heat under the hammer is ab-
solutely necessary. The heated bar is set
upon its side, across the anvil, and is
hammered from a given point to its tip,
starting the stroke lightly and increasing
its weight as hammering proceeds. It is
next set flat upon its side and hammered
in the same manner, though less heavily
than on the narrow side. Hammering alter-
nates from one side to the other until the
metal is drawn out. Constant watching and
an accurate adjusting of the stroke to fit
the need is of great importance if a smooth,
gradual taper is to be made. If the taper
is to be round, continue as described in
step *i* following.

e) Drawing in within a length (*E*, Fig.
89) as used on scrolls, feet, and so on. The
heated iron is placed on the end of the
slightly crowned shoulder of the anvil, or
on the anvil face, and is drawn between
given points with an oval-faced hammer,
starting lightly, increasing toward the center and fading out toward the end. Next,
it is laid down flat, straightened, reheated,
set up and drawn to the proper dimension,
and aligned by sighting down its length and
tapping to shape. Drawing should be done
conservatively. Drawing in round sections
is begun by squaring the section to be
drawn, then drawing and rounding it as
directed in step *i* on page 53.

f) Spreading (*F*, Fig. 89) as used on scrolls. The heated iron is hammered along one edge between given points, then along the opposite edge, and so on alternately, until it is spread. Hammer blows start and end lightly, and the hammer is tipped outward a few degrees to effect a crowned surface (see *A*, Fig. 91). As a rule the hammer marks are continued beyond the spread section in each direction. Spreading is done very conservatively, the curve fading into the adjoining edges.

g) Drawing out flat and straight from a square or narrow bar (*G*, Fig. 89) as used in forks, chisels, and so on. The heated iron or steel is placed on the anvil for the length to be drawn and hammered flat progressively from a given point to its tip. Next it is revolved and straightened along its edge. Then it is reheated and drawn alternately on its flat side and on its edge as explained, until drawn out to the required parallel dimension. It is then aligned. If it is a carbon steel chisel blank, the metal must at all times be red while under the hammer. The blank is slightly thinned out at the tip.

h) Shouldering as used on lamp feet, hooks, and so on (*H*, Fig. 89). The heated iron is placed beyond the edge of the anvil for the distance to be reserved for the ball, disk, or foot (*C*, Fig. 91); or it may be placed on the near side for the length of the neck or offset if there is no head. The hammer, striking up to the edge of the anvil, narrows the part of the metal thus supported. The narrowed part then is drawn out to a taper (steps *b* and *d* preceding), the wide part always remaining over the edge of the anvil untouched, to be forged later. In the case of the foot illustrated in *H*, Figure 89, the point is drawn out first. The metal may be held at an angle to obtain a tapered neck as shown in *C*, Figure 91. The procedure then is setting the metal in place, hammering away from the shoulder, reversing the metal and doing the same, turning it flat to straighten, and so on, until it is drawn in. It is then aligned.

i) Drawing a round bar or a round taper from a square (see step *d*). The heated square is set up on its corner and is hammered progressively from a given point to its tip, first along one corner and then along an adjoining one, until an octagon of equal sides is drawn out. The reheated iron then is hammered lightly along each of its arrises. Cold finishing by constant watching and turning produces a smooth hard finish (*I*, Fig. 89).

j) The square is drawn from the flat piece as in step *b* preceding.

k) Drawing narrower all along is a process of hot or cold hammering, by which iron is given a texture for rings, arms, and lamp legs. It is set on its edge and hammered along the length, then flattened slightly if necessary, and trued (*K*, Fig. 89).

4. Drawing in pipe ends, such as are used as husks and rings for lamps illustrated in Plates 46, 47, 50, 52, and 53, is done in the following manner:

a) The pipe is heated red and placed at an oblique angle against the step of the anvil (*D*, Fig. 91).

b) The end is lightly tapped while the pipe is rotated. Repeated tapping at red heat will draw it in. A three-point reducing force is exerted at every blow. Cold drawing will tend to open the seam.

5. Upsetting, such as is used on the foot scraper in Plate 44, is best done as follows:

a) The bar is heated bright red, grasped 1½ in. down by heavy tongs, set at an angle against the shoulder of the anvil, and hammered or upset by heavy blows squarely on its hot end. This procedure should be repeated. Bending must be avoided. The metal may also be held in a vise during the process.

b) Finishing to a round or oval head is

done over a bottom fuller or a similar form (see Fig. 92).

c) It also may be drawn out into a flared scroll, the upsetting providing more than the ordinary amount of metal.

6. Squaring a right-angle bend is described in the text for Plate 35 (Fig. 207).

7. Scrolls. The same introduction that preceded the section on forming of scrolls is applicable here.

a) The primary curve or the inside end is forged as follows:

(1) The heated and flared metal is laid over the curved edge on the far side of the anvil, where it extends slightly.

(2) The hammer, held at an angle over the edge, bends the extreme tip down around the curve (Fig. 93).

(3) The iron is now fed steadily over the edge while the hammer continues striking at intervals of ⅛ in., until enough has been bent to make a primary curve as shown. Steady controlled feeding is easier if the feeding hand is pressed against the leg and the latter is slowly bent toward the anvil as hammering proceeds.

(4) The scroll is then heated and placed on the anvil in reverse (*A*, Fig. 94).

(5) Light, well-directed blows while the metal is rocked from high to low position, as may be seen in *A*, Figure 94, will close the curve to its proper size.

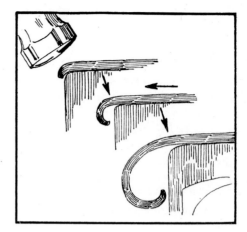

Fig. 93. Making scroll on an anvil.

b) The secondary curve.

(1) The metal is reheated and placed upon the horn of the anvil or on its face over the edge, curve down.

(2) More metal is bent into the curve as in the beginning (*B*, Fig. 94).

(3) It is reversed, placed upon the face of the anvil and worked in as before, the eye directing the operation so that the volute flows gracefully (*A* and *B*, Fig. 95). This process is repeated until the scroll is complete.

(4) Corrections may be made in a vise (see *X* at *B*, Fig. 95).

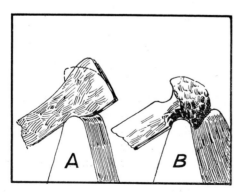

Fig. 92. Finishing round or oval heads.

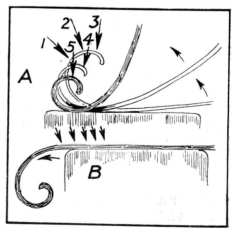

Fig. 94. Further steps in making scroll.

(5) If a correction involving the opening of curves is necessary see the text on Straightening and Figure 23. It is best to work the curve too large rather than too small, and to complete the primary curve before proceeding further. In each case, after reheating for the secondary work, the primary curve is cooled in water to keep it from jarring out of shape.

8. Hot forming is a process of bending hot metal around forms.

a) Scrolls may be made as follows:

(1) The primary curve is bent as shown in Figure 93.

(2) The metal is reheated and the primary curve is slightly cooled in water so that it will not bend.

(3) The piece is then hooked over an iron form which fits into the anvil or the vise (Fig. 81), and drawn down, completing the scroll.

This is the method employed in professional work for duplicating scrolls. However, the process illustrated in Figure 82 also may be used in this instance, and it is recommended for classwork.

b) Leaves in iron may be shaped hot over forms similar to those shown in Figures 80, 81, 82, and Plate 52. Veining and any other modeling is done previously.

c) Knobs, such as are used in lamps (Pls. 46, 50, and 52), are formed hot of heavy nuts held on the end of a threaded iron rod or pipe. All arrises are hammered down while the nut is revolving on the anvil face.

d) Chisel blanks may be formed into gouges (Pl. 59) in grooves on the block shown in Figure 96. The round bar need not be attached as shown, but it is a decided convenience. The chisel blank is drawn out and heated bright red, placed in the groove under the bar, and driven into shape by hammer blows much like drop forging. The same may be done by a cross peen against the anvil shoulder.

9. Hot forming by grasping instruments — scrolls.

a) Hot forming of scroll ends on thin stock, such as used for Plates 27, 29, 30, 34, 55, and husk-leaf ends as in Plate 52, are formed in round-nosed pliers kept expressly for hot work. Owing to the immediate cooling of the ends upon being grasped by cold pliers, several attempts are necessary before such scroll is satisfactorily formed. Large pliers and the use of gloves will aid in performing work on diameters otherwise deemed too heavy. A high red heat always is necessary.

b) Scrolls on bars and difficult curvatures as the double curve in Plate 30 are

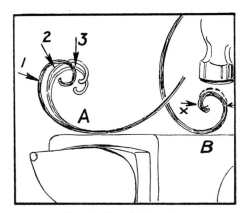

Fig. 95. Completing volute.

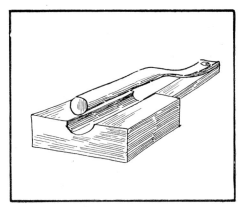

Fig. 96. Block for forming chisels.

easily made by the use of forks like the one shown in Figure 23. The interval between the prongs must be sufficient for the thickness of stock to slip easily over the bar. The forks are worked in opposition to each other. By skillful direction of pressure, a long section or an entire scroll may be shaped at one time.

CHAPTER IV

SURFACE DECORATION AND FINISHING

CHASING

1. Chasing is the art of small-scale modeling by means of punches called chasing tools. These vary in size and in shape according to the metal and to the form and textures of the units upon which they work. Their points, however small, must conform exactly to the curvatures of the areas or lines upon which they are used. Therefore, chasing is nothing more than small-scale planishing.

The standard tool, used for silver, bronze, brass, copper, and so on, is 3½ to 4 in. long, made of carbon tool steel, the blanks being ⅛, 5/32, and 3/16 in. square at their wide sections. These are filed to shape and tempered. The tools to be used for lining, background flatters, and modeling, are illustrated in *A*, *B*, and *C*, Figure 97. Pewter tools may be made of iron nails, copper rod, or even hardwood, and tools for sheet iron are made of cold-chisel stock. The tools used in Plates 5, 10, and 16 for leaf and rosette veining are wide (*D*, Fig. 97).

2. Holding of work. (*a*) Work, such as simple leaf and rosette veining, is placed on the end grain of a wood block and held by small nails or strap (Fig. 98).

b) Work requiring a higher type of chasing including side and vertical pressure, on pewter, silver, or bronze, is mounted on jeweler's pitch. The metal is thinly oiled on the reverse side, both pitch and metal are heated and the latter is pressed into the pitch. When all is cool, the metal is ready to be worked upon.

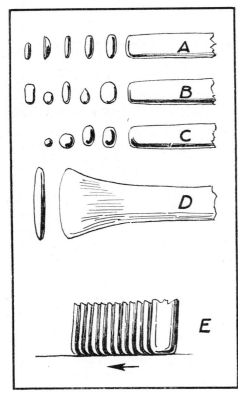

Fig. 97. Chasing tools.

Fig. 98. Holding work.

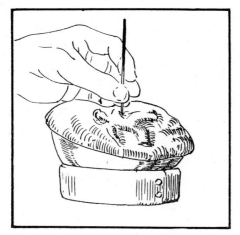

Fig. 99. Pitch container set in leather coil.

c) Pitch may be purchased or made. One pound of either Burgundy or shoemaker's pitch is melted in a pot. To this are added ½ oz. of Venetian turpentine and ½ in. of wax candle. Into these is slowly stirred enough plaster of paris to make a very stiff lump. This is pressed into a container (Fig. 99). A very efficient container may be made of a cheap aluminum pot, raised to half spherical form on wood and filled 1/3 with lead. The pitch should fill the remainder and come above the rim about ½ in. Such spherical pitch cups are set into coils of leather belting (Fig. 99). Pitch and pitch bowls may, of course, be purchased.

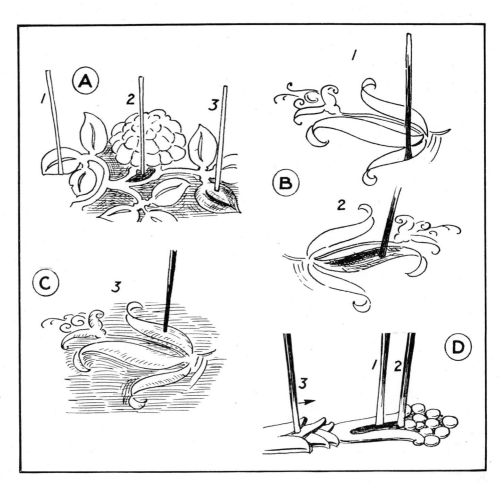

Fig. 100. Chasing processes.

3. General process. (*a*) Low-relief chasing procedure follows:

(1) The design is outlined (*A*, Fig. 100, 1). (See step 4, *b*.)

(2) The background is worked down and away from the outline, leaving the object in relief (*A*, Fig. 100, 2).

(3) The object is modeled (*A*, Fig. 100, 3).

b) High-relief chasing or repousse.

(1) The face side is outlined (*B*, Fig. 100, 1). (See step 4, *b*.)

(2) The metal is reversed on the pitch block and the object is worked up from the underside within the outline. This is done as nearly as possible to the general shape of the final design, the highest points on the face side being driven deepest into the pitch on the reverse side (*B*, Fig. 100, 2).

(3) The metal is reversed once again and modeled on the face side (see *C*, Fig. 100, 3).

c) High, over-all relief, with little background, is not worked from the underside unless it saves time. In other words, if the motifs predominate in area, it is economical to work the background from above.

d) High relief in heavy metal.

(1) The pattern is first outlined.

(2) The low levels or backgrounds are carved by a chisel.

(3) The piece is modeled over all partly by carving, and is finished by chasing (*D*, Fig. 100). Flat gravers, mentioned in the

next section, are used for this type of metal carving.

e) Chased, over-all motifs overlapping one another, giving the effect of many levels often seen in modern work, are used on the spoons in this course (Pl. 57).

(1) The design first is outlined.

(2) The backgrounds, if any, are carved and then chased down.

(3) Working away from the overlying motif, the next level is chased down around its base and faded off toward its high edge (*D*, Fig. 100), and so on, at each level.

f) Bronze castings meant to be highly finished are machined or scraped and filed, if possible, before chasing. Chasing alone, however, is regularly done on the ornament and broad surfaces of monumental and pattern work.

4. Practice. (*a*) The position of the hand and fingers. Smooth work, covered by a sheen of tiny facets produced by punch and hammer, is of necessity a matter of system and exact tool control.

The thumb presses the tool against the fingers, the third being held tight to the tool bottom and the fourth being pressed against the third. In this position the lower fingers drag on the work and act as guides to the motion of the tool (Fig. 101). At the same time, they serve as cushions against which the tool is pivoted to produce short but clean and graceful lines. The action may be described as a rhythmic sketching motion. Thus, metal may be modeled or forced into desired directions by both vertical and oblique chasing with the resultant effect of a slight overlap.

b) Tool work—outline. The tool is in constant motion while it is being tapped. There is no appreciable interval between taps.

The selection of tools is important. As a rule, one uses the largest convenient tool that fits the area. The tool should not be too smooth. If it is, it should be hammered into fine emery cloth.

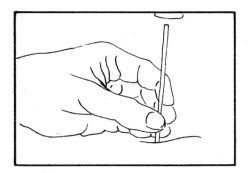

Fig. 101. Holding the chasing tool.

It is set on the line, tipped slightly backward, held tightly to the metal, drawn slowly forward, or more correctly, allowed to vibrate forward, while being tapped a sufficient number of times so that the blows overlap and present a continuous line. By tipping the tool, the rear end of its face is dragged in its track, while the front, being above the surface, is directed over the line (*E*, Fig. 97). The work is so placed that the hand will pivot on the inside of curves.

c) Background. The flat-faced tools, held slightly tipped, drive the background down by courses which start at and work away from the outline in the general direction of the design, unless a different background texture is desired. They are laid down in short, sketchy series, extending as far as the fingers allow, as already explained. The work is turned so that the hand may operate on the inner side of the curve being traced.

d) Modeling. Flat tools are used on convex areas and rounded tools on concave areas. These must be selected to fit their particular work perfectly on the one hand, and on the other, to blend well with that done by other tools on adjacent areas. The tools move in courses similar to those explained in step *c*, their purpose being to emphasize the direction and character of the unit. A knowledge of natural form and a feeling for rhythm are valuable to the worker in this, the highest phase of metal arts.

Excellent chasing of small floral motifs and initials on plate and tray centers is being done by students on seventh- and eighth-grade levels. On the other hand, chasing on pewter vases, plates, and boxes has become the focus of interest for many people in adult-education classes.

5. Chasing jigs for tracing parallel lines on plate rims (Fig. 102) and on bowls and vases have been recently developed and used to advantage in the author's classes. A ¼-in. setscrew is ground to the shape of a line chasing tool, and fastened by two nuts into the upper end of a 14-gauge by 1½ mild steel band bent over into a spring of flat-C shape. Directly under the chasing tool is fixed the polished head of a cap screw to serve as an anvil. This unit is screwed to a heavy wood block to fit into a vise. On its sides are screwed two bars

Fig. 102. An endless variety of line designs may be engraved on metal.

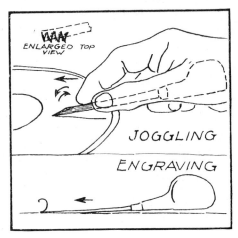

Fig. 103. How to hold the engraving tool.

of wood extending beyond to support the plate, and on the forward end of these are fixed adjustable blocks that serve as gauges. Against these gauges and between the chasing head and anvil, the plate is slowly rotated while the chaser is vibrated by a hammer. Narrow and wide lines, double lines, and moldings may be thus produced.

ENGRAVING

This art may be applied to bronze, brass, and pewter work of modern as well as period design (Fig. 102), and manipulation is comparatively simple so that it may be recommended for school use. It consists of cutting and joggling lines, either by means of extremely sharp tools mounted specially into handles or by fine chisels.

The joggling tool for use in pewter may be made of a nail or of tool steel, the latter being the better all-around tool. Three square tools are necessary, 1/32, 3/64, and 1/16 in. wide at their points respectively. These may be purchased as flat gravers.

One diamond-shaped graver is all that is necessary for line work (Fig. 102). A blank, No. 6 or 7, should be purchased. This is mounted in a graver's handle so that it may be used horizontally or almost flat on the metal as shown in Figure 103. It is held in the palm of the hand after mounting, the thumb is extended along the blade as far as possible, and this is cracked off in a vise at a point opposite the tip of the thumb. The tool is then ground tapering from a 1/32-in. diamond point to full section three quarters of the distance back. Sharpening is the key to successful engraving. This is done on an Arkansas or razor stone. The two lower sides are ground flat and the point, held in exact position by means of a holding device, is ground square across its face on a plane 60 deg. from the bottom edge. The device may be made of a block of wood to which the tool is fastened by means of a small clamp. The point is tested through a strong

magnifying glass in which dull edges reflect light. These precautions may seem superfluous yet they are important.

1. Joggling is a means of making decorative lines on metal, especially characteristic of native work, but also used to advantage in modern work. The process is as follows:

a) The design is transferred to the metal (see Marking).

b) A tool of proper width is held in the fingers, point on the line, the blade in a 45-deg. position.

c) With a medium forward pressure on the point, the tool is revolved to one side and the other in the fingers in an approximate 90-deg. arc, at each end of which it jogs forward (Fig. 103).

d) Uniform pressure and revolution and a steady arm are necessary for a fairly straight line. A natural variation in the line adds to its individuality. If desired, a long, straight line may be cut against a straightedge.

e) The line is darkened by means of a weak nitric-acid solution applied by a toothpick between frequent rinsings.

2. Engraving is a means of making a variety of clean lines by cutting. The tool described can make a hairline and also a wide, shaded line. To do the latter, the point is tipped as far as desired, depending upon the width of the cut, and turned back to shade it to a hairline at the end. The process is as follows:

a) The design is transferred (see Marking).

b) The metal to be engraved is set upon a wax or leather surface or on one which offers some resistance to movement.

c) The graver is held in the palm of the hand, with the fingers in such position on the blade and handle that they may not interfere with the freedom of movement and yet that the thumb and first finger may retard the movement at will. The graver is held almost flat (Fig. 103).

Fig. 104. Etched designs.

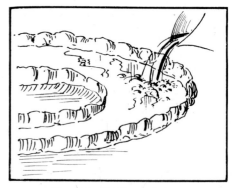

Fig. 105. Etching a design.

d) When making a curved line the metal is fed into the graver.

e) The graver is pushed over the metal when making a straight line.

ETCHING

Etching is an acid process of surface decoration often used to excess in the past. Present-day trends are toward native forms and motifs applied with reserve. The illustrations in Figure 104 suggest the use of Indian, Greek, and Chinese motifs for plates and bowls.

1. Etching a plate rim. (*a*) The plate is cleaned in hot soap and water, rinsed, and dried.

b) The design is traced into the plate by a scriber against cut-out paper patterns or by any similar method in which no grease or wax substances are used. Finger marks are to be avoided.

c) The design is painted out, leaving the part to be cut unpainted. This is done with fresh asphaltum paint and a fine brush kept free from thickened paint in turpentine. Time given to accurate painting is well re-

paid. Scratching out errors is not satisfactory though it is the means used to correct overlaps. The application must be of sufficient thickness to insure safety for the edges and covered areas. Dust in the paint may form a wicklike channel through which acid penetrates to the metal surface.

d) If a container is used, the plate is entirely painted. Since this requires a large supply of acid, the following method is preferred:

e) A wall of wax is built to within ½ in. around the rim and, if desired, also inside the rim so that acid may be run between the walls, otherwise the inside of the plate is also painted. Beeswax and rosin are melted together in the proportion of 2/3 to 1/3 and this is applied with the fingers when partially solidified (Fig. 105).

f) One part of nitric acid is added to four parts of water in a glass container and poured over the work to a depth of at least ¼ in. It is well to stir the solution gently by feather or swab of cotton tied to a stick. A solution of 1 to 2 is too violent and often tends to loosen paint not perfectly applied. Acid should be used several hours after the painting. The paint should not be permitted to become hard and brittle.

g) After five to ten minutes of application the acid is poured into a bottle with glass stopper to be saved for further use. The wax is broken off and laid aside, also for future use, and the asphaltum is soaked and washed off with turpentine, benzine, or gasoline.

h) The plate is repolished, if necessary, especially if etched motifs require high lighting. If the acid color is removed more than desired, it may be recovered with dilute acid on the point of a stick between frequent rinsings.

2. Etched motifs on vase bodies, bowl and plate bottoms, and so on, are applied in a similar manner.

3. Scraped lines on prepainted surfaces have the disadvantage, from an artistic standpoint, of being too mechanical and hard. They are nevertheless justified in some instances. Designs 1 and 2 in Figure 102, and 2 and 4 in Figure 104 are adaptable to this process. If they are used, the plate or bowl rim is cleaned, painted, and sufficiently dried, a marking gauge is supplied with chisel point of the necessary width, and the parallel lines are scratched

in (*A*, Fig. 106). A nail may be used for the point. Cross lines are scribed along a soft leather-backed strip of wood. Scraping other than straight lines is done around heavy cardboard patterns, followed by the foregoing procedure.

BEADED EDGES

Beaded edges may be scraped into plate and bowl rims independently or in addition to turned edges. The moldings thus made are quite like those customarily soldered on. The process is similar to the scraping in step 3, preceding, the nail point of the marking gauge being widened by hammering and then filed in reverse of the design. The gauge is held tightly to the edge of the plate, the point dragging until it has cut to the necessary depth (*B*, Fig. 106). Chatter marks are removed by rubbing with emery cloth held to the sharp edge of thin brass.

PLANISHING

Planishing is a smoothing and hardening process of ancient origin applied to thin metal surfaces following the rough shaping described under low and high raising. It is done by means of polished hammers over polished metal forms called stakes. It

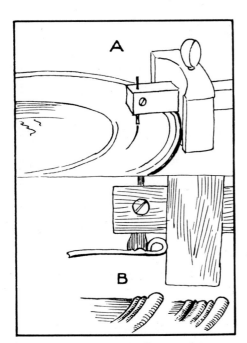

Fig. 106. *A*. Scribing lines on plate.
B. Scraping beaded edges.

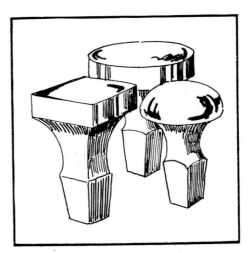

Fig. 107. Stakes for planishing.

imparts a rich texture to the flat and curved surfaces on plate and bowl work (Pls. 13 to 18). Smoothly finished work also is planished, the marks being polished and buffed out.

1. Tools. (*a*) The hammers used, whether they are the standard planishing hammers (see Tools and Equipment) or substitutes, such as claw or ball-peen hammers must be free of all marks and highly polished. Otherwise each flaw is impressed upon the metal surface over and over.

A flat-faced hammer is used on convex surfaces, a slightly crowned face on flat surfaces, and one highly crowned on concave surfaces. In the latter case, planishing is usually done on the reverse or convex side. Work possessing a combination of curves is more difficult to planish uniformly. The proper selection of hammer curvatures and the weight of the blow are very important. Work displaying hammer marks of varying size and shape is inferior; the ideal is uniformity.

b) Stakes. Stakes should be free of marks and highly polished. They should accurately fit the area under which they are used. To find or make such stakes is a major problem of the work. They usually

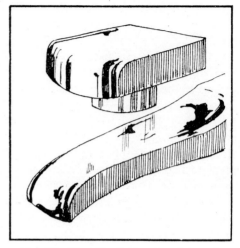
Fig. 109. Planishing stakes for plate and vase bodies.

come made of cast iron in a large assortment of standard shapes (Fig. 107). However, polished short lengths of cold- or hot-rolled iron bars serve well (Fig. 108). A few with flat ends, and some with curves for bowls, a few for plate planishing and one or two for vase bodies make up a good selection (Figs. 107, 108, and 109). To make or reshape such tools and hammers, they are ground or filed roughly, drawfiled to a semifinish and polished with medium and No. 220 abrasive cloth. Accurate curves are filed with the aid of brass templates.

2. Process. Three types of planishing

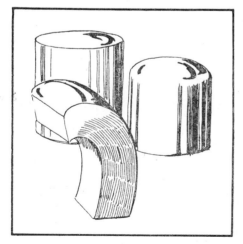
Fig. 108. Stakes made of common materials.

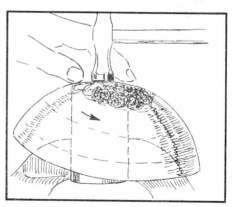
Fig. 110. Planishing a bowl.

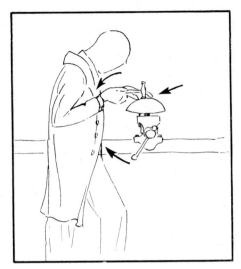

Fig. 111. Planishing a bowl.

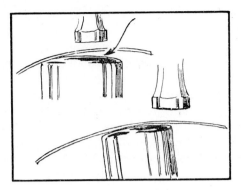

Fig. 113. The bowl must be down
tightly on the stake.

processes are explained in the following
outline, each having its own holding problem and a definite place in metalwork.
Special holding devices are used where
possible.

a) The most elementary of the processes
and that recommended for beginners is the
planishing of bowls by small areas. Bowls
should be raised to perfect spherical form
as explained under low raising, step 4, *c,* no
matter what the final shape, so that planishing may be accomplished over a single stake
with greatest ease and uniformity.

(1) A stake of accurate curvature is set
into the vise. If not exact, the deviation

should be in the direction of a smaller arc.
However, an exact arc is not difficult to file,
and the time spent perfecting it will be
amply returned in the end. A shop will in
time accumulate stakes of useful contour.

(2) The inside of the bowl is placed over
the stake and held down tightly (Fig. 110).
If the bowl is large, the fingers may bear
down on each side of the area above the
stake (Fig. 110). If the bowl is small, the
following standard method is used. The
fingers are held beneath the bowl with several of them touching the stake, if possible,
for purposes of location. The area over the
stake must be held in perfect contact with
the thumb and fingers.

(3) The hammer is held in a manner to
minimize the difficulty experienced when
work is held at inconvenient positions.
The body is braced against the bench (Fig.
111) and the wrist is pressed to the body
so that the hammer handle is on a horizontal plane and the hand may deliver a blow,
machinelike, over the center of the stake
with the center of the hammer face, both
being on a like plane at this point (Fig.
111). If the hammer strikes otherwise, an
inferior quality of work with oval and half-
moon marks will result.

(4) For uniformity in the size of planishing marks, the weight of the blow is important. It is controlled by the height to which

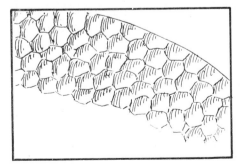

Fig. 112. Good planishing produces
uniform facets.

the hammer is lifted and dropped. Note that the hammer is merely lifted and dropped from ½ to ¾ in., while the metal is moved under it. The handle should be held somewhat loosely.

(5) It is not to be expected that planishing be done in one round. The first round is merely a preliminary flattening. After the second or third round, however, round facets of uniform size completely cover the metal surface, each slightly overlapping the other (Fig. 112).

(6) The system of area planishing requires the least amount of skill, and its use in bowl planishing is recommended as a first problem. By it, the metal surface is slowly moved about under the hammer, until an area of approximately 1-in. diameter in the center of the bottom is uniformly planished over all. The work then progresses to the next area of the same general size, one width toward the rim and then the next, and so on, until the edge is reached (see Fig. 110).

(7) The surface is now examined, and its marks are brought into sharp outline by rubbing with steel wool. A second and third planishing is probably necessary, though sometimes a last touching up is sufficient. All intervals between marks, however, must be closed, and any undesirable marks are

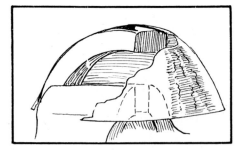

Fig. 115. Segmental stake for planishing.

worked out. If the bowl is not smooth, either it was not held down tightly to the stake or the hammering shifted from the stake center to the stake edge (Fig. 113).

b) Planishing by radiating courses, a process confined principally to platework, bowls, and vases, where stakes fit but one of a number of contours and the saving of frequent change of position, as explained in step *c,* is an advantage. In this process, the metal surface is struck five or six times in each position as against once in process *c,* the marks being laid down on lines radiating from the center instead of on concentric lines (Fig. 114). This process is recommended for schools if plate planishing is done at all. Average low raising of plates is good enough to require planishing only on a band immediately inside the curve.

(1) The plate is set to partially hang from the stake at 60 to 75 deg. so that its

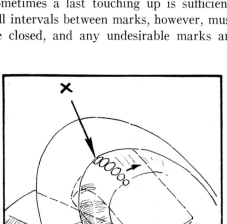

Fig. 114. Planishing by radiating courses.

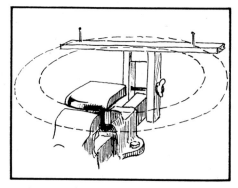

Fig. 116. Frame for holding work in planishing.

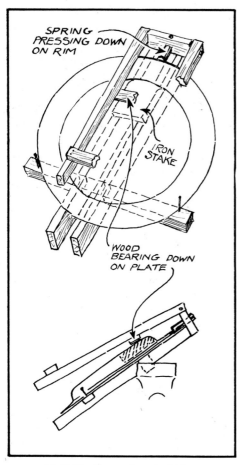

Fig. 117. Frame for planishing.

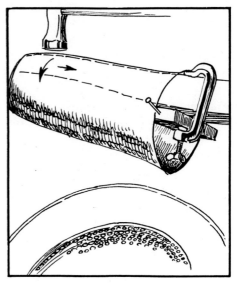

Fig. 118. Planishing by courses.

weight serves to hold it tightly to the stake. The fingers hold the plate against and into the curve of the stake, as in step *a*, (2) and progress is essentially the same as in step *a*, (3), (4), and (5).

(2) The square-headed hammer is held so that marks may be made as closely as possible to the inner corner without striking the underside of the rim (*X*, Fig. 114). From that point, the blows follow the contour of a line radiating toward the center as far as possible without moving the wrist from the body. The radiating courses overlap around the entire plate, after which a second width is hammered toward the plate center to a point slightly beyond the limit

of irregularity left by the raising process. There, the marks fade off.

c) The concentric course process is the traditional method and while it requires greater skill and experience, it is the most beautiful if correctly used. Therefore, ways should be devised to simplify this process to the point where the novice may make a success of it.

(1) Stakes. The ideal stake is one that fits the entire surface accurately so that the object to be planished does not need to be moved. However, to make such a stake is highly impractical. The second choice, a most practical and economical one, is to make a segment of such a stake, wide enough for convenient hammer work (Fig. 115). It is either forged or rough filed and polished. The last resort is a stake fitting an area or part of the segment. Its use brings the worker face to face with a holding problem which can be partially solved by devices such as frames, bars, supports, and so on, an example of which may be studied in Figures 116 and 117.

(2) Practice. Planishing usually begins in the center of the bottom of bowls, plates,

cups, and so on, and at the lower end of cylinders, and progresses in concentric circles to the outer or upper rim (Fig. 118). Overlapping facets of uniform shape and size should completely cover the area worked upon. If not, the process is repeated.

Frequent rubbing with steel wool will bring the hammer work into sharp relief so that accurate work may be more easily accomplished.

The rule of procedure given is not always practical and must frequently be set aside for one that fits the work and the student.

Feeding in all course planishing is by the rhythmic system described under low raising, step 4, *a*, the thumb bearing down and in on the work in opposition to the fingers below. The latter are the key factors in correct holding to the stake in this process. Hammering takes place while the metal is moved $\frac{1}{8}$ in. per blow toward the right, the object being held down by the hammer after the third blow while the thumb slides back for a new hold, and so on to the end.

A hollow sound is a signal of faulty contact. Attention to body and wrist rigidity and weight of blow is of greatest importance. The face of the hammer must at all times strike on its center at which point the work comes into contact with the stake.

d) Flat surfaces are particularly difficult to work. Light blows of uniform weight and size are always essential for the best results.

CHAPTER V

FASTENING

DRILLING

1. Marking and holding. (*a*) As a rule, the position of holes before drilling is marked by a center punch.

b) The drill should enter the metal on a horizontal plane, otherwise it may work over and break. Drilling on inclined planes is done by means of jigs with hardened bushings or by chiseling horizontal working planes.

c) Holes on inclines may be drilled if the work is held on an incline (see Fig. 119).

d) Work that may roll or shift during the drilling operation is held by a clamp in V blocks, in drill-press vises, or in wood blocks built to fit such work. Most drills are broken by the shifting of work.

2. Speeds (general). (*a*) Small drills are revolved quickly to stiffen them and to give them an efficient cutting speed. If not operated in high-speed machines it is often economical to use stub ends and feed slowly. In drilling aluminum, and most brass, tools are run at comparatively greater speeds than those used in other metals.

b) Large drills revolve more slowly. Time is gained on work in iron and steel by drilling pilot holes of small diameter. For a technical handling of the subject of speeds, consult drill manufacturer's data.

3. Lubrication. Cast iron requires no lubrication while being drilled. Generally, lard oil is preferred when drilling any other kind of iron or metal. Mineral oils are not used. Hard metals, poorly conditioned tools, and heavy feeding present most of the difficulties.

4. Means. (*a*) For deep drilling iron and hard metals a bench drill is generally necessary. Good progress, however, may be made when a hand drill is forced by wood lever.

b) Small holes in brass and bronze are drilled easily by a hand drill.

c) Soft metals, such as lead, tin, aluminum, and copper clog slowly moving drills. If such is the case, the drill is cleaned frequently and the front angle is ground straight to make a light bite possible.

5. Hardened steel should be annealed before drilling (see Annealing).

6. Holes partially drilled off center may be corrected by drilling obliquely until the hole is brought back, chiseling or chasing the hole to center, or by drilling through a hardened bushing held in a fixture clamped over the center. Such a fixture may be made of mild steel, drilled and casehardened.

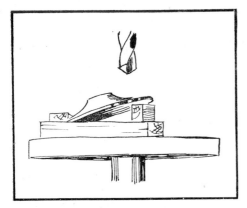

Fig. 119. Drilling on inclined surface.

69

CENTER PUNCHING

Center punching is the operation preceding drill work that provides a mark in which the drill position may be easily maintained.

1. This mark is usually made at the intersection of lines scribed by measuring and marking instruments. It is made light at first, in case it is not accurately centered.

2. For greater accuracy, the crosslines are scribed long enough so that they may be seen while drilling. Rings may be scribed around center-punch marks to check drilling after the center marks are obliterated (Fig. 120).

PUNCHING HOLES INTO THIN METALS

Punching is preferred to drilling in metals too thin or soft to remain flat under the drill. For example, 24-gauge copper tears and climbs up on the drill unless special means are used to keep it flat. Punching is a simple timesaver.

1. The lines are laid out as in center punching.

2. Punching is done over the end grain of a hardwood block or into a lead block. One sharp blow is preferred to a number of light blows, for the latter tend to stretch the metal down before cutting.

3. Punches of round, square, or any odd shape may be made of tool steel or drill rod (see Hardening).

COUNTERSINKING

When rivets or screwheads are to be driven in flush, countersinking is necessary (*A*, Fig. 121). A countersink bit or a drill of larger size than the hole, given several turns, will taper the hole.

RIVETING

1. Rivets, to be inconspicuous, are countersunk and hammered down flush.

2. Rivets, to be decorative, are left round. A head displaying the uniform facets of hammering is preferred to one set with a rivet set (*A*, Fig. 121), and for the same reason a ball-peen hammer is preferred to a riveting hammer.

3. The part of the rivet to be peened should extend from the hole a distance slightly less than the diameter. A 3/16-in. rivet will extend $\frac{1}{8}$ to 5/32 in. from the hole (*B*, Fig. 121).

4. Peening proceeds around the edge of the rivet rather than at the center. A flattened rivet is too weak to be of use (*A*, Fig. 121).

5. If a number of rivets are used on one unit, all but the first hole through the second piece are drilled after the first rivet is in place at least temporarily (*B*, Fig. 121).

6. Usually a rivet head rests upon an anvil face while it is being hammered home.

Fig. 120. Center punching.

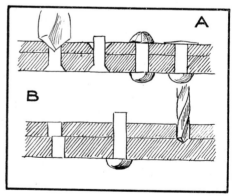

Fig. 121. Countersinking and drilling rivet holes.

However, if the head is inaccessible and the metal may not be bent temporarily away, riveting is done over a bar held in the vise. If the work is too large to handle, a heavy weight is held to the rivet head while its other end is peened down. It is recommended that only one rivet be used in each foot of lamp projects, as more may create discouraging complications (Pls. 45 to 53).

TAPPING

Successful tapping depends upon the following:

1. Drill size. A 75-per-cent thread for cast iron and brass, and a 60-per-cent thread for mild steel and other soft metals will fill all strength requirements and save time and taps as well. A drill larger in proportion than is given in tap-drill tables therefore is recommended for this work.

2. Lubrication. Mineral oil retards cutting and causes breakage. Lard oil is recommended as the best lubricant. Cast iron usually does not need a lubricant although liquid soap often is used.

3. Design of tap. A full thread may be tapped with comparative ease by using a tapered tap rather than a plug tap. The latter, however, may be ground to a long taper if necessary.

4. Method of tapping. The tap, being very hard, must not be turned beyond its elastic limit. Chips bind it despite lubrication. Short back turns, therefore, at every half turn, tend to break the chips and keep it free.

5. Broken taps may be resharpened on a grinder by squaring off and tapering each side back at a cutting angle.

6. Broken taps are extracted with difficulty. If not too deep, they are driven out by a nail set from below. They may be annealed and drilled out if the nature of the work is such that it is not damaged by heating.

7. Accurate tapping is done on a bench drill, the tap being held in the chuck and the work lying flat on the table or in a drill-press vise. After the thread is safely begun, the job may be continued by a wrench out of the drill press.

8. Sheet metal may be tapped into a hole drilled small and driven to tap size by means of a tapered tool.

THREADING

1. Short threads are made by die and wrench, started carefully and slowly, by pressure against the rod or pipe, using a lubricant.

2. Long, handmade threads and those used in pipe assembly must be started accurately. Such threads are made either by drill-press chuck and die held flat to a drill table by means of a wrench, or if pipe, by pipe-threading stock and die whose collet acts as accurate guide.

3. For lubrication, animal-lard oil or soap is used.

SOFT SOLDERING

1. Solder and flux. (*a*) A 50-50 solder (tin and lead) in wire form, melting at 401 deg. F., is recommended for the work proposed, except for pewter which requires a 60-40 solder, melting at 368.6 deg. F. Solders of still lower melting point contain bismuth. A superior pewter solder may be purchased from the pewter manufacturers. A commercial soldering paste, sold under the name of "Lotan," is recommended for some of the ironwork in the text. This powdered, low-melting solder is mixed with flux, and is of great strength and wide utility. It is well suited for parts otherwise brazed or welded. The latter processes, because of the high temperatures required, are not discussed. For convenience and economy in flame soldering, it is recommended that wire solder be cut into $\frac{1}{8}$-in. round pellets, and that solder used for pewter, if bought as $\frac{1}{8}$-in. wire solder, be rolled or hammered to

Fig. 122. Holder for soldering materials.

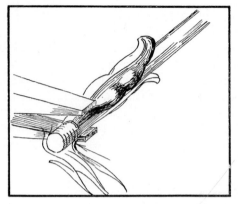

Fig. 123. Soldering pieces of unequal weight.

paper thickness, scraped bright, and cut into 1/16-in. strips and then into 1/16 by 1/32-in. pieces just prior to use. In this form it will melt readily at low heat. Pewter solder may be purchased in 1/16-in. wire form, however. This is merely snipped into short pieces just before use.

b) The flux, recommended for all-round utility, is an ammonium-chloride preparation commonly sold as "soldering salts." Such salts are conveniently diluted in water, and are useful for iron and steel as well as for copper, brass, and pewter. A further recommendation for this salt is its efficiency as a cleaner for the soldering copper. Both flux and cleaner may be kept together·in a box to prevent loss and damage by tipping of bottles (Fig. 122).

c) Other fluxes may be used. For example, 1 oz. of glycerine and 5 drops of hydrochloric acid make an excellent flux for pewter. Zinc chloride or soldering paste may be used on copper, brass, and tin, and hydrochloric acid on zinc.

2. General rules for soldering. (a) Contact points or surfaces on metals to be soldered must be clean. Bright tin and fresh copper and brass are sufficiently clean. Dull pewter and heat-tarnished tin should be brightened with steel wool. Discolored and scale-covered copper and brass should be cleaned in an acid bath and scoured, and failing that, it should be rubbed with emery cloth and a scraper. Iron always requires a thorough brightening by a file.

Particles of dust, emery, steel wool, and pencil marks retard and even stop the flow of solder. Therefore metal is wiped clean before fluxing.

b) Metals must be kept clean at all useful temperatures. This is the function of a flux.

c) Metals are soldered by means of alloys of lower melting point. The soldering metals fuse with the adjoining molecules in the metals soldered if their entrance is unobstructed. To maintain this free entrance is the particular purpose of a flux.

d) Contact points must fit closely. Solder will run in tight joints by capillary attraction and will stop at the least opening. In such instance and within reasonable limits more solder may be fed in from the end of a wire of solder flattened to wedge shape by a hammer. Enough solder will run up by capillary force to fill the opening, but this will occur only after the solder has risen to the same height in the entire joint for the extent at least of the molten area. Large openings are better refit, or backed with metal. One other recourse remains if others are impractical, that of filling the opening by a soldering copper used at low temperature. A cloth may be held back of the opening. Solder will run to the hottest point, to the closest joint, and if too much is applied, it will run down grade, its weight being greater than the total attraction.

e) Heat sources. Solder is run into a joint by properly directed and distributed heat. The following heat sources are used:

(1) A direct flame, such as a Bunsen burner, its equivalent, as an alcohol lamp, the excess flame from the door of a gas furnace, or a gas torch. The first are fixed and supply heat from below; the last is free and is used over and around the metal.

(2) A soldering copper. A common copper bit receives its heat from a flame. It is a simple reservoir of heat. An electric soldering iron supplies constant heat, though this is sometimes a disadvantage.

(3) Flame and soldering copper methods are often used together, as for example in the sweating process.

3. Heat distribution and range. (*a*) In joining two pieces of metal by solder, each piece heated must attain a temperature above that of the melting solder (401 deg. F. for 50-50 solder). If but one of the pieces attains this heat, solder will adhere to that one and not to the one below 401 deg.

(1) When two metals of like thicknesses are joined, the heat is distributed evenly over both.

(2) When metals of wide varying weights are joined, heat is directed mainly on the heavy metal until both are equally hot (Fig. 123).

(3) When two alloys are joined, their weight being equal, heat must be directed mainly upon the one of least conductivity. For example, if copper is soldered to brass, the heat is directed mainly toward the brass until both metals are equally hot.

(4) Heat is quickly wasted to the point of failure if work is held by oversize tongs, on the metal vise, or to cold metal bench tops. The vise is never used for soldering unless lined with a nonconducting material.

The same may be said of a bench top. Sheets of asbestos and firebrick are ideal foundations for the soldering operation. Failing these, a nonresinous wood such as bass or walnut is good. Pine may not be used.

b) The temperatures of metals being soldered should never rise to the point of heavy oxidation, and certainly not to that of the burning point of tin.

(1) This danger point is attained especially in instances where one metal directly contacts the flame.

(2) However, it is more often attained when the flame is directed toward the light metal rather than the heavy, or the conducting metal rather than the nonconducting. This metal, then, rises in temperature to the burning point, while the other piece has risen barely to the melting point of solder. The working-heat range then is limited. When the solder becomes a thin fluid the heat should be removed because correct temperature has been attained.

4. Direct-flame soldering. The Bunsen burner is used as the standard heat source throughout this work, though the flame of an alcohol lamp or the surplus flame from the door of a bench furnace will produce good results. A gas torch is convenient for most purposes because of its mobility, but its use is hazardous in schools. This may, of course, be overcome by proper insulation with sheet asbestos and firebrick and with an annealing pan of lump pumice.

5. Examples:

Example 1. A seamed cylinder is soldered preparatory to being flared. The same procedure is applicable to box corners, lap joints, and flowerpot seams.

a) The seam is fluxed on the inside, and a few small pieces of solder are laid on it. Then it is held by light tongs over a soft flame (Fig. 124).

b) The cylinder is rocked as necessary. It should be remembered that solder, being

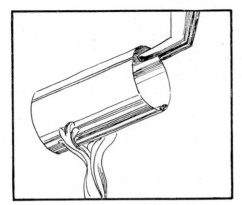

Fig. 124. Preparing a seam for soldering.

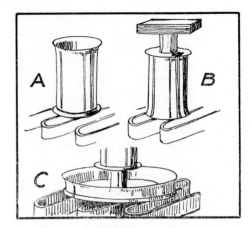

Fig. 126. Soldering a cup and stem.

heavy, flows downward and toward the hottest point. A strong heat is to be avoided.

Example 2. A candlestick cup is soldered to its base (Pl. 1). This process is also used in the soldering of bases to flowerpots, dished bottoms to vase bodies, etc.

a) The contact points are cleaned by means of steel wool.

b) Flux is applied by bamboo stick or brush.

c) The base is set on a rack under which the flame may play (Fig. 125).

d) The cup is set over the center of the base and three pieces of wire solder, ⅛ in. long, are distributed inside the cup.

e) A slow flame is used.

f) Close watching of the joint will soon

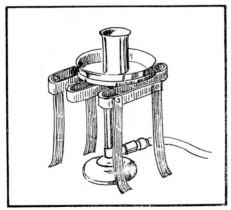

Fig. 125. Heating base of candlestick for soldering.

disclose a stream of bright solder running completely around the cup, at which point the heat is turned off. It is cooled before moving. If the solder does not run around, the metal does not fit closely, the work is not set level and solder will not run up grade, or foreign matter is obstructing free running. An application of more flux will remedy the latter.

Example 3. A cup and stem are soldered to a base (Pls. 13, 15, etc.). The same process is used in the soldering of stemmed vases.

a) A bottom disk is soldered to the cup by the same process as steps *a* to *f*, Example 2 (*A*, Fig. 126).

b) It is turned over and a stem is soldered to the lower side of the cup in the same manner. The original soldering will melt, but, if it is held down by weight (*B*, Fig. 126), enough solder will remain in the joint to hold it. Do not move it until set.

c) Pack the cup with damp paper, or paint it with yellow ocher, or whiting, mixed with water. A low heat then will not affect that part.

d) Punch a small hole into the center of the base for a gas vent.

e) Set the soldered cup and stem over the base with several pieces of solder inside, both contacts having been fluxed (*C,* Fig. 126).

f) Apply the heat and turn it off the moment the solder has run.

Example 4. Feet are soldered to the bottom of a lamp base. The same process is used for the soldering of handles to covers, rosettes to tray bottoms, etc.

a) The parts are cleaned — if iron, filed bright — and fluxed.

b) The base is laid in reverse on the soldering rack (Fig. 125). Feet are placed on their marks, a small piece of solder next to each, and a pencil line marking off the soldering area. Solder under ordinary conditions will not cross the line.

c) The flame is applied to each separately while it is held down firmly by a bamboo stick.

d) The soldered foot is allowed to set. Then it is painted with water to cool. It is covered with yellow ocher or whiting, or damp paper for protection, and the soldering proceeds on the next foot.

Example 5. Projecting arms are soldered to a disk (Fig. 127).

a) The parts are cleaned and, if they are of iron as in Plates 30, 50, or 53, filed bright at joining areas, and fluxed.

b) They are assembled under a holding ring of pipe and held aligned in light tongs bent to hold them between parallel jaws.

c) The solder is placed inside next to each arm.

d) Placed over a flame, they are soldered, allowed to set, and cooled in water. The flux should not run up to the ring.

Example 6. A leaf is soldered to a rod. This process is the one most widely used in part assembly in this book. For example, a brass arrowhead is soldered to an iron rod, petals to a stem, rosettes to the side of a flowerpot, shade arms to a stem, handles to disks and reflectors, and handles to bowls.

a) If necessary, the parts are cleaned and then fluxed. Iron parts are filed bright.

b) They are held together by light tongs (Fig. 123), pliers, clips (Fig. 128), fine wire, fire clamps, or they are pressed together on a soldering rack by a stick or weight (Fig. 125).

c) The solder is dropped into place.

d) The aligned assembly is held over a flame (see Soft Soldering, step 3). The piece is revolved and tipped if practicable, allowing the solder to run into all joints.

Example 7. Parts assembled by rivet and those in need of reinforcing, such as feet on iron lamp bases, hooks to backplates, scrolls, and husks to lamp stems, are soldered to prevent turning.

a) All parts are cleaned, except iron which is filed.

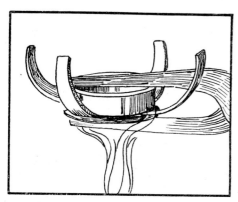

Fig. 127. Heating arms and cup for soldering.

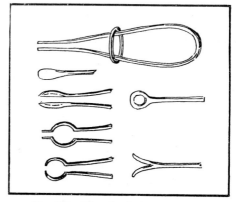

Fig. 128. Clips for holding light and heavy pieces.

b) When ready, the parts are fluxed, care being taken to confine the flux to limited areas.

c) Solder is placed next to joints by means of tweezers.

d) The object is held over a flame, revolved, and tipped until solder runs into the joints. It is then cooled in water. The work described in Examples 5, 6, and 7, when it concerns iron, is simplified and great strength is obtained by the use of Lotan soldering compound. As this mixture already contains flux, the procedure is as follows: The parts are filed bright, assembled, and held as directed. Lotan is applied by means of a cup-ended iron wire, and soldered over a flame.

6. Sweating and tinning. When solder may not be placed into a joint satisfactorily because of the width of the surfaces to be joined, because of the absence of a suitable ridge, or to keep adjacent metal clean of solder, the process of sweating is employed. This consists of coating or tinning one or both pieces to be joined with a thin layer of solder, and then holding them together over a flame until the coatings fuse together. Tinning is done either by soldering copper or flame. In the latter instance, the metal is cleaned and fluxed, a piece of solder is laid over it, and both are held in the flame to spread the solder. If the latter does not run of itself, it may be distributed by a cloth or fiber brush. The piece is then washed.

Example 1. Arms are soldered to a beam. This process is applicable to an endless list of problems, especially in fastening leaves to a lamp stem, arms to a disk or rod, feet to lamp bases, rosettes to flowerpots, petals to stems, and so on.

a) The parts are cleaned, unless it is iron, which is filed bright.

b) They are fluxed, tinned by a soldering bit, or after applying solder, they are placed over a flame and tinned.

c) Then the tinned pieces are assembled, held together by light tongs or other holding devices except screw clamps (see Figs. 126, 127, and 128), and melted (sweated) together.

Example 2. Two thin pieces or a thin and thick piece are sweated together. This process is used on such problems as laminated book ends and bases.

a) The joining surfaces are tinned as shown above, or if one extends beyond the other and is to remain clean of solder, the smaller joining surface is tinned, while the other is cleaned and fluxed.

b) The parts are clipped together, using enough clips to hold them tightly at all points (Fig. 128). Screw clamps will not do for this work.

c) The unit is passed back and forth through the flame until evenly heated and soldered. It is held so that surplus solder may drop out without running over the clean areas. If it is found that spaces remain unsoldered, holding devices having held all points tightly, more flux is added, and if this does not draw the solder, more of the latter is added from a wire of solder hammered to a thin wedge until all edges are filled. If other parts are now to be soldered to this piece, the clips should remain in place. In some instances polishing before further soldering saves much labor, especially if such additions make machine buffing impossible. Clips then are removed for polishing and are replaced for the next soldering.

Example 3. Pieces, having been polished and fitted, are soldered to the cleaned and polished base by sweating together as shown in Example 2 (Pl. 23).

a) All contact ends on the pieces to be added are tinned sparingly.

b) The base is fluxed only where necessary in order to avoid discoloring the metal. A pencil line is drawn around the soldering area in order to confine the solder.

c) The base piece is clipped because the next operation will melt its solder.

d) All parts are set up on the soldering rack and aligned. Those needing pressure to hold them are weighted down.

e) A flame is played evenly over the bottom until the parts are sweated in, when it is immediately turned off and fanned to cool rapidly. Do not use water to cool until the solder has set. Example 3 may be more readily done, however, by means of a small gas torch or other mobile flame if available. By this method the parts are prepared and set up as before, and a hot flame is concentrated upon the area around each upright, thus soldering without the general melting of the base.

7. Soldering-copper practice. (*a*) Function. The flame is preferred on work demanding an enveloping heat that draws solder toward and under points not reached by the copper. Soldering thus is confined to smaller areas and is cleaner and inconspicuous in appearance.

However, if the flame may injure soldering already done, if a copper bit is more convenient and practical, if a flame will warp thin surfaces as in tinwork, or if it may discolor the metal unnecessarily, the soldering copper should be used.

b) Theory and care. The soldering copper is a heat reservoir. A light copper holds

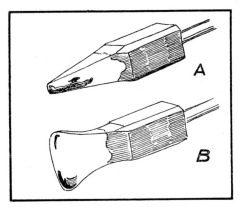

Fig. 129. Special forms of soldering coppers.

too little heat for practical purposes. A $\frac{1}{2}$- to 1-lb. tool is recommended. Enough heat must be available to raise the temperature of an object above the melting point, and maintain it there as long as necessary. If conditions require working within a limited area on a larger object, enough heat must be supplied to maintain the melting temperature and allow for the loss of heat through adjacent cold areas.

Such an amount of heat may not run out of a small or clogged opening. The purpose of a clean tinned tip, whose flat surfaces rest in fluid solder, is to provide a large heat outlet. The wide surfaces of both pieces to be joined must be in perfect contact. That this may be the case:

(1) The point is forged long and fine (*A*, Fig. 129), or it is shaped for special work such as inside bottom work (*B*, Fig. 129).

(2) It is filed smooth on each surface.

(3) The point is tinned by heating the copper until the furnace flame burns green around it, and until the bright copper turns iridescent bronze and purple. It is then laid flat on a brick of sal ammoniac and its four faces are rubbed in a pool of solder. It also may be rubbed on a thin metal surface in a pool of flux and solder.

(4) The point must be kept tinned and clean.

(*a*) Avoid overheating the soldering bit. A high temperature will burn off the tin and pit the copper. Before it may be used again, therefore, it must be refiled and tinned.

The proper temperature for a soldering bit is calculated by means of the full green flame enveloping it and by the thin iridescent film on its tinned point. Just beyond lies a destructive range of heat.

(*b*) It is well to wipe the bit on a muslin cloth before using or to dip it into a weak solution of soldering salts.

c) Practice.

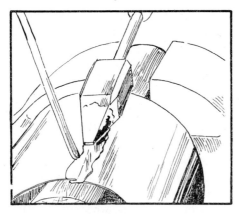

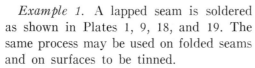

Fig. 130. Soldering a seam.

Fig. 131. Soldering the reflector plate.

Example 1. A lapped seam is soldered as shown in Plates 1, 9, 18, and 19. The same process may be used on folded seams and on surfaces to be tinned.

a) The seam is cleaned, if necessary, and fluxed.

b) The soldering copper is removed from the fire, dipped into the cleaning solution, and charged with several pellets of solder lying on a nonconducting surface. These, when touched by the heated tip, are melted and drawn up. It is best to take up just enough solder for the job.

c) The work, having been hung over a wooden rod extending from the vise, is held down at one point by a bamboo fluxing stick while the soldering copper is set over the joint on the far end of the cylinder, its broad surface down flat.

d) As soon as the solder runs on the metal, the bit is slowly drawn down to the opposite end, the stick holding the soldered portion until set (Fig. 130).

If the job is not smooth, the copper was drawn too quickly to maintain an even temperature throughout, it was not held down flat to the joint, it was too cold, or too much solder was applied.

If the parts are still loose, too little solder was used, or the copper was not in contact with *both* members of the joint, or the bamboo stick failed to hold the seam until set (Fig. 130).

Example 2. Tacking process. If the joint to be soldered is long and otherwise difficult to hold; if its parts tend to spring while being held, or if parts are to be temporarily placed for appraisal, they are tacked. A planished tin cover, sprung out of true, is soldered to a watering can (see Pl. 9).

a) The can is held next to the operator's body and the cover is forced into place. The soldering points are fluxed by a bamboo stick. The bit is cleaned, charged with a little solder, and touched to a center point to tack the cover in place. If it is now found to be incorrectly placed, it may be easily loosened and shifted. It is then forced into place at the end and touched with solder. The opposite end is tacked likewise. In touching the copper to the points of contact heat should be equally distributed to both sides and enough solder should be deposited to complete the joint.

b) Now being held in place, the joining edges are fluxed completely. The bit is removed from the fire, cleaned, charged, set into the joint, contacting *each* member as fully as possible. It is drawn slowly so that the pool of solder remains in a fluid state. If the supply of solder fails, the bit is re-charged and the soldering is continued. The important point in this step, however, is to solder, first the sections not tacked, allowing a safe interval between the tacked points and working sections, and finally filling in and finishing. The reflectors in Plate 2 are similarly soldered (see Fig. 131), the only possible difference being that tongs or clips may be utilized as shown. Rings on shade tops are also soldered by the same process.

Example 3. A hemmed upright is sol-dered to a reflector. This method also may be applied to the soldering of feet to a base, a holder to a shade, handles to trays and reflectors, and joints in boxes and trays.

a) The parts to be soldered are cleaned and fluxed.

b) They are held over a nonconducting material. The part to be soldered is held down by a bamboo stick or its equivalent (see Fig. 132).

c) The soldering bit is cleaned, touched to the solder supply, and laid into the angle of the joint, flat on the bottom and tight against the added side, allowing it to rest until the solder runs into the joint. The bit is drawn slowly so that the solder penetrates.

Example 4. A handle is soldered to a sprinkling can or candlestick. This method also is used in the soldering of spouts to cans, handles to lanterns, and crossbars to shades.

a) The parts are cleaned and fluxed.

b) The soldering copper is taken from the fire, cleaned, and touched to the solder.

c) The handle, held in the fingers, is pressed to the can which again may be held against the operator or the bench.

d) The copper is placed into the angle of contact (Fig. 133), and held there until the solder melts. It is then moved back-ward in the pool of solder for the extent of the joint.

If solder runs out of the soldering area, too much solder was used, or the work was not held properly. Since solder runs down grade as well as toward the hottest part, the joint should be held in horizontal posi-tion. Some cases are better worked in a V position (Fig. 133).

PEWTER SOLDERING AND WELDING

1. Soldering. Generally speaking, pewter is flame soldered much the same as other metals. Owing to its low melting tempera-ture (between 425 to 440 deg. F.), extreme caution is advised in the application and proper distribution of heat.

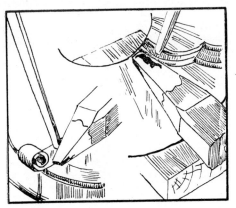

Fig. 132. Soldering feet and arms.

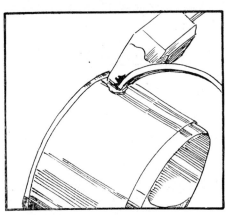

Fig. 133. Soldering a handle.

a) First of all, a lower melting solder should be used; namely, a 60-40 solder, melting at 368.6 deg. F., a gain of 33 deg. in range.

b) Another important point is the use of thin, freshly scraped solder (see Soldering). If this is disregarded, the heat may rise to the softening point of pewter before the cores of the solder pieces reach a melting point. The result is a badly pitted pewter surface. Then further, a film of insulating foreign matter on unscraped solder may ward off heat until dangerously near 425 deg., when, by a slight further application, both pewter and solder melt. Very thin, clean solder, then, is a necessity.

Pewter solder of 1/16-in. diameter may be bought from pewter manufacturers. Both this alloy and size are recommended.

c) A most important element in successful soldering of pewter is heat distribution. The recommended heat source is a combination of Bunsen burner and small gas torch. Either will do and even an alcohol lamp or a gas blowpipe will answer the same purpose (see Soldering 3, step *a,* and Fig. 134).

Since solder is a lead alloy of gray color and modern pewter is almost pure tin, much whiter in tone, solder should be used sparingly. As a rule, butt joints are not soldered. They are welded (see Welding). If solder is hidden in the shadow of angular joints, however, its use is not objectionable.

Fig. 135. Preheating to the vaporizing point of flux.

2. Practice. Soldering the base of a bowl. (*a*) The edges to be joined are filed to fit accurately. A close fit provides a strong capillary attraction through the joint. All contact surfaces and edges are then thoroughly cleaned of all foreign matter.

b) The pieces are held, if flat, so that the flame may play beneath as well as over them (Figs. 135 and 136), while at the same time they are held against the danger of buckling or sinking down. Pewter is quite soft at 400 deg. F.

c) The closed spaces are drilled from below before soldering to provide vents for gases.

d) The seam is fluxed, the glycerine-hydrochloric acid solution being preferred (see Soft Soldering, step 1).

e) Small pieces, 1/32 by 1/16 in. of thin, freshly scraped solder are placed closely together along the seam by means

Fig. 134. Temperatures above 2000° F. are attained at this point.

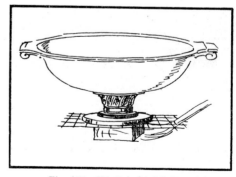

Fig. 136. Heating from below.

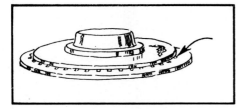

Fig. 137. Using cut pieces of solder for making a seam.

Fig. 138. Soldering parts of a bowl and base.

of tweezers or a fine brush wet with flux (Fig. 137). In some cases, the uncut, thin strips of solder (see Soldering 1, step *a*) may be laid along the joint.

f) Both Bunsen burner and torch are lit and adjusted, the latter to a fine pointed flame. The Bunsen burner is passed back and forth over the metal, heating it all over to about 250 deg. and then near the joint to the boiling point of the flux. At no time should it be held constant over one spot.

g) The torch flame may now be played in the same manner within the more restricted area of the joint until the solder flushes through. This will occur suddenly. The heat is immediately moved to the adjoining section and so on around (Fig. 138). Note particularly that the point of flux vaporization is an indication of the attainment of temperatures within a few degrees of solder fluidity. Great care should be taken at this point. Here the flame is applied less directly. A repeated touching and withdrawing of the flame would more accurately describe this stage of heat application.

The entire operation may be done with either the Bunsen burner or the torch as it is often done, but one can readily see that a small flame is ineffectual on large surfaces and a large one is hazardous on small areas. A torch adjustable by trigger is ideal for this work. On small pieces a torch alone will handle the work satisfactorily.

It has been found practical also to do circumferential soldering of large work on a rotating table constructed out of a used phonograph.

The soldering should be watched very carefully. If any doubt arises as to temperature, more flux should be applied. If the solder begins to melt on one side of the joint, the flame is shifted to the other. From this point the flame is applied a second at a time where needed and removed until the solder suddenly runs. There need be no fear of melting the pewter when using this method.

3. Soldering cast pieces to thin metal bodies. (*a*) The same preparation is made as in the preceding steps *a* to *f*.

b) More heat, however, is directed to the heavy part.

When it has been evenly built up in both heavy and light metal, the torch is passed over the area of the joint, favoring the heavy side, lifted off, applied momentarily and removed, and so on, until the solder begins to melt, when it can be seen on what side to apply more heat. The metal, now within the critical range of heat, is exposed to less volume of flame in successive sections until the solder suddenly flows. If the heavy section is on the bottom of the unit, heat must be applied from below as well as on the joint. If solder remains outside the joint it may have been pushed away from close contact by boiling flux or if rough heat was withdrawn a few points too soon.

c) The work must be watched carefully. When temperatures rise to the melting point, a trifle more heat on one side will draw or melt the solder to that side and leave the joint unsoldered. In extreme cases, more flux or solder is added, but ordinarily, if the eye is quick to judge, heat may be added here or there to distribute it equally and draw the solder into the joint.

d) The flame is more efficient and more easily gauged if played so that it runs off to the side.

4. Pewter welding. Pewter is welded rather than soldered along butt-jointed seams on vases, round boxes, and other joints where the gray line left by soldering is undesirable. Its greatest advantage, however, is that joints, some of which are difficult to match, need no better than approximate fitting, and the problem of holding during assembly, so challenging in soldering, is eliminated. This convenience, added to that of the ease of repairing dents, fractures, short fits, holes, edge faults, seams of built-up cast parts, and filling in of weak corners, brings high raised pewter work within the range of schools and amateurs.

Welding is the process of consolidating

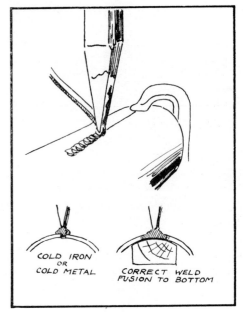
Fig. 140. Welding a seam.

metals by means of a like metal. Soldering is the process of joining metals, using an alloy of lower melting point. Pewter being a metal of low melting point, the preferred heat source used in welding is a soldering copper.

a) Welding the seam of a vase. (1) The pewter is clamped tight to a wood form, closely fitted to the surface under the seam (Fig. 139). If not tight, a pad of

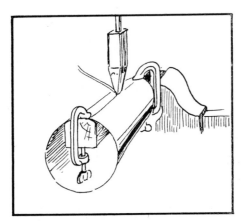
Fig. 139. Holding a cylinder to be welded.

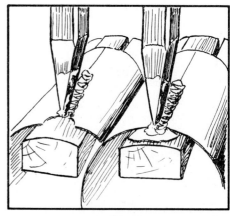
Fig. 141. Running in an end weld.

cloth over the wood will help fill the interval.

(2) It is not necessary to provide a closely filed fit.

(3) The seam is fluxed.

(4) A long tapered soldering copper is heated to a point where the flame is green and its tinned surfaces are iridescent. Further heat is ruinous to the coated tip.

(5) It is removed from the fire and, if not in perfect condition, the tip is rubbed in a pool of pewter on a sal ammoniac block and wiped on a cloth. A jar or soldering flux, a jar of soldering salt solution for cleaning the copper, and small pieces of scrap pewter on asbestos sheet should be near the object to be welded.

(6) Welding procedure. The heated copper is dipped into a cleaning solution and held in a vertical position. A drop of pewter then is fed into its tip and applied to the joint. The heat of the copper passing through the melted drop, fuses it with the pewter. At the fusing moment, the copper, still held in the molten metal pool, is moved down the seam (Fig. 140).

If it were possible to feed the proper amount of pewter into the heated tip with the left hand, and the tip were moved at a constant speed to the end of the seam, the operation might be beautifully done. In practice, a hot iron tarnishes and the flow becomes increasingly irregular until it is recleaned in the solution. It is, therefore, a good policy to clean the iron, take up a fresh drop, and proceed to the end of the supply, repeating the procedure as often as necessary.

The ideal weld is one which penetrates through to the bottom of the joint cleanly at all points, and utilizes all superfluous pewter drops having a top seam only slightly higher than the body itself.

Enough metal should be deposited so that, after filing both inside and outside, the seam will not show.

(7) Capillary attraction is responsible for the running in of end welding. To close the end, a scrap of pewter is set against it and the interval is welded shut and trimmed down (Fig. 141).

b) Welding a hole burnt into a pewter vase. If the hole is large, it is filled with a patch cut to the approximate size of the hole. Accuracy is not necessary. If small, it is filled by the drop method as follows:

(1) The hole is trimmed back to the clean metal.

(2) A wood form is fit tightly under the hole and held by any suitable means. Almost as good is a tightly folded cloth pad.

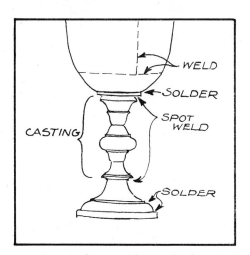

Fig. 142. Some articles require both welding and soldering.

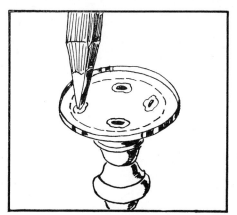

Fig. 143. Spot welding.

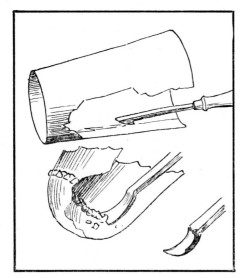

Fig. 144. Superfluous welding metal may
be removed with gouges and scrapers.

(3) The copper is dipped into the cleaning solution and pewter is fed into its tip
until the drops fall into the hole. These
are fused together with the metal edges by
stirring. If the hole does not close, an in-
sufficient amount of pewter drops were fed
in. Here, the weight of pewter must coun-
teract the capillary force.

(4) The weld is then filed, scraped, and
finished.

(5) The large hole is trimmed, supported
from beneath by a wood form, filled with
a patch bent to the correct curvature, and
welded by the seam-welding process. It is
then filed, scraped, and planished. The purpose of the wood support is to reduce inside filing and chiseling or scraping to a
minimum.

(6) With care, melted edges and ornament parts, heretofore discarded, are built
up with pewter by the welding process and
thus repaired. This method has so many
applications in pewter work, particularly
at its critical and discouraging stages, that
one is compelled to assign to it a high
place of importance as an aid in the con-
duct of successful classes.

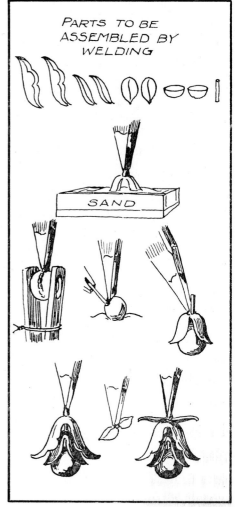

Fig. 145. Assembly of ornament by welding.

c) Spot-welding pewter. The spot-welding process is a convenient means of fastening certain types of pewter parts in a way
that renders seams invisible to the observer.
The advantage of the process is its ease of
application to parts otherwise soldered, the
convenience of fastening parts difficult to
hold during soldering, and finally its speed
of application.

For example: (1) The spot welding of
base pieces before being soldered into a
unit to the body of a vase, bowl, or cup
as shown in Figure 142.

(*a*) The contact points are fluxed.

(*b*) The two sections are set, one on another, their inside surfaces in close contact or, if necessary, in contact through an intermediate piece.

(*c*) These are aligned and held down by a finger or a stick. The work usually rests on a nonconducting material such as an asbestos sheet.

(*d*) At this point, the heated soldering copper is cleaned in the salt solution and held vertically in the hand.

(*e*) The point of the copper is set over one of the most logical fastening areas and plunged in to the lower level of the unit, taking with it molten pewter. This is fused to the lower piece, thereby welding all together. The same process is repeated in three or four other areas as shown in Figure 143.

(2) With expert care it is possible to spot-weld base units to the thin layers of underbodies, especially if slight eruptions on the inside surfaces, due to the melting through of molten welding metal, are easily removed. This is done with comparative ease by the use of gouges of the carving chisel type, riffles, and scrapers (Fig. 144). Rotary files and small abrasive wheels are particularly useful in this work.

(3) Fastening an ornament consisting of two twin leaf units and a ball (Fig. 145).

(*a*) Each pair of leaves is held in sand and welded. The ball is made of two halves, each driven into wood with a rounded punch. These are held between wood as shown, and the seam is welded, then filed, scraped, and burnished.

(*b*) A stem is welded to the ball, and its joint is filed clean.

(*c*) The ball unit is placed into the inner leaf unit and spot-welded from below. The ball unit may be wedged into an immovable position by paper wads and held in the fingers.

(*d*) The ball-and-leaf unit is then welded to the lower leaf unit (Fig. 145).

(*e*) If small parts become too hot to hold, they are encircled in cloth, wood, or asbestos pads.

CHAPTER VI

CASTING

The casting process requires no expensive equipment, in fact, the metal may be melted over a gas flame in a tin can and poured into wood. Wood molds are quite durable for small work and are hardly scorched if rightly used.

1. Standard equipment. A small gas melting furnace and ladle, plaster of paris and fine molding sand, small flasks, and materials for patterns are required for this work.

2. Low-melting alloys are numerous, the most beautiful being britannia, melting at 440 deg. It usually contains about 92 per cent tin, 6 per cent antimony, and 2 per cent copper. However, other alloys containing antimony are useful for decorative work, as for example:

> White metal — 33 lead, 54 tin, and 10.6 antimony
> Type metal — 60 lead, 10 tin, and 30 antimony
> Babbitt — 78 lead, 6 tin, and 16 antimony
> Linotype metal — 85 lead, 3 tin, and 12 antimony

The sundial was cast in type metal, its antimony content giving it the desirable property of expanding on cooling, thus sharpening its detail. Lead is least expensive, but melts at 618.8 deg. F., the highest fusing point of the recommended metals. Lead has been used satisfactorily for centuries on architectural detail and is noted for its durability.

3. Casting covers the following work: patterns; molding; core making, if the casting is to be hollow; and pouring or casting.

THE PATTERN

The pattern may be made of clay, soap, wax, wood, or metal.

1. Turned patterns should be split, that is, they are turned from wood having previously been glued in two halves with paper in the glue joints. After turning, they are split and provided with short pins for convenient parting in the molding operation (Fig. 146).

2. Other patterns or models are carved in clay, plaster, soap, wax, or wood, with ample provision for draft; that is, the angles of all planes, both above and below the parting line, must converge sufficiently to allow free drawing of the pattern from the mold (Fig. 146).

3. Wax models are the exception, if they are meant to provide but one casting (waste-wax method). In such case, they are cast in a two-part plaster mold, then melted out over a slow heat (usually overnight). The vents and casting channels are cut in, the metal is poured, and the molds are broken away, since they may not be lifted from the casting because of undercut portions in the wax and in the metal.

4. Wood, clay, plaster, or soap models (and wax also if carved with proper draft) are well shellacked and thoroughly, though thinly, greased with heavy cup grease, floor

wax, or liquid soap and oil before being cast into plaster-of-paris molds. They are merely well shellacked if molded in sand.

MOLDS

1. Plaster molds. After the pattern is greased, enough plaster is mixed in water to make the lower half of the mold. The plaster is sprinkled into water until the saturated mixture appears above the surface. When this also has absorbed water, the batch is stirred from below to avoid bringing down air bubbles. It is then run into a cardboard box and shaken to bring up any bubbles that may have formed. The pattern is immediately laid

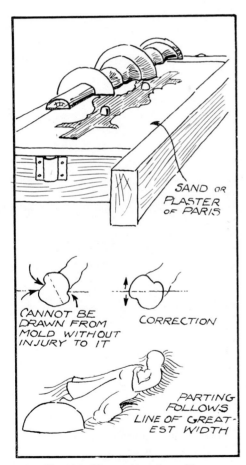

Fig. 146. Place pattern in mold so that it may be withdrawn.

into the plaster up to its center. When the plaster is set and partially cooled, it is trimmed down to the parting line and the pattern is lifted out. If the mold is as perfect as possible, it is replaced, the plaster is greased for parting, and the upper half is cast and shaken. After setting, the pattern is removed and the mold is thoroughly dried. A good plan is to set it on a heating furnace overnight.

Dental plaster (investment) is ideal for this work except for its cost. It may be dried out by a torch and used immediately while hot, a decided advantage in itself. Furthermore, the dental-plaster molds last indefinitely, while the usefulness of plaster-of-paris molds seldom extends beyond three castings.

2. Sand molds are made in flasks (Fig. 147), and may be used immediately after molding. When the pattern is small, fine, damp Albany or French sand, obtained at a brass foundry, is rammed into the drag (bottom), the pattern is pressed in up to its parting line, and sand is tamped and trimmed around it. Parting sand then is dusted over the mold. The wooden cope (top of the flask) is set over the drag, the sprue and riser pin are set, and sand is rammed over the pattern.

The process is simplified if the pattern is such that it may be made split, when

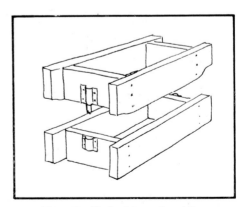

Fig. 147. Flasks for sand molding.

the flat half is laid on the table inside the drag and sand is rammed around it. Reversed, and the second half of the pattern added, the process proceeds as before.

VENTS

The pouring hole or sprue as a rule leads to the heaviest or highest point of the pattern. It should be of such diameter and height that the weight of surplus metal cast into it tends to force that below it into all extremities of the cavity. The riser is set at a heavy point near the opposite end of the pattern and serves as the indicator of a filled mold.

After the cope is filled with sand, the flask is carefully opened, and the pattern, together with sprue and riser pin, are removed. Air and gas vents should lead outward from every point at which air pockets are likely to form (Fig. 148). In plaster, these are cut on the parting surface as hairlines with a pin or knife. In sand they are made by puncturing the mold with fine wire. About 90 per cent of the success of casting depends on proper venting. Therefore, sand molds are superior to those cast of plaster.

POURING

The metals must be sufficiently hot not to cool before reaching the fine cavities and extremities of the mold. Temperatures above this requirement, however, tend to cause violent boiling and probably failure. A successful casting will show metal at the riser.

WOOD MOLDS

Metal cast into wood (Fig. 149), previously cut to the general contour of the

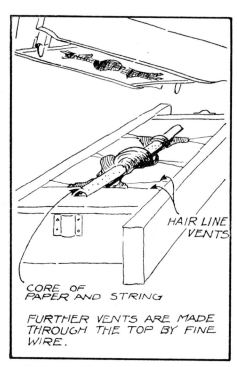

Fig. 148. Proper venting is of great importance.

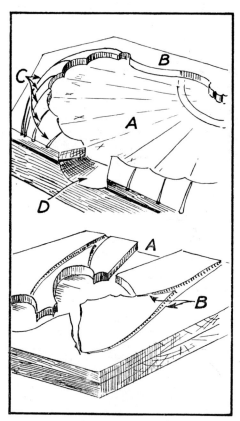

Fig. 149. Flat castings made in wood molds.

model, is cast at a low temperature. No patterns being used, the castings come out flat and need modeling (see the spoon project) except in such instances where the mold itself may be easily carved as in the sundial project. Castings are modeled by a process differing only slightly from that of wood patterns. The metal, being soft, may be chiseled, scraped, cut by knife, filed, and chased (see the book-end figures).

HOLLOW CASTINGS

Since melting temperatures are low, paper tubes with string wound about them are excellent core materials. Sand cores may be employed for advanced work (Fig. 148).

PEWTER RODS

Pewter rods, useful as handles and stems in built-up floral and fruit ornaments (Fig. 145) are cast into paper cylinders through paper funnels, the cylinder being rolled around wire, rod, or pencil, and stopped below by a paper wad.

Blanks for turnings, such as knobs, stems, finials, drops, etc., are cast in the same way. Blanks for turned lamp, bowl, and vase bases are cast on paper-wound wood blocks, the latter having been mounted and turned on a faceplate to the outside diameter of the blank with a step equal to the thickness of the cast wall, leaving a center mass which in the casting is its hollow core. Around the widest portion of the wood under the step, paper is wound to the height of the casting and tied with string. The faceplate with its mold is then set down, the casting made and cooled, the paper removed, and the blank is ready for turning. Such castings usually include a layer cast over the core in which case a match stump held into that portion of the molten metal will give vent to the gases.

FLAWS

Holes caused by air and gas pockets, sand falls, and low pouring temperatures are repaired by welding (see Welding).

CHAPTER VII

FINISHING

Each metal has an accepted finish expressing the quality of that which has been built up around it in its associations throughout history. This quality is effected by use, period, conditions, etc. The same may be said of metal forms and textures. Except for finishes accepted as bright, as on old silver, britannia, colonial brass, and modern metals of all kinds, those which have won the esteem of connoisseurs on old bronze, brass, iron, and lead-bearing pewter are patinas produced by handling and wear over their natural oxides, carbonates, and sulphides. Antique finishes are simulations of these. They may be approached by chemical and mechanical means, on which volumes have been written. The few such finishes, suitable for the projects of this course, are given in this chapter.

Viewing the work as a whole, the following is a résumé of finishes recommended: Tinwork may be polished like the old pewter it resembles, tin being the coating of one and the predominating metal in the other. The thin metalware, designed after that of the French Revolutionary period, is painted, decorated, and glazed. Copper bowls are acid colored and waxed. Brass is left bright to conform to modern practice, and is lacquered. Pewter is merely polished. Iron is fire oxidized, high lighted, and waxed, and if it is to be used outside, it is fired and coated.

Since all work not painted is polished by hand or machine, that process and the steps preceding it are discussed first.

POLISHING

Finished surfaces, except those on iron projects, are mirror smooth, a condition approached by gradual stages. A prime consideration then would be the protection of sheet metal from abrazing agents prior to and during manipulation.

1. The surface finishing process first in rank is planishing, which see. Chasing holds the same rank on small areas. By these processes, all waves, creases, kinks, and shallow scratches are easily removed. Buffing follows immediately.

2. Otherwise light scratches may be rubbed out by means of a burnisher, as shown in *E*, Figure 150, then a fine abrasive cloth and crocus cloth, prior to buffing, or prior to replanishing and buffing, as the

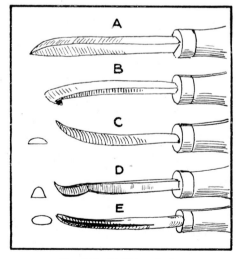

Fig. 150. Finishing tools.

case may be, in the order given, each step completely removing the marks of that preceding.

A burnisher produces high luster on metals, is used principally on small work such as jewelry, and consists of a mirror-smooth, file-hard blade of oval section. The preferred tools are slightly bent and may be made of files, or purchased.

3. *a*) Deep scratches and marks are scraped prior to the above order of procedure. Scraping is accomplished by means of short-bladed tools, ground from files, some of which are shown in Figure 150. They may be shaped to fit any need and are honed to a sharp edge. Scraping is just what the name implies and calls for no special direction except that the tendency of the tool to chatter is overcome by alternate cross scraping. For further exception, see step 4, following. Deep scraping within a limited area must be avoided or otherwise feathered so gradually to adjacent areas as to present no perceptible depression on the final mirrored surface.

b) Corners and deep areas, especially those on castings inaccessible to a file, are also scraped prior to further finishing processes, as noted.

4. Weld and solder patches are, generally speaking, too rough to scrape until they are chiseled or filed to uniformity with adjacent areas. Chiseling is the usual process in concavities such as, for example, insides of vases, and this in pewter and solder is done with wood-carving gouges, Figure 144; in harder metals with cold chisels.

As already mentioned, rotary files and small abrasive wheels attached to flexible shafts or hand motors are fast replacing the chiseling and scraping processes.

Filing is recommended for convex surfaces, a coarse file being used for pewter and solder. Gummed paper may be temporarily applied to immediate areas as protection against scratches. Following either of these processes are those of scraping, burnishing, rubbing with abrasive cloth, crocus cloth, and the buffing process, in order.

5. Abrasive and crocus-cloth polishing, mentioned in the foregoing paragraphs, includes the use of wood blocks over which the cloth is held and by means of which pressure at any point is correctly applied. Flat surfaces may be obtained only by the use of flat blocks. Shaped wood blocks for moldings, and wood sticks, felt-covered sticks, and felt and leather pieces will meet a variety of needs, especially if the latter are covered with powdered abrasive over glue.

Rubbing is done in the predominating direction of the part being polished, with the primary motive of a design, with the rim, or with the length of the object.

6. Buffing by hand is a rubbing process with cloth, felt, felt-covered stick, felt eraser, leather or brush, charged with tripoli, an abrasive in brick form supplied by hardware houses catering to the industries. The practice will approach the effectiveness of the machine process with little more expenditure of time and effort.

Streaks caused by the uneven pressures of dried-out and hardened cloths are eliminated from surfaces by the freer use of abrasive and a soft and evenly folded polishing cloth. Remaining unavoidable streaks are removed with a clean, soft cloth.

The film consisting mainly of abrasive binder, a wax, is finally washed off with kerosene. Great care is necessary during the entire buffing procedure to avoid picking up particles of emery dust in the cloth or tripoli brick.

7. Rouge polishing follows that of tripoli on such metals as pewter, bronze, silver, etc., if a still higher finish is desired. The process is identical with that described in the preceding paragraphs. The action of rouge is to burnish rather than to cut.

Fig. 151. Polishing and buffing wheels
may be mounted on a grinder.

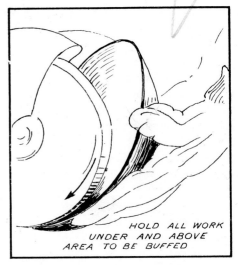

HOLD ALL WORK
UNDER AND ABOVE
AREA TO BE BUFFED

Fig. 152. Buffing a bowl.

8. Machine polishing and buffing by cloth wheel is a great convenience, and one should be set up if possible. A hand grinder or lathe may be utilized for this purpose.

a) The wheels as used are built up of two or three 6-in. sewed cotton wheels, each about ⅜ in. thick, sold at mill-supply stores. In the absence of standard equipment, they are mounted in the lathe, or improvised grinder lathe, shown in Figure 151, between washers and nuts, on a ½-in. bolt whose ends are drilled and slotted to fit against the spur on one end and a dead center at the other.

b) The mounted wheels are then prepared as follows: They are covered with hot glue, and when almost dry, are rotated, scraped true, and edges rounded with lump pumice or file held against a tool rest. They are dried and recoated with glue, and immediately dipped into a tray of 120 grit abrasive powder and redried. In this state they are exceedingly hard and coarse and need cutting down on rough work before being used on fine bronze, brass, or pewter. The fact is that none but very worn wheels should ever be used on pewter, and then with reserve. Machine polishing is ideal for bronze turnings and for marks and scratches in brass, bronze, and copper, but even for these, wheels must be smooth and soft. They may be softened with a hammer.

Pewter, copper, and solder tend to clog polishing wheels and should be held lightly against them. It is good practice to prepare a number of wheels at a time and to have them available in various stages of wear.

c) Buffing is grainless finishing with abrasive compounds of extreme fineness, as already explained. These are bought in brick form and are used by being pressed against the clean rotating wheel as needed during the operation. Wheels are mounted as before, usually in threes, occasionally single if the work is irregular as a handle, or deep and narrow as in the base of a bowl. The work then proceeds as follows: The metal is held against the freshly charged rotating wheel and moved sidewise and forward to produce a uniform polish. It will be noticed that scratches and pinholes become lines under the wheel unless the metal is revolved, alternated in direction, and constantly moved. Pressure is necessary, and since this produces considerable heat, pewter is quickly softened and drawn unless constantly moved to areas within safe temperatures. Other metals are not so affected, but it is suggested that work be held in canvas gloves. Buffing wheels need repeated replenishing during use. Black streaks on metal and a metallic glaze on the wheel is a signal for the application of more abrasive.

Wheels must be maintained in a soft condition. Caked wheels are cleaned by combing while in rotation with a nail-studded wood block or file end. Final removal of buffing streaks is done with a soft, clean wheel left uncharged.

Minute scratches on buffed surfaces are caused by particles of emery dust on the wheel or on the abrasive brick. Combing or discarding the wheel for a fresh one is the only remedy.

d) All flat work is held against the wheel within its surfaces, on its trailing edges, or on side edges, the hands being beneath the point of contact and above, as shown in Figure 152. The latter position is important as it provides resistance to the pull of the wheel. Otherwise the wheel may draw the project out of balance, catch its upper edges, and throw it down. Thin edges and open-work objects are too easily caught in the wheel. Handles, small open ornaments with projections, etc., are held flat on a glove, pad, or on an old buffing wheel, as shown in *A,* Figure 153. Hollow sections,

such as lamp stems, are held on rods and spun against the wheel, as shown in *B,* Figure 153.

SPECIFIC FINISHES

Bright finishes on pewter, tin, brass, bronze, and copper: (*a*) Antique luster is obtained by rubbing with No. 4/0 steel wool charged with lava soap and water. Frequent rinsings will disclose irregularities in finish and direction of stroke. The latter should follow predominating motives in decoration, the length of rectangular surfaces, and the rim of circular and oval pieces.

Steel wool without soap will produce a high luster.

b) Satin finish is produced by rubbing a damp surface with a wet cloth pad charged with fine pumice powder. It should be rinsed frequently.

c) Semisatin finish may be made over the satin finish with a damp cloth pad charged with rottenstone.

d) High finish is obtained by rubbing with a cloth pad or buffing wheel charged with tripoli compound as explained in the preceding section. It is finished with a clean cloth, wiped with a kerosene cloth, and washed in soap and water.

e) Mirror polish is a continuation of the

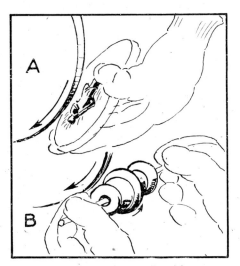

Fig. 153. Buffing small articles.

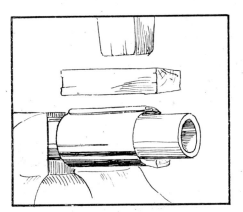

Fig. 154. Making cylindrical part of candleholder.

tripoli finish, rouge compound being used instead. The final cleaning follows as in the foregoing step.

f) Bright finish on iron: Surfaces are drawfiled where possible and otherwise thoroughly smoothed with fine files. They are then vigorously rubbed with several numbers of abrasive cloths, ending with the fine cloth, or polished on wheels in several stages of wear. Corners are polished with abrasive cloth held over a file or stick. Further brightness is obtained with tripoli compound as explained in the foregoing. Machine polishing and buffing is especially useful for iron stakes and hammers.

Antique Iron. After the above abrasive-cloth finish, the iron is washed with soap and water, dried, placed on a bar of iron and set into the furnace to soak at red heat for a few minutes. It is cooled slowly. At no time during the process must the surface come in contact with fingers, tongs, water, or furnace ash, and the result will be remuneration for the trouble. After assembly, it is high lighted to give it the quality of human contact, that of having been worn by use. Edges and extending parts, easily worn, are rubbed bright with abrasive cloth, blended into those of less importance, and led by imperceptible gradation of tone from the outer surfaces to the dark, untouched corners and con-cavities which do not wear, until all melt into a unified composition with emphasis on parts which draw attention. In general, parts nearest the observer and those near or at the top and outer edges receive most rubbing.

Heavy scale, the result of extended soak-ing at red heat, will produce unusual effects in iron, as shown in Figure 216. Rubbing, as usual, will remove some of it, but by hammering along surfaces to be high lighted, an irregular mottled appearance may be obtained. By repeating the soaking, a pitted effect that looks well on hardware, as shown in Figure 202, is obtained.

The final finish is heavy wax, thoroughly dried and rubbed. Dried wax in corners adds to the effect. Wax over rusted parts produces a very desirable brown.

Painted iron, and the linseed-oil coating of hot iron, are definitely not recommended because such coatings except for outside work, are unnecessary on the one hand, and on the other they destroy the beauty of the material. Soldered work is fire col-ored before assembly.

CLEANING, WASHING, AND CHEMICAL CLEANING

Cleaning, washing, rinsing, and drying precedes all acid and enamel coloring.

1. Grease, foreign matter, and even finger marks are a bane to coloring. Grease from buffing compounds is wiped off with kero-sene followed by a soap and water bath. Otherwise it is brushed in scalding water containing a washing-crystal grease solvent, and then rinsed and dried. Work to be painted is cleaned of soldering acid by scouring. Ironwork may be washed in warm soapy water, rinsed, and dried.

2. Though a small shop may quite satis-factorily continue cleaning tarnished cop-per, brass, and bronze pieces by the abra-sive method, it may adopt part or all, modestly or more fully of the following acid method since these metals are more easily and thoroughly cleaned by chemicals.

a) Book ends, for example, assembled from prebuffed pieces, are tarnished lightly by the heat and flux and require a bright dip and rinsing before lacquering.

b) Tarnished copper and brass whose contours are cut so deep as to exclude buffing come out of the acid pink. The following formulas will be found effective:

(1) Acid bath commonly called pickle. Into a stone crock pour 25 parts water and into it pour 1 part commercial sulphuric acid. The work is suspended in this solu-tion on a copper wire from 5 to 10 seconds, rinsed in running water, scrubbed, rerinsed,

and finally dried. If necessary, the operation is repeated in order to obtain uniformity of metallic color.

(2) Into a crock pour 4 parts water and into it 1 part commercial nitric acid. The work is suspended in it in the same manner as in step 1.

Either of these pickle baths is recommended, but the former is preferred for schools. The latter is very fast in its action.

3. Bright dip. (a) Pour 2 parts commercial hydrochloric acid into a crock and slowly add 1 part nitric acid. Then allow it to cool. To 1 quart of the foregoing, add 1 tablespoon of salt. When the boiling subsides, the solution is ready. Owing to the fumes generated during this operation, the mixing should be done outside, if the fumes may not be drawn off otherwise.

Articles are immersed on a copper wire for one or two seconds, swilled in water, and dried. Coloring or lacquering should follow immediately.

b) Another good solution consists of 2 parts pure sulphuric acid, 1½ parts nitric acid, and 1 per cent by weight of salt. The boiling should be allowed to subside. Neither of the bright dips are safe in schools, except with special precautions against splashing, dripping, etc.

COLORING BY ACID

For simplicity only three coloring solutions are given. These will be found both adequate and beautiful for the bronze and copper projects offered. They are as follows:

Solution 1. Into a crock or enameled pan, pour 1 part of powdered barium sulphide and dissolve it in 25 parts of hot water (approximate).

Solution 2. Into a crock or enameled pan, pour 1 part of lump potassium sulphide and dissolve it in 25 parts of hot water (approximate).

Solution 3. Into a glass container or crock, pour 1 part of lump copper sulphate, and dissolve it in 5 parts of hot water; then dissolve 1 part of crystal ammonium chloride in the above (water approximate).

No specific brass coloring solution is mentioned because the brass projects are recommended to be left in their natural state.

1. Brown on bronze and copper is obtained as follows: (a) The piece to be browned is thoroughly cleaned and rinsed. It must not be touched by the fingers, but should be handled with wire.

b) It should then be dipped into Solution 1. If the object is too large for the receptacle, the solution may be brushed on with a swab made of cotton waste tied to a stick. Iron-bound brushes should not be used. Hairbrushes are destroyed in this solution. A fiber kitchen brush will do. If work is immersed, it is handled by string or copper wire. The fingers should be kept out of the solution.

c) When the object is darkened sufficiently, it is rinsed and lightly polished on a rotary brass brush, or rubbed lightly with extra fine steel wool until a metallic sheen appears.

d) This operation is repeated until a fine brown is obtained. The work then is given a final rinsing and dried.

e) Aging may be produced by hand rubbing the parts or edges naturally becoming worn in time. Light buffing on new dry wheels will do the same thing. Dry rottenstone may be used, but buffing compounds should be avoided, because the grease they deposit necessitates rewashing.

f) Sheet-metal projects are usually thickly waxed, dried, and rubbed, and cast-bronze projects are lacquered. Similar colors on bronze may be obtained by the same method, using sodium sulphide instead of barium sulphide.

2. Black on copper is produced in Solu-

tion 2. The metal is left in the solution only as long as required to turn it dark. As it then appears, it is quite satisfactory as a modern finish on bowls and vases (Pls. 13, 14, and 15), although on several of these it is used only on the underside, the inside being left natural.

To be used merely as a color, however, as is the brown of Solution 1, it is cold and entirely out of harmony with the characteristic warmth of copper. It has a further use in the following formula:

3. Antique patina on copper, brass, and bronze, being a beautiful Pompeian green, is widely used, especially on classical work.

a) The metal is cleaned, rinsed, and dried, avoiding finger marks.

b) Copper or bronze is given an undercoat in Solution 2. In its absence, Solution 1 will do.

c) Solution 3 is stippled over the surface with a fiber brush and allowed to dry. The effect is better when the brush is not too wet with solution. Heat should not be used for drying.

d) The stippling is repeated until antique green uniformly covers the surface, its shades varying from a milky blue to yellow, depending upon the depth of the coating.

e) Aging is accomplished as in the preceding process, the natural color of the metal edge showing through the green.

f) The work is heavily waxed, dried, and rubbed.

PAINTING

American colonial tinware was painted but did not have the variety of color found on old French Tôle ware of the French Revolutionary period. This work is not to be confused with ordinary painted work of monotonous tone and raw color. Rather, it may be found in fine shops, in colors as Chinese red, oriental yellow, bone white, Nile green, or turquoise blue, over which there is a conservative decoration in gold, and a warm overtone called a glaze. This soft warmth over rich color sets it apart and recommends it for its present application. The process is as follows:

1. The object is scoured and dried as explained.

2. It is coated with a quick-drying enamel of the color recommended. (*a*) The paint is well stirred with a clean metal rod, applied on a clean surface with a clean brush, and then left to dry in a room free from dust and dirt. Two thin coats are better than a thick one though a single coat should be adequate. Brush marks are stippled out. When dry, the entire surface is steel wooled to an eggshell luster.

3. Strips of gummed gold paper and simple classical cutout designs are now glued to the surface (Pls. 4 to 12 and 16 to 20). Original Tôle decorations were beautifully hand painted, but, unless the student is adept with a brush, the paper method is recommended. This is done as follows:

a) Silver or gold gummed paper is cut into 1/16-in. strips or into various forms, as for example, leaflets of a palm branch (Pl. 6).

b) The object is moistened in the area of the first application with a brush and diluted soap water. Soap will spread the water evenly.

c) The strips are laid on with a wet brush and tapped with a damp cloth.

Chinese silver leaf paper also may be used. This, however, having no gum, is applied with vegetable glue. Surplus glue should be washed off immediately.

4. Glazing is an aging process applied as follows: (*a*) Make a mixture of 5 parts raw umber in oil, 5 parts linseed oil, 1 part varnish, and 1 part turpentine.

b) Apply a thin coat of glaze over the entire piece with a soft 1-in. brush used extremely dry. If the brush is dry and the color very thin, the latter may be worked in by stippling and brushing so that the lower portions are darker. Next, all surfaces are blended by stippling with a perfectly dry brush until the concavities, corners, and rarely handled parts are deeper in color, and the upper and center portions and those handled are quite free of glaze, blending off into the deeper portions.

PRESERVING METALS

1. As has been mentioned, tin and pewter work need no protective coatings because they retain their luster indefinitely. Tarnish may be removed from these metals by means of the original polish.

2. Tôle work needs no further coating.

3. Bright sheet brass, copper, and bronze work, as well as acid-colored cast bronze work is coated with a dull lacquer applied by a soft 1-in. brush. A spray may also be used, in which case the lacquer is thinned 10 per cent or more. A 10-cent fly spray is quite serviceable. The black and antique green finishes are waxed heavily.

4. Ironwork is usually waxed. If it is to be kept in damp locations, it is lacquered and rubbed dull with steel wool. This finish is preferred to paint; otherwise a thin coating of asphaltum, rubbed dull, will preserve it very well.

CHAPTER VIII

WIRING

TERMINAL THREADS

1. A standard lamp fixture fits over a ⅛-in. threaded pipe having at least ¼-in. free thread. The method by which this fixture terminus is supplied varies with the lamp design. For example, brass nipples are soldered into position on lamps shown in Plates 4, 18, 19, 20, and 48; short iron or brass nipples are turned into drilled and tapped holes in the lamps in Plates 45, 49, and 51; and the threaded ends of the ⅛-in. pipes on which the lamps in Plates 46, 47, and 50 are assembled, serve as fixture terminals. In the latter instances, the sockets screw down over the parts and serve as locks to hold them together. In any case, the nipples must be cut or filed square at the ends. Burrs left by saw or file are removed with the die, a center punch being rammed into the nipple to hold it for this operation. Furthermore, accurate threading is of importance (see Threading) if the fixture is to stand upright.

2. Where it is necessary to draw the assembly down tight as in bronze lamp parts, iron nipples are better than brass.

3. Where the work requires soldering, brass nipples are most practical.

4. Nipples may be cut from threaded ⅛-in. pipe bought in 3-ft. lengths. Short nipples, however, may be purchased.

5. All cut nipples must be filed (see Filing) and reamed with a tapered pipe reamer, countersink, or large drill, so that the cord will not cut or wear through on sharp edges.

6. In the lamp shown in Plate 51, parts are held to a ¼-in. pipe below by nipple and lock nut, and above by ⅛-in. pipe and threaded upper arm. A ⅛-in. threaded pipe fits into a tapped ¼-in. pipe.

ELECTRICAL FIXTURES

1. Ordinary sockets are not used on decorative work. Candle sockets may be bought in 2- and 4-in. adjustable sizes, the former being preferred for most work. A 4-in. standard candle socket may be lowered by cutting and retapping. A 2-in. socket may be raised on a length of pipe.

2. A fiber tube (1¼ in. O.D.) painted off white, is recommended as a candle cover. This tubing can be purchased at any store that handles electrical fixtures. The ordinary drip cover is not appropriate because, in the first place, its decoration is a detraction from the point of interest, and it is too large in diameter. The candle tube must not overshadow the rest of the design.

3. The cord should be quiet in tone, either silver or gold. About 6 ft. of cord should extend from the lamp.

4. Standard twin covered wire is used for single lamps. French cord is recommended for the inside wiring of double lamps because it is very thin, and four strands may be easily drawn through ⅛-in. pipe.

5. The plugs with handles are recommended.

WIRING

1. Single lamps are wired in the following manner (see Lamp, Pl. 45).

a) The candle cover is removed.

b) The negative and positive screw terminals are partly unscrewed.

c) The cord is split and about ½ in. of each wire covering is removed from both ends of the cord. These are scraped and twisted. Care should be taken not to cut the wire while scraping.

d) The cord is fed through the tubing into the socket. The negative and positive wires are wound once around their respective terminals in the direction of the closing screw, loose wires and all exposed ends being confined within their terminals.

e) The candle cover is slipped over the wiring.

f) The cord is now drawn through the plug and the wires are attached as in the socket. The common practice is to draw the wire around its prong to the terminal.

2. A single lamp with the socket screws not within reach is shown in the lamp in Plate 49.

a) The socket is unscrewed and wired as in the preceding step 1, the cord being drawn through in the same manner.

b) The lamp is held so that the cord may revolve and the socket is screwed tight.

c) The other wiring is completed as described in the foregoing.

3. Double-light lamp (Pl. 51).

a) Four French cords are brought through the pipe far enough to complete the wiring.

b) One is passed out to the side of each figure and the arm is screwed into place. The cords are protected by damp paper and the figures are soldered. The cups and sockets are tightened and the cords are fed in from below. They are pulled out and attached to the sockets as explained in *d*, step 1.

c) Below, the wires are cut short and ½ in. of the insulation is removed from each. A standard twin cord also is uncovered at both ends, one of which is attached to a plug.

d) The two French cord positive wires are twisted with that of the standard cord. The same is done with the negative. It makes no difference whether one or the other is taken for negative or positive, but one of each is twisted, making three wires in each twist. These are soldered and well taped, yet not so heavily as to extend beyond the lamp.

4. Double-light lamp (Pl. 20).

a) The outer light is wired as described in step 1.

b) A piece of French cord is cut to fit between the lights. The light already wired is now rewired, that is, the French cord is wired over the first wiring, so that two wires lead from each of its terminals. The French cord then is brought across and wired to the other light.

LIGHT SWITCHES

Key and snap sockets, chain-pull sockets, and switches set into the wire are not recommended. The best switch for service and appearance is a small one, inserted into a hole in the base. This is switched by the mere turning of a small knob.

a) A ⅜-in. hole is drilled into the base.

b) It is filed by a round file until the disassembled neck of the switch fits. It is then set in, the top is screwed down tight, and the button is replaced.

c) An inch of insulation is removed from the cord where it leaves the base so that it can be conveniently connected to the switch. In the middle of this section the wire is cut. Each end of the wire is twisted and fastened to the switch wire. It is then soldered and taped.

SECTION III

PROJECTS

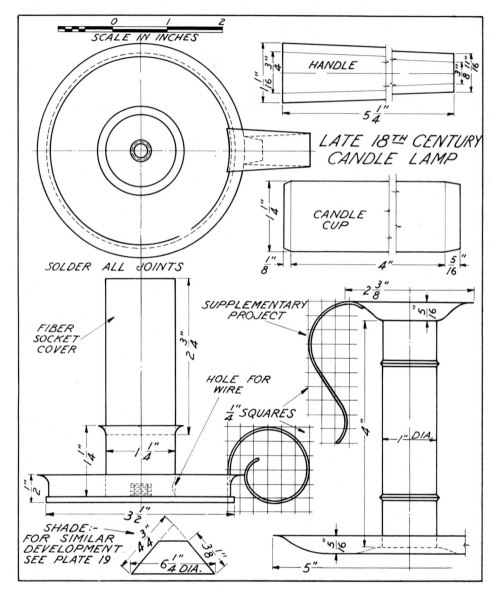

Plate 1.

Bill of Material

Material: All pieces made of tin-can stock.

Pieces		Thickness	Width	Length
1	Base	3½D. Can	Bottom of can	½ high
1	Candle cup		1¼	4 7/16
1	Handle		1 1/16	5¼
1	Shade-holder ring		⅜	7¾
2	Ring straps		¾	2
1	Shade	Large can	7⅛	9½

Bill of Material
(Supplementary Project)

Material: All pieces made of I.C. Bright coke tin sheet — Imperial No. 3 grade; or substitute 12-oz. copper sheet.

Pieces		Width	Length
1	Base	5	5
1	Stem	4	3½
1	Cup	2⅜	2⅜
1	Handle	1⅛	3⅜

Plate 1.   Tin Can to Candle

Candles and candlesticks are of ancient origin. Of the more recent types, the medieval candle prickets and coronas in iron were severely simple, often featuring the fleur-de-lis with banded column, while those of the Renaissance in pewter, bronze, and brass were quite ornate with figures, festoons, etc., over stems of heavy turnings, in which the urn and tripod base were usual parts. Early American settlers, however, used the simplest iron fish-oil lamps, candles being reserved for holidays. Tin candleholders appeared as early as 1630 in quaint styles still greatly appreciated, and these soon gave way to many beautiful creations in pewter and brass as these metals became available.

The candlestick in Figure 155, right, designed as a bedroom light, is described in the following procedure. The one to the left is an adjustable reading light, in early days hooked to the back of ladder-back chairs.

Procedure

1. On a standard can of 3⅝-in. diameter, a line is drawn ½ in. from the bottom. The procedure may be seen in Figure 8.

2. The can is cut down on each side of the seam, the seam is bent out and cut off. The rim then is cut off. Again, see Figure 8.

3. The can is now cut to the point shown at the Gauged Line 1, Figure 8. The line is followed closely around, thus cutting off the bottom. The worker should be careful not to bend or mar the tin.

4. The pieces for the cup and handle are laid out and cut.

5. The edge of the base is flared over a rounded wood block with a wood mallet. For the processes involved, see Flaring, steps 1 and 2, and Figure 44.

6. Both ends of the cup piece are folded on alternate sides. See Folding, steps 1 to 4.

Fig. 155. Tin can to candle.

7. The piece is bent into a cylindrical form over a pipe, locked together, and flattened down, the lock being held in place with a piece of wood. See Figure 154.

8. The seam is locked by driving it to the inside over a bar. See Grooving and Figures 50 and 60.

9. Both sides of the handle are hemmed and bent into a volute on forms. Consult Figures 38, 39, 41, and 42, and follow the directions for step 6, Bending.

10. The seam of the cup is soldered. See steps 1 to 3, and 5, Example 1 under Soft Soldering, and Figure 124.

11. The top of the cup is flared by pressing it into a bench drill chuck. The process is explained in step 4, Flaring, and is shown in *B*, Figure 46.

12. The cup is soldered to the base over a flame. See Example 2, Soft Soldering, step 5.

13. The handle is soldered to the base in the same manner.

14. The candlestick is washed and dried, and polished with steel wool.

If a lamp is preferred, feet may be made by following directions for step 8, Bending. In soldering the feet, consult Example 4, Soldering. A shade may be made as described in Plate 4, step 7, and wired following directions given under Wiring.

Fig. 156. Reflectors.

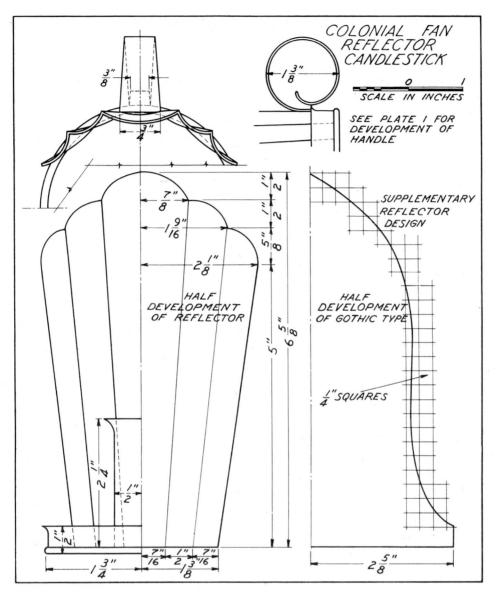

Plate 2.

Bill of Material

Material: All pieces made of tin-can stock; or substitute I.C. Bright coke tin sheet.

Pieces		Thickness	Width	Length
1	Base	3½D. Can	Bottom of can	½ high
1	Cup		2¼	3⅝
1	Handle		1 1/16	4½
1	Reflector	Large can	4¼	6⅝

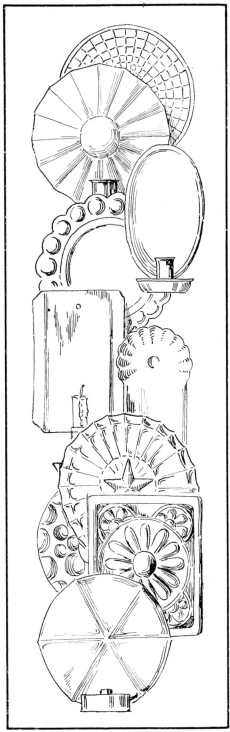

Fig. 157. Reflectors for candleholders may
be made in endless variety.

Plate 2. Eighteenth-Century Colonial Reflectors

The advantage of reflectors was recognized at an early date in Europe as well as in the American colonies. Many tin oil lamps and candleholders, particularly wall sconces, were supplied with a variety of tin reflectors. They not only increased the amount of light, but acted as draft deflectors and as a protection from fire. A variety of reflectors are shown in Figures 156 and 157.

Procedure

1. The directions for cutting the can and making the base, candle socket, and handle are the same as for Plate 1. The handle, however, is bent to the design shown in the drawing by means of a wood form and a mallet.

2. A piece of sheet tin is cut to size. The reflector pattern is either directly laid out or a paper pattern is fastened by wetting. The reflector then is cut, the bottom being square with the center line. See Cutting, Thin Metal. The lines for the flutes are drawn, and the flutes are bent. See Folding, steps 1 to 6, and 9. The reflector is then curved to the back and soldered to its base. See steps 1, 2, 3, and 7, Example 2, Soft Soldering, and Figure 131. The handle is soldered to the reflector. See step 7, Example 3, Soft Soldering. The entire piece is washed and dried, and rubbed with extra fine steel wool.

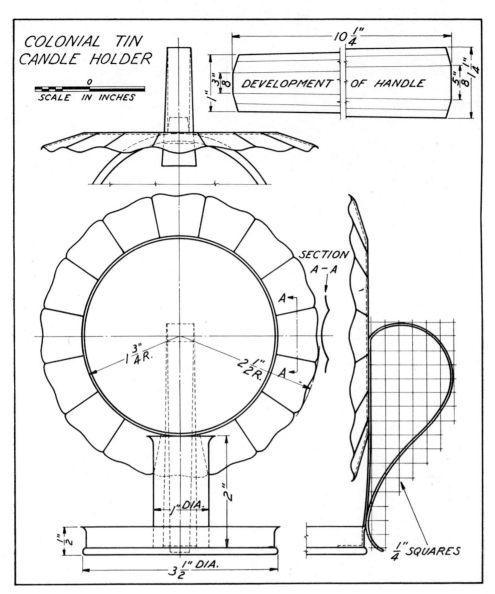

COLONIAL TIN
CANDLE HOLDER

SCALE IN INCHES

DEVELOPMENT OF HANDLE

SECTION A–A

$1\frac{3}{4}$ R.

$2\frac{1}{2}$ R.

$10\frac{1}{4}''$

$\frac{3}{8}''$

$\frac{5}{8}''$

$1''$ DIA.

2''

$\frac{1}{2}''$

$3\frac{1}{2}''$ DIA.

$\frac{1}{4}''$ SQUARES

Plate 3.

Bill of Material

Material. All pieces made of $3\frac{1}{2}$-in. diameter tin-can stock or substitute I.C. Bright coke tin sheet.

Pieces		Width	Length
1	Base	Bottom of can	$\frac{1}{2}$ high
1	Candle cup	2	$3\frac{5}{8}$
1	Handle	$1\frac{1}{4}$	$10\frac{1}{4}$
1	Reflector	5	5

Fig. 158. Pie-crust reflector.

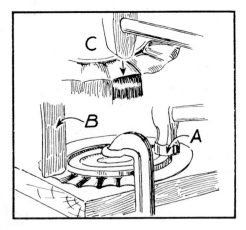

Fig. 159. Making pie-crust edge on reflector.

Plate 3.　Pie-Crust Reflector

The reflector candlestick of the eighteenth century is an excellent example of the development of early American design. Our early colonists used forms of homely inspiration, such as fruits, vegetables, flowers, animals, etc., and the reflector on the candle in Figure 158 is one of these, a sunflower or pie-crust type.

Procedure

1. The soldering of the base, cup, and handle is described under Plate 1. The handle, however, is bent over a form cut to the design shown in the drawing, Plate 3.

2. The reflector blank is cut from sheet tin large enough to enclose a form like the one shown in Plate 3 or like one of those shown in Figure 157.

3. All lines of the design are transferred to the stock and the outline is cut out. See Cutting, Thin Metal.

4. The design of the reflector may be chased as described under Chasing, but a process resembling stamping is more simple. Stamping may be used on a number of the other reflectors shown.

a) The side tin is trimmed off the base of a tin can. This base then is centered over the reflector and both together are clamped to a piece of softwood (Fig. 159).

b) The can edge is hammered all around making a circular impression on the reflector (*A*, Fig. 159).

c) While still clamped, a punch, made of ⅛ by ¾-in. band iron, filed as a blunt chisel and curved (*B*, Fig. 159), is placed over each radiating mark on the outer rim, and struck so that all the lines are uniformly driven in. These lines extend from the can base to the outer edge, resulting in a crimped, sloping edge.

d) The reflector now is placed over the end of a rounded block and the edge at the center of each space is curved forward with a mallet (*C*, Fig. 159).

5. The handle is soldered to the back and both are soldered to the base with a copper bit. See Soft Soldering, steps 3 and 7, Examples 3 and 4. This is the procedure on all reflectors. The small rounded impressions shown on reflectors in Figure 157 are made by driving the metal into the end of a softwood block by means of the ball of a hammer, or with a properly shaped and polished punch.

Fig. 160. Early nineteenth-century lamp.

Bill of Material

Material: All pieces made of 3½-in. diameter tin-can stock except as noted.

Pieces	Material	Use	Width	Length
1		Base	Bottom of can	½ h'gh
4		Feet	⅜	2¾
1		Chimney base	1¼	8½
1		Shade ring	1 1/16	8⅞
1		Shade handle	1	5¼
2		Sides	1	8½
1	I.C. Bright coke tin sheet	Shade	9 7/16	10⅜
1	⅛-in. Pipe nipple — brass	Fixture base		½
2	Roundhead copper rivets	Handle		⅛
1	Lamp chimney	Chimney	2½ base	7¼
1	Candle socket	Light		2
1	Socket cover			2
1	Cord			8 ft.
1	Plug			

Plate 4. Early Nineteenth-Century Lamp

An exact date for the interesting lamp shown in Figure 160 is not available, although it probably is a development of the early nineteenth century. The glass chimney was a chance discovery by the staff of the Swiss chemist, Aimé Argand, in 1783.

Shades, though used as lantern tops in early times, did not appear in Europe and America as lamp reflectors until the latter part of the eighteenth century.

Procedure

1. The base is made in the same manner as the one for the candlestick in Plate 1, steps 1 to 5.

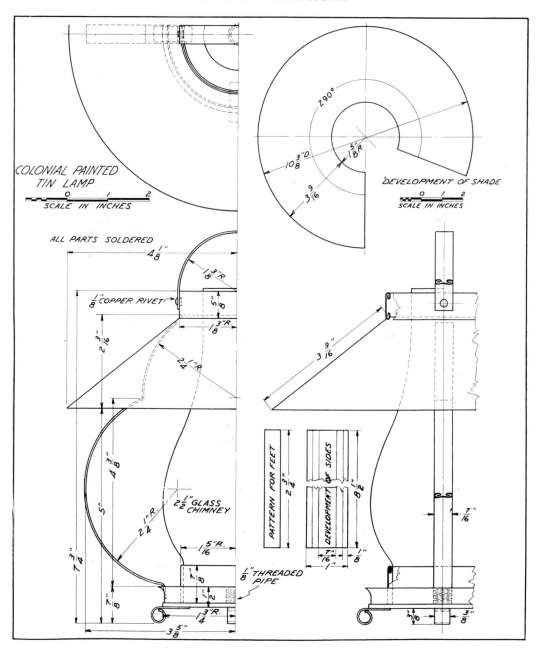

COLONIAL PAINTED
TIN LAMP

SCALE IN INCHES

DEVELOPMENT OF SHADE

SCALE IN INCHES

ALL PARTS SOLDERED

Plate 4.

2. A hole is punched in its center for the cord. See Punching.

3. The chimney base ring, the shade ring, the shade-supporting arms, and the top handle ring, are laid out, cut, and double hemmed. See Folding, steps 1 to 6.

4. The rings are bent over pipe, as described in Bending, step 4, and the chimney and shade rings are soldered. See Soft Soldering, steps 1 to 4, and 7, Example 1.

5. The shade-supporting arms are bent sharply in a vise and are curved over large round forms.

6. The chimney ring is held together with fine wire and set over the base. A pipe nipple is set over the center as explained under Wiring, Terminal Threads, and is soldered to it. See Soft Soldering, step 5, Example 2.

7. The shade is laid out full size on paper, cut, and checked, allowances being made for seams. Then it is laid over metal stock and cut. See Cutting, Thin Metal, steps 1 and 2. If the shade is to be made of tin-can stock, it may be lapped at two points. One lap is soldered. See Soft Soldering, step 7, Example 1, and Figure 130. The metal then is drawn over a round form by hand, the palm directing its curva-ture as it moves. The seam is soldered as in the foregoing. If cutting and fitting are carefully done, the top and bottom are on parallel planes; otherwise, trimming is necessary.

8. The crowning ring is soldered to the shade. See Soft Soldering, step 7, Example 2.

9. The supporting arms are soldered to the shade and the base. See Soft Soldering, step 7, Example 3, and Figure 132. The top handle ring is riveted or soldered in the same manner.

10. The feet are bent as directed under Bending, step 8, and soldered. See Soft Soldering as in the foregoing.

11. The lamp is now washed, and polished with steel wool, or it is painted. See Finishing, Painting of Tôle Work. Finally it is wired. See Wiring, Fixtures, etc.

12. A glass chimney may be purchased at a fixture house.

Plate 5. Pots for Flowers

Pots like those in Figure 161 have no direct historical pattern. The type, however, as characterized by their painted and decorated surfaces, is called tôle, a development of the French Revolutionary period.

Fig. 161. Pots for flowers.

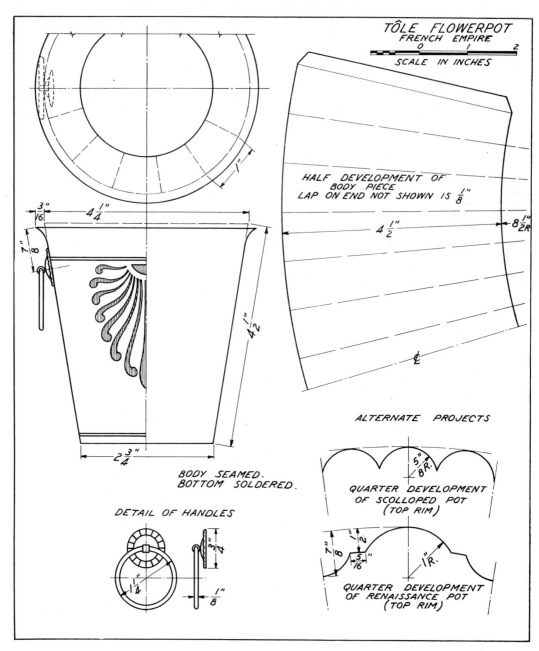

TÔLE FLOWERPOT
FRENCH EMPIRE

SCALE IN INCHES

HALF DEVELOPMENT OF
BODY PIECE
LAP ON END NOT SHOWN IS ⅛"

BODY SEAMED.
BOTTOM SOLDERED.

DETAIL OF HANDLES

ALTERNATE PROJECTS

QUARTER DEVELOPMENT
OF SCOLLOPED POT
(TOP RIM)

QUARTER DEVELOPMENT
OF RENAISSANCE POT
(TOP RIM)

Plate 5.

Bill of Material

Material: All pieces made of cold-rolled annealed copper sheet except rings, which are made of half-hard copper wire.

Pieces		Thickness	Width	Length
1	Body	12 oz.	5 9/16	12 15/16
1	Base	24 oz.	3	3
2	Rosettes	24 oz.	3/4	3/4
2	Ring eyes	24 oz.	3/16	1 1/4
2	Rings	1/8 D.		7 1/8

Procedure

1. The pattern is drawn full size on paper, cut out, and checked. If correct, it is transferred to the metal stock, allowing for seams, and then cut. See Cutting, Thin Metal.

2. The seams are folded. See Folding, steps 1 to 6.

3. It is then laid over a large cylindrical form and bent carefully until the ends lock. The seam is flattened over a pipe with a mallet and block, and is driven inward over a groove. See Grooving and Figures 50 and 60.

4. The seam is soldered. See Soft Soldering, steps 1 to 4, and 5, Example 1.

5. A disk is cut ¼ in. larger than the bottom. See Cutting, Thin Metal. This is flattened with a soft mallet. See Straightening, step 1.

6. The bottom side of the pot is trued to round and filed to fit the base.

7. The bottom is placed on a soldering rack as shown in Figure 125, with the body

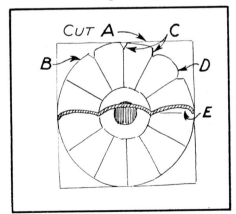

Fig. 162. Making a rosette.

set upon it and held down by a weight. It is then fluxed, charged with solder, and soldered. See Soldering, step 5, Example 2.

8. After cooling, the pot is trimmed and tested. Leaks may be closed with a soldering copper. See Soft Soldering, step 7, Example 1.

9. The top rim is flared. See Flaring, steps 1 and 2, and A, Figure 70.

10. Square blanks are cut for the rosettes. They are laid out, cut, and filed to line as shown in Figure 162, A to D. The center is driven into the end grain of a softwood block or the sharpened end of a ⅜-in. pipe by means of a ball-peen hammer. The radiating lines are punched with a blunt chisel as shown in Figure 159. This process is explained in step 4, under Pie-Crust Reflector.

11. A center hole is punched for the ring straps. See Punching.

12. A 3/16-in. copper rod is bent twice around ½-in. pipe, cut off into two rings, and straightened.

13. The straps are cut, bent around the rings, and pinched at the back with pliers or vise as shown in Figure 196. They are then inserted into the rosette holes and bent back on the inside as shown. The assembled handle is tinned and then sweated on. See Soft Soldering, step 6, Example 1.

14. The pot now is washed, dried, painted, decorated, and glazed. See Finishing, Painting Tôle Work.

15. If the top is to be scalloped, the directions in Cutting, Thin Metal, step 6, should be followed.

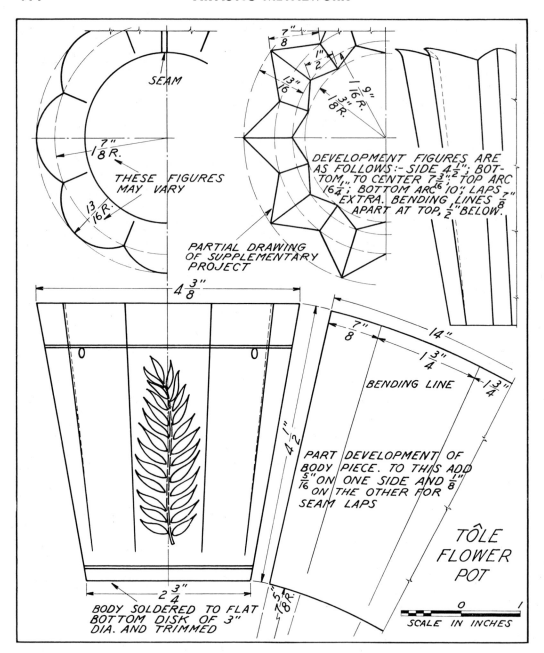

SEAM

7"
$\frac{7}{8}$R.

THESE FIGURES
MAY VARY

$\frac{13}{16}$R.

DEVELOPMENT FIGURES ARE
AS FOLLOWS:- SIDE $4\frac{1}{2}$"; BOT-
TOM, TO CENTER $7\frac{3}{16}$" TOP ARC
$16\frac{1}{4}$"; BOTTOM ARC 10" LAPS $\frac{7}{8}$"
EXTRA. BENDING LINES $\frac{7}{8}$"
APART AT TOP, $\frac{1}{2}$" BELOW.

PARTIAL DRAWING
OF SUPPLEMENTARY
PROJECT

$4\frac{3}{8}$"

$2\frac{3}{4}$"

BODY SOLDERED TO FLAT
BOTTOM DISK OF 3"
DIA. AND TRIMMED

$\frac{5}{8}$R.

$4\frac{1}{2}$"

$\frac{7}{8}$"

14"

$1\frac{3}{4}$"

BENDING LINE

$1\frac{3}{4}$"

PART DEVELOPMENT OF
BODY PIECE. TO THIS ADD
$\frac{5}{16}$" ON ONE SIDE AND $\frac{1}{8}$"
ON THE OTHER FOR
SEAM LAPS

TÔLE
FLOWER
POT

0   1
SCALE IN INCHES

Plate 6.

Bill of Material

Material: All pieces made of cold-rolled annealed copper sheet; or substitute tin sheet.

Pieces		Thickness	Width	Length
1	Body	12 oz.	5¾	13 3/16
1	Base	24 oz.	3	3

Plate 6. Fluted Pots

Tôle was used extensively in France, England, and Russia in many useful forms, such as boxes, candlesticks, flower urns, lamps, tea caddies, and trays. These were

Fig. 163. Fluted pots.

painted in gold over black, red, green, cream, turquoise, etc. In France, floral motifs, with figures and medallions, classic borders and scenery were used, while in England the motifs were Chinese and floral. The pot in Figure 163 is modern, and the decorations are of the Empire period.

Procedure

1. A full-sized pattern, including folding lines, is laid out on paper. It is then cut out, folded, and tried for size and taper.

2. If the pattern is satisfactory, it is placed on the metal, and the exact pattern, including enough metal for the seam, is laid out.

Fig. 164. Scribing the bottom of a fluted pot.

3. The pattern is cut to the line. See Cutting, Thin Metal.

4. Using the jig described under Folding, it is folded as explained under Folding, step 9. See Figure 59.

5. The piece is removed from the vise, and the seams are tapped down. See Figure 52.

6. The flutes are trued over a pipe with a mallet.

7. The body of the pot is now carefully bent over a large form with the palms of the hands.

8. The seam folds are engaged, tapped tight over a pipe, and grooved. See Grooving, Figure 60.

9. The body is trued up and placed on a flat surface, where a line is scribed around the base as shown in Figure 164. This line is trimmed with a shears and filed so that the edges meet the table all around.

10. The soldering of the seam, the making of the bottom and its soldering is described in the text under Plate 5, steps 5 to 8.

11. It is now washed, dried, and painted. See Finishing, Painting Tôle Work.

Other projects may be made by the same process. The pot to the left in Figure 163 is folded alternately outward and inward.

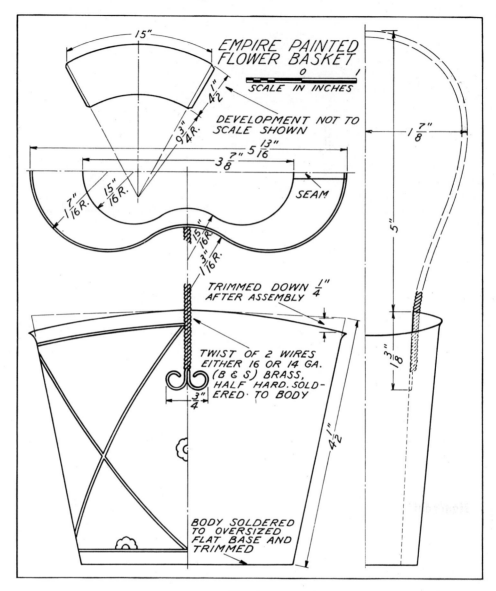

Plate 7.

Plate 7. More Flowerpots

This project is adapted from modern pottery, but because of its decoration is still in the tôle category. The oval flowerpot in Figure 165 is true to the tôle tradition.

Bill of Material

Material: All pieces made of cold-rolled annealed copper sheet — or substitute tin sheet — except the handle, which is made of half-hard brass wire.

Pieces	Thickness	Width	Length
1 Body	12 oz.	5 13/16	14½
1 Base	24 oz.	2⅛	4⅛
1 Handle 14 Ga. (B&S)			45

Procedure

1. The layout, cutting, shaping, and assembling of the flowerpot is described

Fig. 165. More flowerpots.

under Plate 5, steps 1 to 9. The trimming of the bottom, however, is better described in Plate 6, step 9, and should be done after the body has been bent to the pattern. The seam should fall at an end. The bending is done over a pipe with the hands.

2. The top is flared to a considerable lip at each end. This fades out completely at the handles. See Flaring, step 2.

3. The handle is made by the following

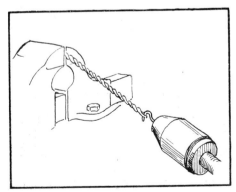

Fig. 166. Twisting the handle.

process: The two loose ends of a wire are set into a vise and the middle is drawn to a loop. This is placed over a hook set into a hand drill, as shown in Figure 166. The wire is then turned until twisted tight.

4. The ends are cut, straightened, and bent to the pattern with a round-nose pliers.

5. The handle then is bent. It is fluxed, held to the body with light tongs, and soldered. See Soft Soldering, steps 1 to 4, and 5, Examples 4 or 6.

6. The entire piece is washed, dried, and painted. See Finishing, Painting Tôle Work.

The oval fern dish is made like the pot in Plate 5. The top design is cut before folding, and held down with a weight while it is being soldered. The bottom is supported by rods to keep it from sagging. Feet are added. See directions for Plate 5, step 7. The modern pot has a square base and is folded down as described under Bending, step 1.

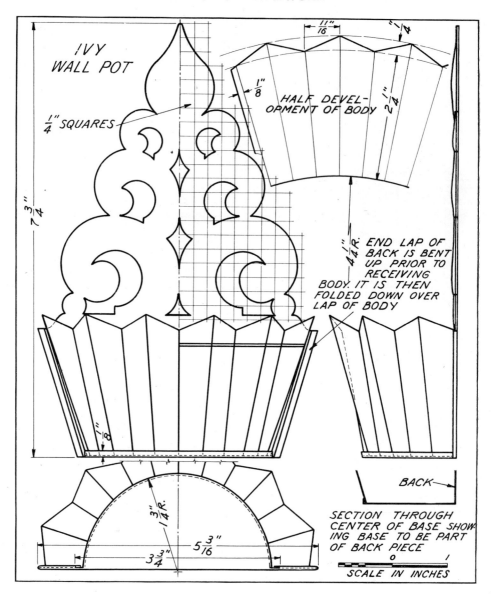

Plate 8.

Bill of Material

Material: All pieces made of cold-rolled annealed copper sheet.

Pieces		Thickness	Width	Length
1	Back and bottom	32 oz.	5½	9⅝
1	Body	24 oz.	3 5/16	7⅞

Plate 8.   Fluted Wall Vase

The tôle vase in Figure 167 is modern Renascent in style. It suggests a wide field in which other motives may be applied.

Procedure

1. The design is drawn full size on pa-

Fig. 167. Fluted wall vase.

per, one side of which is drawn accurately. The paper is folded down the center and the pattern is cut to the line. It is then attached with thin glue to a piece of metal stock. See Cutting, Thin Metal.

2. The straight lines are cut with a shears.

3. The scrolls are cut with a cold chisel. See Cutting, Metals of Medium Thickness, steps 7, 8, and 15.

4. The piece is filed to the lines. See Filing, steps 1 to 4.

5. The bottom rim is bent up over a wood pattern. See Bending, step 1, and Figures 31, 32, and 52.

6. The sides are folded forward on the same pattern, as is also the bottom rear fold. See Folding, steps 3 and 4.

7. The front piece is laid out full size on paper, checked, laid out on the metal stock, and cut. See Cutting, Thin Metal.

8. It is folded on the lines as directed under Folding, step 9, and Figure 59.

9. It is bent to the proper curvature in the fingers, and its fluting is flattened out with a mallet over a round form toward the bottom.

10. It is cut to fit tightly to the bottom and side folds, set into place, and soldered below. See Soldering, steps 1 to 4, and 5, Examples 1 and 2.

11. The sides of the back piece are folded over the ends of the front piece, fluxed, and soldered in the same manner.

12. The top is shaped on the end grain of a block of wood so that each scroll is rounded slightly outward, as shown in Figure 61.

13. The whole is washed, dried, and painted. See Finishing, Painting of Tôle Work.

The top may be altered in design to conform to any period.

Plate 9. A Watering Can

The watering can shown in Figure 168 is a modern convenience, finished as a tôle piece.

Procedure

1. A 1-lb. coffee can is used for ·this project.

2. The cover is cut as shown in the plate, and planished until all die marks are removed. See Planishing, steps 1 and 2a. During this process the metal will stretch providing for the curvature of the top.

3. The inner edge is trimmed and folded. See Bending, steps 2 and 3.

4. The spout and handle material is laid out and cut. The handle is double hemmed. See Folding, steps 1 to 6.

5. The spout piece is rounded along both joining edges over a ⅜-in. rod with a mallet (A, Fig. 169). It is then held over a tapered form of metal or wood and bent around by hand. See Bending, steps 4 and 5. It may also be bent with a block and mallet as shown in Figure 169.

6. If the laps do not close properly, the spout is laid on the table and rolled and tapped until closed.

7. It then is soldered. See Soft Soldering, steps 1 to 3, and 7, Example 1.

8. It is trimmed to fit the can. The can is scribed around it, placed over a rounded

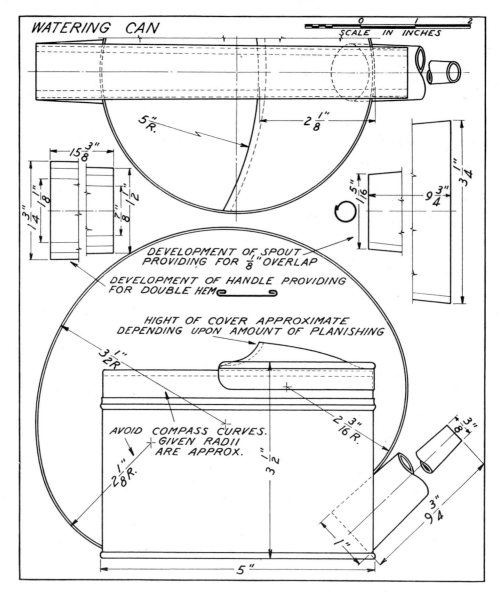

Plate 9.

Bill of Material

Material: All pieces made of large tin-can stock or I.C. Bright coke tin sheet — Imperial No. 3 grade, except as noted.

Pieces	Material	Use	Width	Length
1	Body of 1-lb. coffee can	Body		
1	Cover of 1-lb. coffee can	Cover		
1		Handle	1¾	15⅜
1		Spout	3¼	9¾

Fig. 168. Watering can.

block, and the hole is cut just inside the line with a chisel. See Cutting, Metals of Medium Thickness, steps 6 and 7.

9. The spout is forced into place, bent upward, and soldered. See Soft Soldering, step 7, Example 4. It is soldered below from the outside and above from the in-side of the can.

10. The cover is soldered on. See Soft Soldering, step 7, Example 2.

11. The handle is soldered on. See Soft Soldering, step 7, Example 4.

12. It is washed, dried, and painted. See Finishing, Painting of Tôle Work.

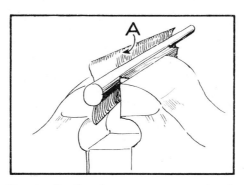

Fig. 169. Bending the spout on a tapered rod.

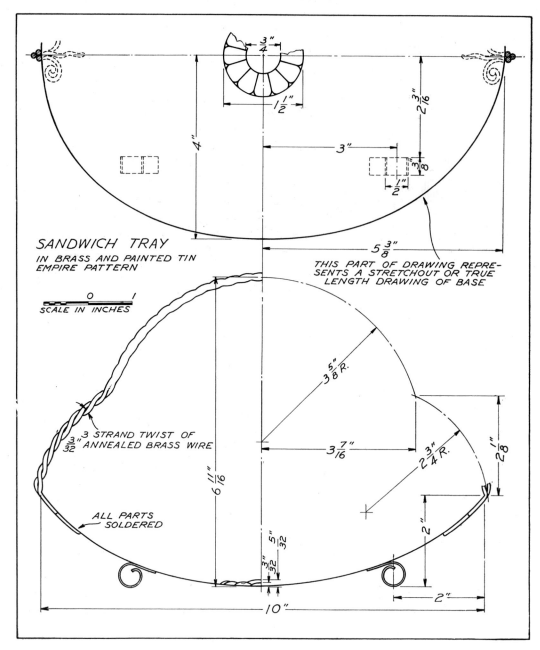

SANDWICH TRAY
IN BRASS AND PAINTED TIN
EMPIRE PATTERN

THIS PART OF DRAWING REPRE-
SENTS A STRETCHOUT OR TRUE
LENGTH DRAWING OF BASE

3 STRAND TWIST OF
ANNEALED BRASS WIRE

ALL PARTS
SOLDERED

Plate 10.

Bill of Material

Material: All pieces made of I.C. Bright coke tin sheet — Imperial No. 3, or substitute galvanized sheet 30 gauge, except as noted.

Pieces	Material	Use	Thickness	Width	Length
1		Bottom		8	10¾
4		Feet		⅜	2¼
3	Brass wire — half hard	Handle	14 Ga. (B&S)		22
1	Brass sheet — soft spinning	Rosette	22 Ga. (B&S)	1½	1½

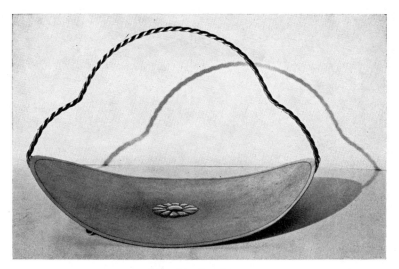

Fig. 170. Bread tray.

Plate 10. Bread Tray

The tray in Figure 170, though modern, is typical of the period which tôle represents. This tray is decorated with one of the simple Napoleonic motives.

Procedure

1. The pattern is laid out full size on paper. It is then cut out and transferred to stock metal of the proper size. This is cut to the pattern line.

2. The piece is bent over a wood form as shown in Figure 171, or over curvatures

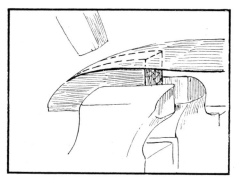

Fig. 171. The tray is bent over a wood form.

such as those on large pipe, paint pails, etc. Wood forms, however, contribute to the uniformity of the work.

3. The handle consists of three wires twisted together (Fig. 166), cut, folded over at the ends, and bent to its general form. It is soldered by the process in Soldering, steps 1 to 3, and 6, Example 1.

4. The rosette is laid out, cut, and filed, as shown in Figure 162. The center is driven into softwood with a sharpened $\frac{3}{8}$-in. pipe, and radiating lines are punched with a blunt tool as shown in B, Figure 159. The petal tips are shaped over a block as shown in C, Figure 159, and E, Figure 162.

5. The rosette is soldered, the flame directed away from the previous soldering. See Soft Soldering, as above.

6. The feet are cut and bent as described under Bending, step 8, and Figure 39. They are soldered as described under Soft Soldering, step 7, Example 3, and Figure 132.

7. The entire piece is now cleaned, washed, and colored. See Finishing, Painting Tôle Work. The brass is polished and lacquered last. See Finishing, Polishing, step 6, for this work.

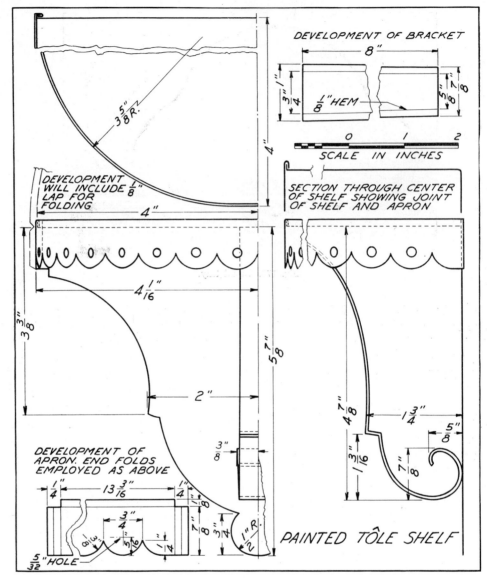

Plate 11.

Bill of Material

Material: All pieces made of 24-oz. cold-rolled annealed copper sheet; or substitute tin sheet.

Pieces		Width	Length
1	Back and top	8¼	10
1	Apron	1	13 11/16
1	Bracket	1	8

Plate 11. Flower Shelf

The shelf shown in Figure 172 is another example of tôle work. Its lines are strongly Renaissance, and its treatment is typical of the French Revolution.

Procedure

1. The one-piece shelf top and back is sketched full size on paper. The paper is folded on its center and cut to the pattern. It is applied to the metal blank by wetting.

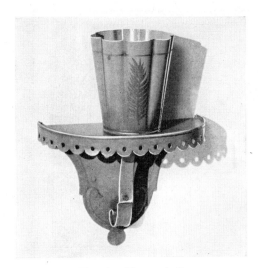

Fig. 172. Flower shelf.

The blank is then cut to the pattern. See Cutting, Thin Metal.

2. The right-angle fold on the shelf front is made between two pieces of wood. See Bending, step 1, and Figure 32.

3. The back is bent down at a right angle over the same form, and the sides, just under the shelf, are folded back to meet the ends of the apron.

4. The apron is laid out as described under Cutting, Thin Metal, step 6. Its holes are punched into the end of a hardwood block by pin punch.

5. A strip of 18-gauge copper is laid within the latter fold and both are bent around the front of the wood form shown in Figure 32. The copper strip is removed, and the apron is slipped over the shelf lap already formed, and flattened down with a mallet.

6. The seam is soldered. See Soft Soldering, steps 1 to 4, and 5, Example 1.

7. The apron ends are trimmed, bent over the folds made in step 3, and flattened to the back.

8. The bracket is laid out, double hemmed on both sides, and bent into a volute at the large end. See Bending, step 6. It is then bent sharply at the reverse of the curves in hardwood or metal. See Forming, steps 3 or 4, and Figures 86 and 88. The upper shape then is made over a long curvature.

9. Its lower and upper ends are soldered. See Soft Soldering, step 7, Example 3.

10. It is then washed and painted. See Finishing, Painting Tôle Work.

Plate 12. More Trays

The small tray in Figure 173 is modern, of Scandinavian inspiration, while the large one is a typical tôle piece.

Procedure

1. The trays are laid out on stock pieces of metal of the proper size. Lines are checked and edges are filed straight and square. See Cutting, Thin Metal, Filing, steps 1 to 4, and, if necessary, Straightening, step 1.

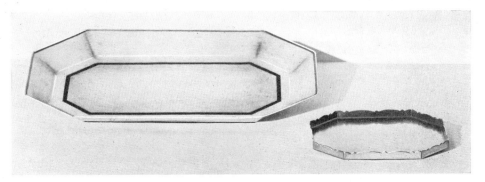

Fig. 173. More trays.

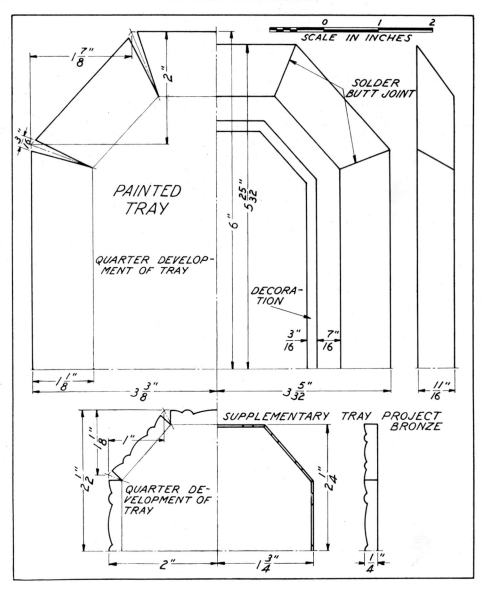

Plate 12.

Bill of Material

Material: Cold-rolled annealed copper sheet (24-oz.), or substitute 30-gauge galvanized steel sheet.

Pieces		Width	Length
1	Tray	6¾	12

2. The corners are laid out, checked, and cut. These trays are not lapped at the corners, the strength of the joint depending upon the stiffness of the metal and the

Bill of Material

(Supplementary Project)

Pieces	Material	Use	Thickness	Width	Length
1	Commercial bronze sheet (Substitute britannia metal, copper sheet, or aluminum)	Tray	23 Ga. (B&S)	4	5

Fig. 174. Pewter plates and trays.

Bill of Material
(Pewter Plates)

Britannia metal No. 1	Plates up to 7 D.	18 Ga. (B&S)
	Plates 8 to 12 D.	16 Ga. (B&S)
	Plates 12 to 18 D.	14 Ga. (B&S)

strength of the solder, which should be more than adequate.

3. If the tray has an edge design, it is laid out, cut with a shears, and filed to the line. See Filing, steps 3 and 4.

4. The rim of the small tray is bent between two pieces of wood. See Bending, step 9, or Folding, step 7. The large tray is bent over the sharp edge of a wood block with a block and mallet. See Folding, step 4.

5. It is not necessary to solder the joints on the small tray. Those on the large tray, however, must be soldered. See Soft Soldering, steps 1 to 4, and 5, Example 1. A pencil mark around the joint will keep the solder within a small area. Yellow ocher mixed with water is painted over finished

joints to protect them in subsequent soldering.

6. The tray is washed and painted. See Finishing, Painting Tôle Work.

Figure 174. Pewter Plates and Trays

Old pewter is an alloy consisting of three parts of tin and one part of lead. Today's britannia metal, an alloy of tin, copper, and antimony, is preferred for its enduring luster, its great ductility, its nontoxic quality, and its soft pewter color.

Procedure

1. The flat piece of pewter is shaped to plate form. See Low Raising, steps 2 and 3. If a rolled edge is used, gauge nails in the forming block are set back an additional amount to provide for it.

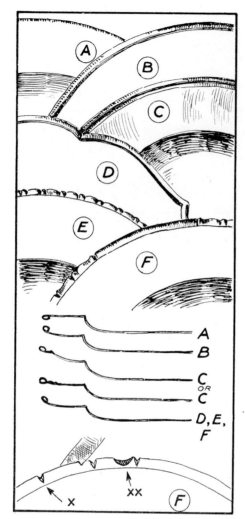

Fig. 175. Designs for pewter plates.

b) The surface of the rim may be curved as in *B* and *C*, Figure 175, using a wood form with a mallet. See Low Raising, step 4, *e*, and *A*, Figure 70.

c) The edge may be cut and hemmed as in *D*, Figure 175. See Bending, step 2. The cuts, if sharp, complicate the hemming operation, and necessitate cutting the corners and welding those not closed. See Pewter Soldering and Welding.

d) The hemmed edge is scraped to produce a double-beaded edge, as in *C*, Figure 175. This is done with the point of a marking gauge, filed as shown in Figure 106. See Beaded Edges.

e) A similar effect is obtained by soldering previously scraped moldings to the unhemmed edge. Such moldings may be drawn through filed dies, the space between their parts being adjusted by screw, *B*, Figure 18. See the drawing. Soldering is done as in Pewter Soldering.

f) The hemmed edges of small plates may be decorated by a file, as shown at *E* and *F*, Figure 175.

(1) All sharp division lines are filed down with the corner of a half-round file, and brought in over the hem. See *X*, Figure 175.

(2) All wide concave surfaces are filed to depth by the round side of the same file, *XX*, Figure 175, and brought over the hem but not too deeply, after which sharp corners are rounded as required.

(3) The design may be scraped, burnished, and buffed. See Finishing, Polishing.

g) Surface decorations, as suggested in Figures 102 and 104, may be done by etching or joggling. See Etching and Engraving.

h) Lines and molded bands may be chased into round plate rims by means of chasing jigs as explained in Chasing, step 5. Many beautiful modern rims may be so executed.

5. Plates are finished as described under Finishing and Polishing.

2. The rim and flat area below the curvature are planished. See Planishing, steps 1 and 2. Particular care is necessary to attain uniformity at the inner edge.

3. The rim is hemmed. See Bending, steps 2 and 3.

4. The rim design should be simple to conform to the character of pewter. It may be distinctly modern, or similar to contemporary Swedish and Danish ware. Several designs are shown in Figure 175.

a) The hem may be turned down or up as in *A* and *B*, Figure 175.

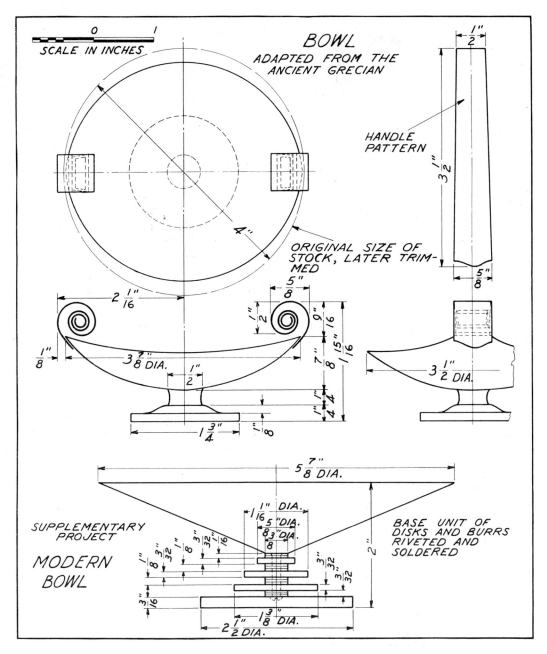

Plate 13.

Plate 13. Modern Bowls

Bowls perhaps are the most successful of school projects; first, because of their universal acceptability, and next because they are ideal vehicles for the teaching of design and mechanical practices. Additional patterns are given in Figure 71.

Procedure

1. The piece of metal for the bowl is cut out of stock and shaped. See Cutting, Thin

Fig. 176. Modern bowls.

Bill of Material

Material: All pieces made of 24-oz. cold-rolled annealed copper sheet — or substitute commercial bronze or britannia metal sheet — except the stem, which is made of half-hard copper tube.

Pieces		Width	Length
1	Body	4	4
1	Base	2	2
2	Handles	5/8	3½
1	Stem		¼

Metal, and Low Raising, step 4, *c*. Annealing is not necessary.

2. It is trued and smoothed on a flat wood surface and planished. See Planishing, steps 1 and 2*a*.

3. The base is made over a wood disk, as directed under Bending, step 1, and the bottom is filed true.

4. It is then reversed and raised by pressure, as in Low Raising, step 6, *b*. By this process the surface is domed upward. See Figure 177.

5. The stem is made of ½-in. tubing. The top and bottom are filed, and flared with a ball-peen hammer. See Flaring, step 3, and *A*, Figure 46.

6. The handles are cut from scrap and rolled with round-nose pliers into the volute given in the drawing. See Bending, step 8, and Figure 39.

7. The base and stem are soldered. See Soft Soldering, steps 1 to 4, and 5, Example 2.

8. The top is soldered. See Soft Soldering, step 5, Example 3.

9. The volutes are soldered. See Soft Soldering, step 6, Example 1.

10. The entire piece is cleaned, colored, and waxed. See Finishing, Cleaning, steps 1 and 2, and Coloring by Acid.

The modern bowl, to the left in Figure 176, is similarly made except that the stem

Bill of Material
(Supplementary Project)

Pieces	Material	Use	Thickness	Width	Length
1	Copper sheet — cold-rolled annealed	Body	24 oz.	6	6
1	Copper sheet — cold-rolled annealed	Base	24 oz.	2⅞	2⅞
11	Copper burrs	Stem	⅜ O.D.		
1	Copper buss bar (Substitute heavy sheet)	Disks for stem	3/32	1⅜	1⅜
1	Copper buss bar (Substitute heavy sheet)	Disks for stem	3/32	1 1/16	1 1/16
1	Copper buss bar (Substitute heavy sheet)	Disks for stem	3/32	5/8	5/8
1	Copper rivet (Substitute copper wire or brass screw)	Stem core	⅛ D.		¾

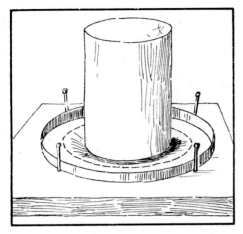

Fig. 177. Doming the base of a bowl.

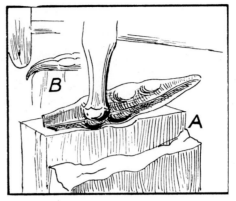

Fig. 179. Leaf ornaments are hammered
on a wood block.

is made of built-up disks. The planishing
is done on a cylindrical stake and produces
radiating, elongated facets.

Plate 14. Copper Bowls of Today

The bowl to the left in Figure 178 is an
example of the refreshing Scandinavian
spirit of today. Here, simple natural forms,
such as berries, leaves, and buds in the
stem offset the severely simple surfaces of
the body.

Procedure

1. The bowl is shaped. See Low Raising,
step 4, *c*. No annealing is necessary. Its
edge is re-turned with a mallet over a
rounded wood block to conform to the
design. See Low Raising, step 4, *e*.

2. It is then planished. See Planishing,
steps 1 and 2*a*.

3. The edge is filed smooth, as directed
under Filing, step 4, and cut to the design
with a file. See Figure 174, step 4, *f*, and
Figure 175.

4. The base is made as described in Plate
13, steps 3 and 4.

5. The leaf ornament is laid out, cut
with a shears to the general form, and then
filed to the lines. The straight leaves are
veined as explained under Chasing, steps
2 and 4*a*, and the other leaves, together
with the leaf tips, are driven into the end
of a block with round-ended punches, much
like the process shown in *A*, Figure 179.

6. The leaves are annealed, bent up over
a ¾-in. rod which may be pressed down
firmly upon their center. Then the leaf
ends are curved outward with a mallet over

Fig. 178. Copper bowls of today.

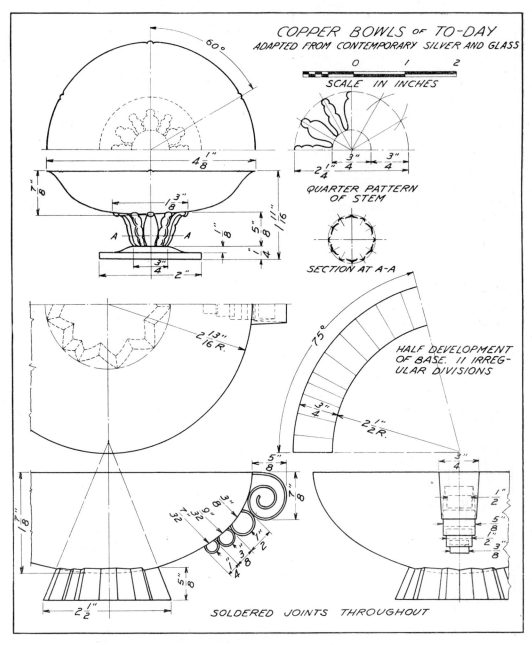

COPPER BOWLS of TO-DAY
ADAPTED FROM CONTEMPORARY SILVER AND GLASS

SCALE IN INCHES

QUARTER PATTERN OF STEM

SECTION AT A-A

HALF DEVELOPMENT OF BASE. 11 IRREGULAR DIVISIONS

SOLDERED JOINTS THROUGHOUT

Plate 14.

Bill of Material

Material: All pieces made of 24-oz. cold-rolled annealed copper sheet.

Pieces		Width	Length
1	Body	4¼	4¼
1	Base	2¼	2¼
1	Stem	2¼	2¼

a rounded block, as shown in *B*, Figure 179. Next they are aligned. Final fitting to the bowl is done by setting the unit on the bowl, bottom up, and tapping the bottom until all points touch.

7. The leaf tips, the bottom of the unit,

Bill of Material
(Supplementary Project)

Material: All pieces made of 24-oz. cold-rolled annealed copper sheet.

Pieces		Width	Length
1	Body	6	6
1	Base	2⅝	6 5/16
2	Handles	¾	3 9/16
2	Handles	⅝	1⅛
2	Handles	½	¾
2	Handles	⅜	9/16

and the base are tinned. See Soft Soldering, steps 1 to 4, and 6, Example 1.

8. The base and leaf unit are soldered as in the foregoing.

9. The bowl is now fluxed below, set bottom up on the rack with the base and leaf unit over it. The parts are aligned and the heat is applied from below. It is removed as soon as the leaves sink into place. If any of the leaves fail to hold, a fine solder wire may be touched back of them. Apply sparingly to avoid running solder.

10. The bowl is cleaned and colored. See Finishing; Polishing; Cleaning, steps 1 and 2; and Coloring by Acid. The modern bowl is shaped in a sandbag in like manner except that one annealing is required. The base is made of a fluted half-circular band, trimmed below after soldering. See Figure 164. The handles are bent with a round-nose pliers.

Plate 15. Fluted Bowls

The bowls shown in Figure 180 are called Modern Renascent. Fluting is found in urn and rosette motifs of the Renaissance and Empire periods, not only having been used in architecture, but in painted decorations, metalwork, and textile design. They come from classic sources.

Procedure

1. The bowl is shaped as described under Low Raising, step 4, *c*. No annealing is necessary.

2. It is planished lightly. See Planishing, steps 1 and 2*a*.

3. It is fluted to the measurements given. See Fluting, step 1.

4. The base is made like that in Plate 13, steps 3 and 4.

5. The center piece is driven up between wood circles, as was the base, though only to 60 instead of 90 deg. The edge of the form over which bending occurs is rounded to provide a bottom curve as shown. The rim petals are laid out and a V cut is filed at their intersections. The leaves are rounded as shown and as directed under Filing, step 3, and each is shaped over the end of a block with a small ball-peen hammer or a round punch. See *A*, Figure 179, for a similar rounding. The tips are bent

Fig. 180. Fluted bowls.

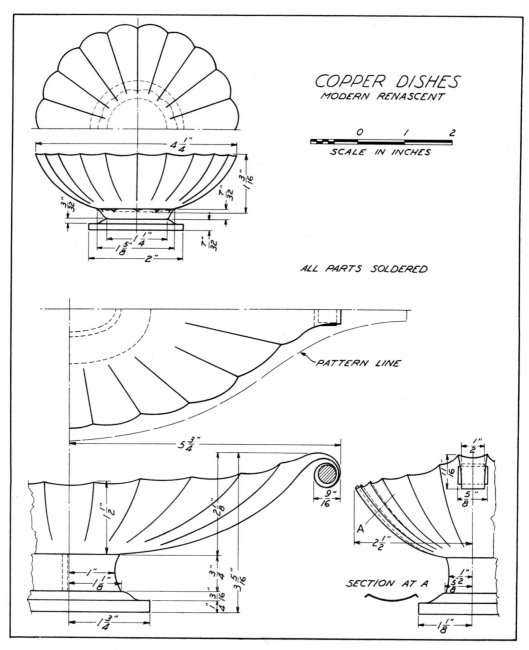

COPPER DISHES
MODERN RENASCENT

SCALE IN INCHES

ALL PARTS SOLDERED

PATTERN LINE

SECTION AT A

Plate 15.

Bill of Material

Material: All pieces made of 24-oz. cold-rolled annealed copper sheet.

Pieces		Width	Length
1	Body	4½	4½
1	Base	2 5/16	2 5/16
1	Stem	1⅞	1⅞

out over the edge of a block, as shown at *B,* Figure 179.

6. The bowl is assembled in the same manner as the one in Plate 13, steps 7, 8, and 9.

7. It is washed and painted, as directed

Bill of Material

(Supplementary Project)

Material: All pieces made of 24-oz. cold-rolled annealed copper sheet except the cores of the handles, which are made of half-hard copper or brass rod or tube.

Pieces		Width	Length
1	Body	5½	14⅜
1	Base	2¾	4
1	Stem	⅞	5 11/16
2	Cores of handles	¾ O.D.	⅝

under Finishing, Painting Tôle Work, or it may be acid colored. See Finishing; Polishing; Cleaning, steps 1 and 2; and Coloring by Acid.

The oval bowl is shaped over a sandbag, with one annealing, to a depth of 1½ in. It is smoothed, planished, and fluted as in the foregoing steps. The ends are curled over wood and soldered to a ⅜-in. rod. The oval neck is seamed and flared, as directed under Flaring, step 5, and the base is made as in the preceding steps. The soldering is similar to that for Plate 13.

Plate 16. Tôle Vases

Vases are bowls under high bodies. The only addition then to the work given in preceding plates is the shaping of cylindrical bodies. This may be attempted without hesitation by those having the foregoing experience. The vases illustrated here are of the French Empire type.

Procedure

1. The full-sized top unit is developed on paper, cut, checked for size and taper. It is then drawn on a piece of metal of the proper size and cut to the pattern lines. See Cutting, Thin Metal.

2. The sides are folded for the seam as explained under Folding, steps 1 to 6, and drawn around a large pipe by hand, locked, flattened with a block and mallet, and grooved. See Grooving.

3. The body is trued either to round or oval, as desired, and soldered. See Soft Soldering, steps 1 to 4, and 5, Example 1.

4. The disk for the body bottom is

Fig. 181. Tôle vases.

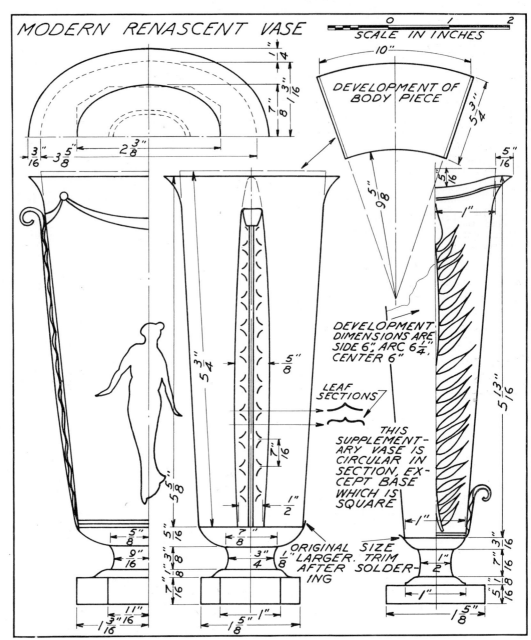

Plate 16.

Bill of Material

Material: All pieces made of cold-rolled annealed copper sheet except the leaves, which are made of half-hard brass sheet.

Pieces		Thickness	Width	Length
1	Body	12 oz.	6¼	10⅛
1	Bowl	24 oz.	2	2½
1	Base	24 oz.	2½	3¼
1	Stem	12 oz.	⅜	3 15/16
2	Leaves	22 Ga. (B&S)	⅝	5¾

Bill of Material

(Supplementary Project)

Material: All pieces made of cold-rolled annealed copper sheet except as noted.

Pieces	Material	Use	Thickness	Width	Length
1		Body	12 oz.	6½	6¼
1		Bowl	24 oz.	1⅛	1⅛
1		Base	24 oz.	2¼	2¼
1	Copper tube — half hard	Stem	½ O.D.		7/16
2	Brass sheet — half hard	Leaves	22 Ga. (B&S)	½	1⅜

shaped, as directed under Low Raising, step 4, *c,* and lightly planished. See Planishing, step 2, *a.* It is made oversize to facilitate soldering, later to be cut down.

5. The stem is cut from tubing, filed at both ends, as explained under Filing, step 10, and flared. See Flaring, step 3. If oval, it is flared over a piece of wood. See Flaring, step 5.

6. The base is cut, placed between prepared forms, and bent. See Bending, step 1.

7. The parts are now set up and filed to fit where necessary.

8. The base is soldered to the neck. See Soft Soldering, step 5, Example 2.

9. A hole is punched into the center base for a gas vent.

10. The base unit is now soldered to the vase bottom. See Soft Soldering, step 5, Example 3.

11. The assembly is set up with the vase body in place. The latter should fit within the bowl unit of the former. Then it is fluxed, and solder is set at intervals into the extending ledge. The soldered parts are painted with yellow ocher for protection, and a flame is directed on the joint until soldered. If the previous soldering is loosened it will not injure the work unless it is actually moved. Consult Soldering, steps 1 to 4, and 5, Example 3.

12. The extending edge is filed off and the top rim is trimmed and flared. See Flaring, step 2. The base corners are soldered. See Soft Soldering, step 7, Example 1. If leaves are desired, they are made as described in Plate 20, step 10, and Figure 179, and soldered. See Soft Soldering, step 7, Example 3.

13. The vase is washed and painted, as directed under Finishing, Painting Tôle Work, and the leaves are polished. See Finishing; Painting; Cleaning 1; and Preserving Metals.

Plate 17. Modern Renascent Urn

Many beautiful Greek urns with painted figures are still in existence, and fifteenth- to eighteenth-century examples in bronze, terra cotta, and stone, together with their representations in wall paintings are numerous. The urn in Figure 182 is a modern adaptation in the manner of tôle work.

Procedure

1. The vase body is made like the one in Plate 16, steps 1, 2, and 3.

2. The body bottom is cut and dished to a depth of ⅝ in. in the three stages as shown in Figure 183. See Low Raising, step 4, *a, b,* and *c.* It is annealed between stages. See Annealing. It is then trued up on a flat surface and planished lightly. See Planishing, steps 1 and 2*a.* The top edge is filed true.

3. The stem is made of a seamed cylinder, grooved inside, as directed under Grooving, and flared over a block. See Flaring, steps 3, 4, and 5.

4. The base is cut and bent over prepared wood forms. See Bending, step 1.

5. The base and stem are soldered. See Soft Soldering, steps 1 to 4, and 5, Example 2, for the procedure.

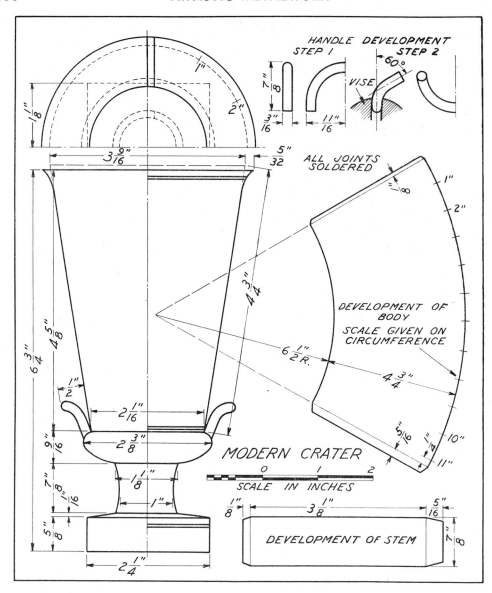

Plate 17.

Bill of Material

Material: All pieces made of cold-rolled annealed copper sheet except the handles, which are made of hard-drawn copper rod.

Pieces	Thickness	Width	Length
1 Body	12 oz.	5 9/16	11 3/16
1 Bowl	24 oz.	2 13/16	2 13/16
1 Base	24 oz.	3½	3½
1 Stem	12 oz.	⅞	3 9/16
2 Handles	3/16 round		2 5/16

Fig. 182. Modern renascent urn.

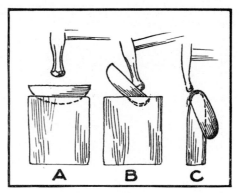

Fig. 183. Raising the base of an urn.

6. A hole is punched in the center base for a gas vent.

7. The base unit is soldered to the vase bottom. See Soft Soldering, step 5, Example 3.

8. The vase body and the bottom are tinned at their points of contact. They are set up, the previous soldering is painted with a protective wash of yellow ocher, and a flame is directed on the joint until the solder runs through.

9. Sections that do not solder may be touched with fine wire solder, or they may be soldered by copper bit. See Soft Soldering, step 7, Example 1.

10. The inside corners of the base are soldered as in the foregoing and the top edge of the body is flared out. See Flaring, step 2.

11. Handles, made of 3/16-in. rod, are bent around ½-in. pipe to a simple arc, as shown on the accompanying plate. The tips at the center of the arch are set into a vise and the ends extending upward are bent over 60 deg. They are then cut to size,

filed, and soldered. See Soft Soldering, step 7, Examples 2, 3, and 4.

12. The vase body is filed inside if necessary, washed, and painted. See Finishing, Painting Tôle Work.

Plate 18. The Whale-Oil Lamp

Whales off our early American coasts were valuable for oils which gave light far superior to ordinary fish oil then in use. Such oil was used until the day of kerosene. During that long period, lamps evolved from the ancient side-burning form to the center-wick type shown in Plate 19, and in Figures 184, 185, and 186. Figure 184 shows the familiar acorn-top whale-oil lamp used in homes and in ships.

Procedure

1. The plate type base is cut as directed under Cutting, Thin Metal, and is shaped over a block with a mallet, working within ⅛ in. of the rim. See Low Raising, step 2.

2. It is planished lightly. See Planishing, steps 1 and 2b.

3. The edge is bent down flat over a smooth, wood edge, as shown in A, Figure 70.

4. It is filed as explained under Filing, step 4, and punched in the center. See Fastening, Punching.

5. The stem is laid out and cut. The beads are pressed in at the top and bot-

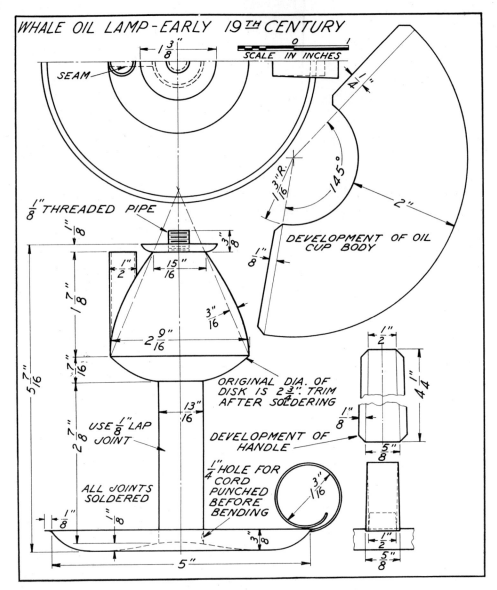

Plate 18.

tom. See Figure 184. This is done over a hardwood block on which a 16-gauge wire is fastened. The tin is laid over the wire, covered with a piece of softwood, and pressed in the vise.

6. It is now bent into cylindrical form, as directed under Bending, steps 4 and 5, and soldered. See Soft Soldering, steps 1, 2, 3, and 7, Example 1.

7. The cup bottom is cut and shaped. See Low Raising, step 4, *a*. This should be made large enough to extend ⅛ in. beyond the outside of the body.

8. The top disk is cut and bent down 30 deg. over a rounded stake.

9. The centers of both top and bottom are punched as was the base.

10. The body of the cup is laid out and

Bill of Material

Material: All pieces made of cold-rolled annealed copper sheet except as noted.

Pieces	Material	Use	Thickness	Width	Length
1		Base	24 oz.	5¼	5¼
1		Stem	24 oz.	2 11/16	2⅞
1		Bowl	24 oz.	2¾	2¾
1		Cup	12 oz.	2 15/16	6⅛
1		Top	24 oz.	1⅜	1⅜
1		Handle	12 oz.	⅞	4¼
1	Copper tubing — half hard	Spout	½ O.D.		1¾
1	Threaded brass pipe nipple	Fixture base	⅛		½
1	Candle socket	Light			3½
1	Socket cover	Light	1¼ O.D.		3½
1	Cord				8 ft.
1	Plug				

folded for seams. See Folding, steps 1 to 4. It is bent around a form, locked, and grooved. See Grooving. Then it is soldered. See Soft Soldering, step 5, Example 1. Its shape is brought out over a block by raising from the inside with a ball-peen hammer. See Low Raising, step 4, *a*. It is lightly planished. See Planishing, step 2, *a*.

11. The handle piece is cut, hemmed on both sides, and bent. See Bending, steps 4 and 6.

12. The stem is soldered to the base. See Soft Soldering, step 5, Example 2.

Fig. 185. Typical whale-oil lamps.

Fig. 184. Whale-oil lamp.

13. The cup bottom is soldered to the stem. See Soft Soldering, step 5, Example 2.

14. The body is trued and filed and the top disk is soldered to it. See Soldering, step 5, Example 2. At the same time a short ⅛-in. pipe nipple is soldered over the hole in the disk. See Wiring.

15. The base and top are now set together and the joint is fluxed. Solder is placed around it, while previous soldering is painted with a wash of yellow ocher for protection, and a flame is directed on it until soldered. See Plate 16, step 11. The surplus edge then is filed off.

16. The spout is cut and soldered. See Soft Soldering, step 7, Example 2.

17. The handle is soldered. See Soft Soldering, step 6, Example 1.

18. The shade is made as directed for Plate 4, step 7.

19. The whole project now is washed and painted. See Finishing, Painting Tôle Work.

20. It is wired. See Wiring, Terminal Threads, Fixtures, and Wiring Examples, step 1.

Plate 19. Painted Tin Lamps

The lamp in Plate 19 and Figure 186, right, a whale-oil type like those shown in Figure 185, is made by much the same processes as that in the preceding plate. The tôle lamp, therefore, is described in the following paragraphs.

Procedure

1. The base, cup, and handle for the lamp to the left in Figure 186 are cut from a 4-in. can as described in Plate 1, steps 1 to 4.

Fig. 186. Painted tin lamps.

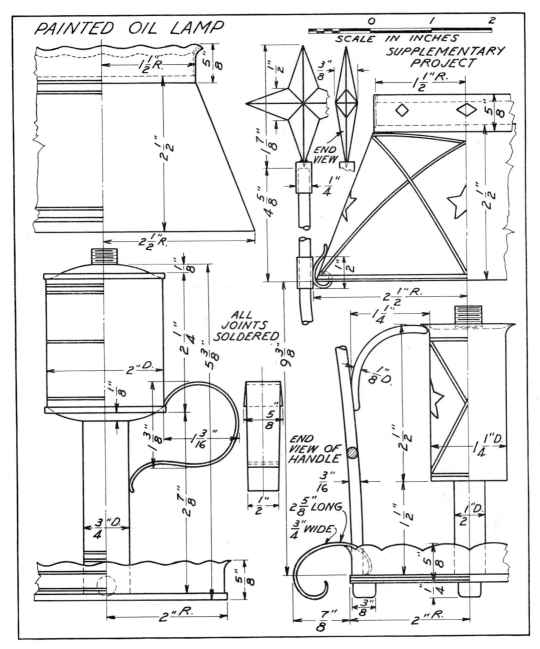

Plate 19.

2. A design is laid out on its rim and cut. See Cutting, Thin Metal, step 6.

3. The edge is filed, as directed under Filing, steps 3 and 4, and flared. See Flaring, steps 1 and 2.

4. The stem is made from a piece of tubing, filed on top and bottom, as explained under Filing, step 10, and flared. See Flaring, step 3.

5. Two top and bottom cup disks are cut

Bill of Material

Material: All pieces made of tin-can stock except as noted.

Pieces	Material	Use	Thickness	Width	Length
1		Base	4D.	Can bottom	5⁄8 high
1		Stem	4D.	2½	2⅞
1		Handle	4D.	⅞	4¼
1		Shade ring	4D.	15/16	9⅝
1		Cup	2D.	Body of can	2⅛ high
1		Cover	2D.	Cover of can	
1		Shade holder		⅜	7¾
2		Holder straps		¾	2
1	I.C. Bright coke tin sheet — Imperial No. 3 grade	Shade		5⅜	11 11/16
1	Threaded brass pipe nipple	Fixture base	⅛		½
1	Candle socket	Light			3½
1	Socket cover	Light	1¼ O.D.		3½
1	Cord				8 ft.
1	Plug				

Bill of Material

(Supplementary Project)

Material: All pieces made of tin-can stock except as noted.

Pieces	Material	Use	Thickness	Width	Length
1		Base	4D.	Bottom of can	5⁄8 high
1		Cup		4⅜	2½
2		Top and bottom disks		1½	1½
1		Shade ring		1¼	9⅝
2		Star	⅜	1⅞	1⅞
1		Handle		1⅜	2⅝
4		Feet	¼	⅜	⅜
1	Brass or copper tube — half hard	Stem	½ O.D.		1½
1	Brass or copper rod — half hard	Bracket	⅛D.		2¼
1	Brass or copper rod — half hard	Shade stem	3/16D.		14
2	Brass or copper tube — half hard	Collars	¼D.		½
1	I.C. Bright coke tin sheet	Shade		5⅜	11 11/16
1	Brass or copper sheet	Shade holder	32 oz.	⅜	1½
1	Brass threaded pipe nipple	Socket base	⅛		½
1	Candle socket	Light			3½
1	Socket cover	Light	1 ¼ O.D.		3½
1	Cord				8 ft.
1	Plug				

larger than needed, and wire holes are punched into the center of each and into the center of the base. See Fastening, Punching.

6. The cup is made like the one in Plate 1, steps 6, 7, 8, 10, and 11.

7. The handle piece is cut, hemmed, and bent. See Folding, steps 1 to 6, and Bend-ing, steps 4, 6, and 7. The project will be more stable if the handle is curved down to the table.

8. The vertical stem and rod for the shade bracket are cut. At their junction is a piece of ¼-in. tubing which may be slipped down for shade adjustment. A length of tubing also is fitted under the

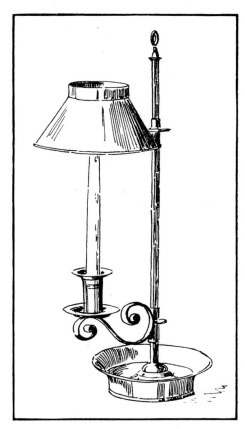

Fig. 187. A colonial candleholder with shade.

ornament. A simple shade-holding device is shown in Figure 187.

9. The lower disk is soldered to the cup. See Soft Soldering, steps 1 to 4, and 5, Example 2.

10. The upper disk is soldered in the same manner. The nipple is set into place. See Wiring, Terminal Threads. It is then weighted, fluxed, charged, and the flame is directed upon it. If the previous soldering melts, no injury is done.

11. The stem is soldered to the cup and the base to the stem. See Soldering, step 5, Example 3.

12. Feet, such as are shown in Plate 4, are cut and bent. See Bendings, step 8. They are then soldered. See Soft Soldering,

step 7, Example 3. The feet shown are filed from rod and are soldered by the same process.

13. The vertical stem, shade bracket, lower brace, and top ornament (see step 19, following) are assembled flat on a board and held with brads while they are soldered. See Soft Soldering, step 7, Example 3.

14. This unit, then, and the handle are soldered to the base, as explained under Soft Soldering, step 7, Example 3, and the lower brace is soldered to the cup.

15. The shade with its top ring is made like the one in Plate 4, steps 3, 4, 7, and 8. The ring is punched with tools filed to diamond shape. These need not be made of tool steel if used but a few times. See Punching.

16. The shade hanger is hemmed and soldered into the shade.

17. The lamp is now washed and painted. See Finishing, Painting Tôle Work, for directions.

18. It is then wired. See Wiring, Terminal Threads, Fixtures, and Wiring.

19. The ornament is laid out on metal and cut from a blank, two parts being necessary. Each half is bent on center lines shown in the detailed drawing, by means of a vise block and mallet, the first bend being made from point to point vertically, and the remaining ones being held in a filed hinge and bent with block and mallet. The hinge is closed over the line in the vise. It is previously sawed down from the extreme left end of its closed edges obliquely inward at about 30 deg. and then straight down leaving an overhanging pointed end which fits to the center of the star without injuring previous bends. After bending, the halves are placed on a flat surface and tapped flat below. These are filed flat, tinned, and soldered. See Soldering, step 6, Example 1, for the proper procedure.

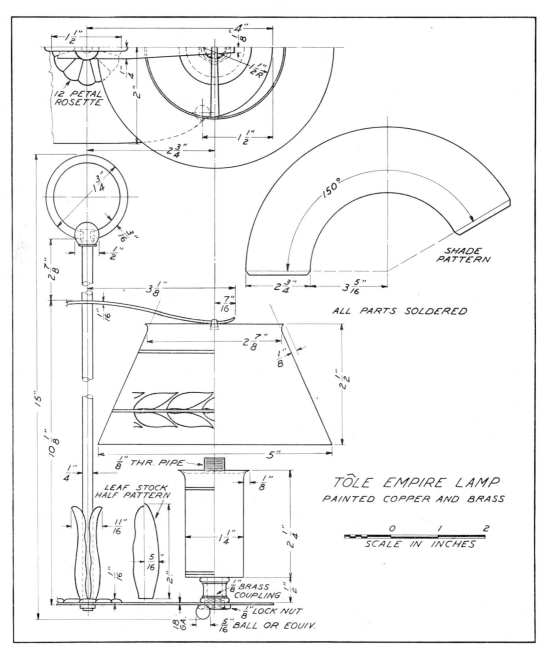

Plate 20.

Plate 20.　Twin Lamp

The tôle lamp in Figure 188 is a charming little Napoleonic lamp in turquoise and gold. It may be varied by using one oval shade, or three candles on a round base with one round shade. The lamp in Figure 187 also will suggest other variations.

Procedure

1. A base is laid out on heavy brass, cut with a shears or chisel. See Cutting, Thin

Fig. 188. Twin lamp.

Bill of Material

Material: All pieces made of soft-spinning brass sheet except as noted.

Pieces	Material	Use	Thickness	Width	Length
1		Base	18 Ga. (B&S)	4	8
2		Leaves	22 Ga.	⅝	2
1		Rosette	22 Ga.	1½	1½
4		Cup disks (Top and bottom)	22 Ga.	1½	1½
2		Shades	28 Ga.	5 5/16	11 9/16
2	Brass pipe couplings	Stems	⅛		½
2	Brass lock nuts	Lock below lights	⅛		
2	Brass tubing — half hard	Cups	1¼ O.D. 1/32 Wall		2¼
2	Brass threaded pipe nipples	Fixture base	⅛		½
2	Brass threaded pipe nipples	Lower lock	⅛		⅜
1	Brass nut	Center stem lock	10–24		
1	Brass rod — half hard	Center stem	¼D.		13⅛
1	Brass rod — half hard	Top ring	3/16D.		4⅞
1	Brass bar — half hard	Shade arm	1/16	½	6¼
2	Brass bars — half hard	Shade holder	1/16	3/16	2⅞
1	Brass rod — half hard	Ring ball	½ O.D.		½
4	Brass rods — half hard	Feet	⅜ O.D.	5/16	5/16
2	Candle sockets	Lights			4
2	Socket covers	Lights	1¼ O.D.		4
1	Cord				8 ft.
1	Plug				

Metal, and Metals of Medium Thickness, step 6. It is straightened, as explained under Straightening, step 1, filed as directed under Filing, steps 1 to 3, center punched, and drilled, as directed under Fastening, Center Punching, and Drilling.

2. The feet are cut from brass rod, filed, and soldered at four points. See Soft Soldering, steps 1 to 4, and 5, Example 4.

3. A piece of 1¼-in. tubing is cut, filed, annealed, and flared. See Cutting Tubing, Filing, step 10, Annealing, step 3, and Flaring, step 3.

4. Four disks are cut slightly oversize and punched in the center. See Fastening, Punching. One disk is soldered to the tubing on the flared end, that end down. See Soft Soldering, step 5, Example 2. It is reversed, and a nipple is set into the center of the top, weighted, and soldered. See Wiring, Terminal Threads, and Soldering, step 5, Example 2. Previous soldering will melt, but this will do no harm. The unit is again reversed and a disk is soldered to each cup bottom in the same manner.

5. The unit is reversed once more, and a ⅛-in. pipe coupling is soldered to it as before, the flame directed only at the joint from above. The coupling is weighted.

6. Each unit now is attached by a short nipple and lock nut to the base, as shown.

7. The vertical stem is cut and threaded below. A ring, cut from tubing, is soldered just above the threads. See Soft Soldering, step 5, Example 6.

8. A shade-holder arm is cut, filed, drilled, and soldered. See Soft Soldering, step 5, Example 6.

9. A finial ring is bent over a pipe. Then it is aligned, cut, and set into a hole in a short, filed, or turned piece of rod, and soldered. See Soft Soldering, step 5, Example 6.

10. The leaves are cut, filed, and bent in a vise with a mallet sharply down the center for the vein. They are then opened and embossed as shown in Figure 179, and bent outward at their tips over a rounded block as shown in B, Figure 179.

11. The leaves are soldered to the lower stem. See Soft Soldering, step 5, Example 6.

12. The rosette is laid out, cut, and chased. See Plate 10, step 4. A hole is punched in the center. See Punching.

13. The stem is now set through the rosette and the center hole and held by a nut below, the latter having been reduced by cutting and filing.

14. The shades are made as described in Plate 4, step 7, the top being flared rather than crowned. See Flaring, step 2. A hanger piece is soldered into each.

15. The lamp is washed and painted. See Finishing, Painting Tôle Work.

16. It is then wired. See Wiring, Terminal Threads, Fixtures, and Wiring Double-Light Lamp, Example 4.

The shades may be attached as shown in Figure 187.

Plate 21. Boxes for Every Use

The small modern box in Figure 189 comes with a cast pewter handle. Such a box may be triangular, square, or octagonal, high or low. The procedure is the same for all.

Procedure

1. The metal blank is cut and filed straight on one edge from which its bottom, sides, and bending lines are laid out with square, scale, scriber, and gauge. If end laps are to be employed, provision is made for them. They are not used, however, on small decorative boxes.

2. The stock is cut as close to the line as possible and, if necessary, filed to the center of the line. See Cutting, Thin Metal, and Filing, steps 1, 2, and 4.

3. With care, the metal may be kept free from marks and scratches. Since dents make planishing and consequent stretching

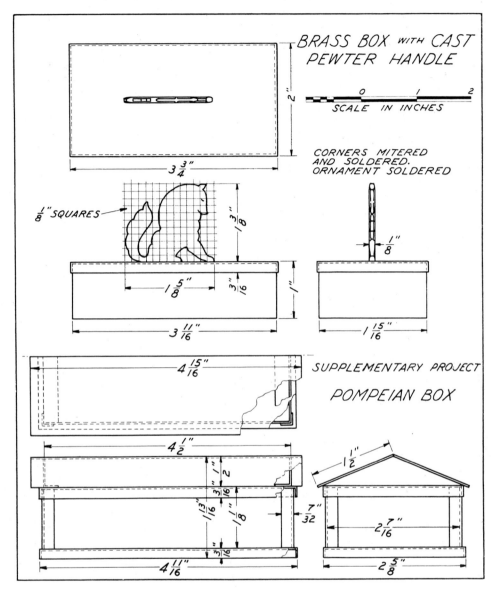

Plate 21.

Bill of Material

Material: Box and cover made of soft-spinning brass sheet; handle of britannia metal scrap.

Pieces		Thickness	Width	Length
1	Box	22 Ga. (B&S)	3 15/16	5 11/16
1	Cover	22 Ga. (B&S)	2⅜	4⅛
1	Handle	½-oz. casting		

of the hammered surfaces necessary, they are to be avoided by all means. Otherwise planishing precedes step 1. Minor waves are straightened by soft mallet after cutting. See Straightening, step 1. Annealing should be avoided, especially after planishing.

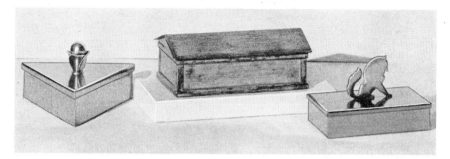

Fig. 189. Boxes for every use.

Bill of Material

(Supplementary Project)

Material: All pieces made of 22-gauge (B&S) soft-spinning brass sheet; or substitute commercial bronze sheet.

Pieces		Width	Length
1	Box	4 11/16	6¾
1	Base	3	5 1/16
1	Roof	3	4 15/16
1	Roof base	3	5 1/16
2	Tympanum	13/16	2½
4	Corners	7/16	1⅛

4. The sides are folded as described under Bending, step 9, and the corners are soldered. See Soft Soldering, steps 1, 2, 3, and 5, Example 1.

5. A cover is made in the same manner.

6. A figure is designed and cast in pewter. See Casting, Wood Molds. It is filed round, scraped, and buffed or burnished. See Filing, steps 5 and 9, and Finishing, Polishing, and Cleaning.

7. The cover is set on a soldering rack, fluxed, and the figure is placed on it. A sheet-iron arch is set over the figure to support it in an upright position. A slotted wood block will also serve for the same purpose. The flame is applied and watched carefully. At the first indication of melting, the flame is removed and cold water is sprinkled on the figure. The slightest delay will result in its melting. Another method is soldering. See Pewter Soldering. The flux used, however, must be soldering salts since the pewter flux will not act on brass or bronze sheet.

8. The box is buffed, washed, and lacquered. See Finishing, Polishing, and Preserving Metals.

Plate 22. Coal Hods in Miniature

The pieces in Figure 190, symbols of the past generation, are relics of the transition from log fire to furnace.

Procedure

1. The pattern is laid out full size on paper, cut out, and transferred to the metal. The metal then is cut as directed under Cutting, Thin Metal, allowing enough for the seam and the hemmed upper edge. The metal is hemmed by a bending tool. See Bending, steps 2 and 3. Its seam ends are folded as explained under Folding, steps 1 to 4. The body is bent around a form, engaged, and grooved. See Grooving.

2. The handle plates also are laid out and cut together with a snips and file. See Filing, steps 3 and 4. The handle wires are cut and bent around pipes to U shape. They are bent out in a vise, and filed to fit the hole in the plates. The back handles are bent down to fit the angle of the body.

3. The base for the hod to the left in Figure 190 is laid out and cut, and set between circular blocks. The edge then is bent down 60 deg. See Bending, step 1.

4. The bottom of the body is trued to round, and filed so as to fit the base to which it is now soldered. See Soft Solder-

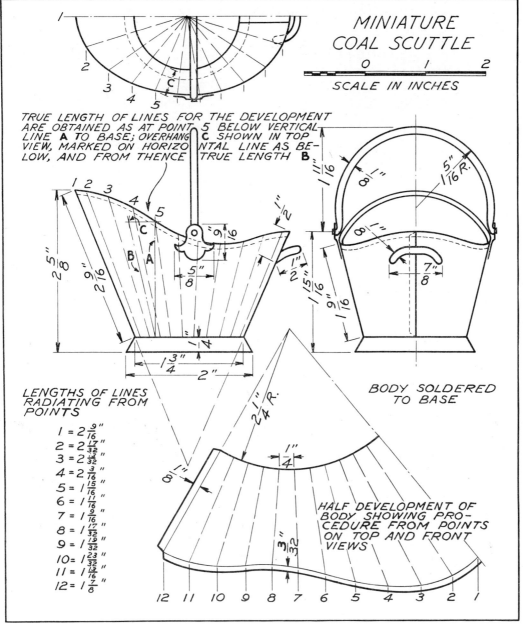

Plate 22.

Bill of Material

Material: All pieces made of soft-spinning brass sheet except handle and grip, which are made of half-hard brass rod.

Pieces		Thickness	Width	Length
1	Body	28 Ga. (B&S)	4¼	7 15/16
1	Base	22 Ga.	2 5/16	2 5/16
2	Handle eyes	22 Ga.	⅝	9/16
1	Handle	⅛D.		5
1	Grip	⅛D.		1⅜

Fig. 190. Coal hods in miniature.

ing, steps 1, 2, 3, and 5, Example 2. The handle plates are tinned inside. See Soft Soldering, step 6, Example 2. The body is marked, fluxed, and the plates, held with light tongs, one at a time are soldered over a flame. The rear handle is attached likewise, held to its angle in a slotted wood holder, while the plates are painted with yellow ocher or covered with damp paper for protection.

5. The whole piece is buffed, washed, and lacquered. See Finishing, Polishing, and Preserving Metals.

The hod to the right in Figure 190 is made in a somewhat similar manner except that the bottom is driven up to 90 deg. and reversed in soldering. Feet are soldered to the bottom while the parts previously soldered are protected as described in the foregoing steps.

Fig. 191. Pyramid book ends.

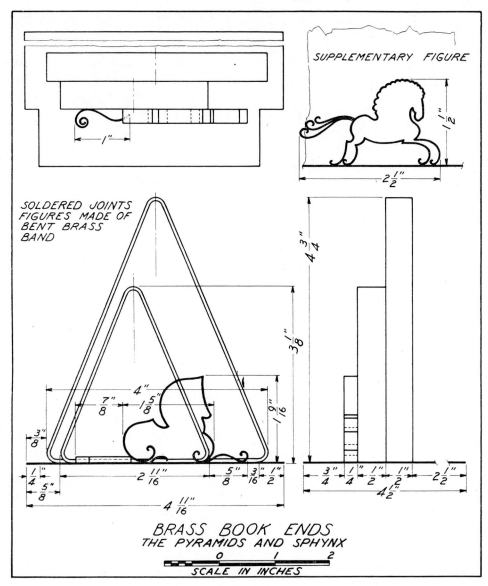

Plate 23.

Bill of Material

Material: All pieces made of soft-spinning brass sheet except the pyramids, which are made of half-hard brass bar.

Pieces		Thickness	Width	Length
1	Base	20 Ga. (B&S)	4 11/16	4½
1	Body of sphynx	28 Ga.	¼	5⅞
1	Front foot	28 Ga.	¼	1⅛
1	Hind foot	28 Ga.	¼	½
1	Tail	28 Ga.	⅛	1⅞
1	Large pyramid	1/16	½	14¼
1	Small pyramid	1/16	½	9½

Bill of Material

(Supplementary Figure)

Material: All pieces made of 28-gauge soft-spinning brass sheet.

Pieces		Width	Length
1	Top	¼	4¾
1	Bottom	¼	2¾
1	Tail	¼	1
1	Tail	¼	1¼
1	Tail	¼	1 7/16

Plate 23. Pyramid Book Ends

Book ends like those in Figure 191 suggest the new fields of modern expression and at the same time are very practical.

Procedure

1. A base is cut as explained under Cutting, Thin Metal. It is filed as directed under Filing, steps 1 to 4, and scraped as explained under Finishing, Polishing. It is carefully straightened. See Straightening, step 1. Annealing should be avoided if possible.

2. The bar for the pyramids and the stock for the sphinx are cut. All pieces are buffed. See Finishing, Polishing.

3. The bar is marked and bent at right angles at each mark while held between wood in a vise. See Folding, steps 1 to 4. It is then placed into a die cut at the pyramid angle, as shown in Figure 192, and driven home by a mallet. A hardwood die should be leather lined. Another bending method is found under Forming, step 3. Heavy paper is used around the metal as protection.

4. The sphinx stock is bent to the design in the fingers with a round-nose pliers. Sharp bends are made with a flat-nose pliers. Bends of more than right angle are made by pinching the bends in pliers.

5. All parts are aligned to fit the base.

6. The pyramid and sphinx pieces are now tinned and soldered. See Soft Soldering, steps 1, 2, 3, and 6, Examples 2 and 3.

7. The parts that discolor are buffed by hand. They are washed and lacquered. See Finishing, Polishing, and Preserving Metals,

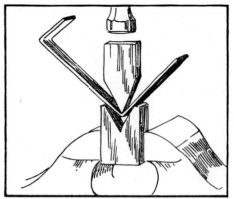

Fig. 192. Bending parts of the pyramid book ends.

step 3. If the discoloration is too great, the book end is bright dipped. See Finishing, Cleaning, step 3.

The soldering, if well done, is barely visible. The book end to the right in Figure 191 is made of sheet brass by the same processes.

Plate 24.   More Modern Book Ends

The pewter figures are framed in a setting of polished brass in the book ends in Figure 193.

Procedure

1. The base pieces are cut and filed. See Cutting, Thin Metal, and Filing, steps 1 to 4. The edges are scraped and straightened. See Finishing, Polishing, and Straightening, step 1.

2. The pieces are tinned and soldered. See Soft Soldering, steps 1 to 4, and 6, Example 2. The base then is buffed. See Finishing, Polishing.

3. The vertical piece, including the bending lines, is laid out, cut, filed, and folded. See Folding, step 9, and Figure 59. The first fold is that on the extreme left. The metal is then reversed and folded in the opposite direction on the second line. While it is still held in the folding device, the flute is curved down by means of block and mallet. No other means is necessary. The metal will bend as shown if driven

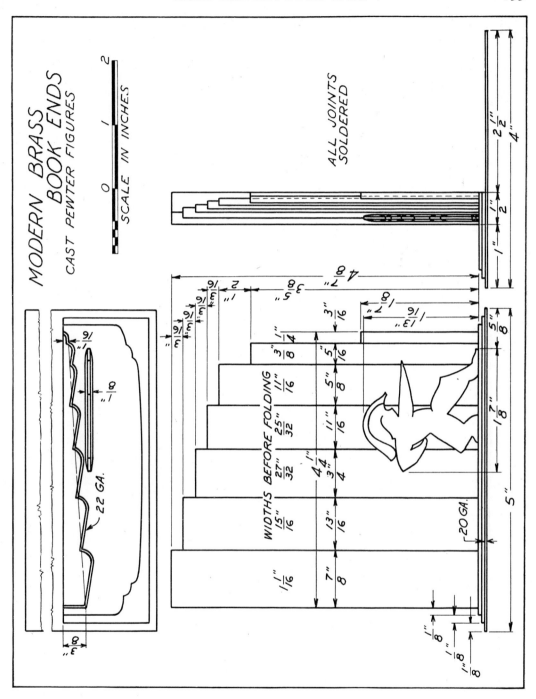

Plate 24.

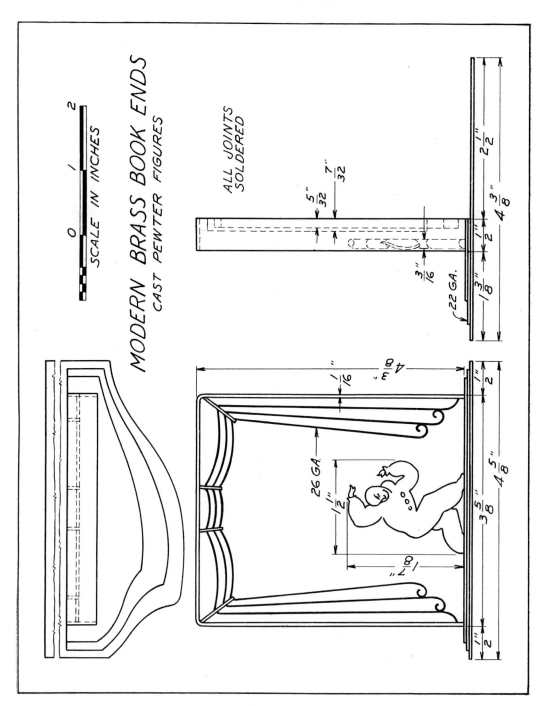

Plate 24A.

Fig. 193. More modern book ends.

Bill of Material

Material: All pieces made of 20-gauge (B&S) soft-spinning brass sheet except the figure, which is made of britannia metal scrap.

Pieces		Width	Length
1	Back	4⅞	5 5/16
1	Base	4	5
1	Second base	1⅜	4¾
1	Third base	1¼	4½
1	Figure — 1-oz. casting		

down sufficiently. The remaining folds are handled likewise.

4. The small flute at the end is bent over a rod by a mallet.

5. The piece is trimmed above the last flute, the corners are filed clean, the edges are scraped, and the bottom is aligned.

6. The project is buffed. See Finishing, Polishing.

7. It is soldered with clips remaining around the base. See Soft Soldering, steps 1, 2, 3, and 6, Example 3.

8. The whole piece is rebuffed, washed, and lacquered. See Finishing, Polishing, Cleaning, and Preserving Metals, step 3.

9. The pewter figure is designed and cast as explained under Casting. It is set on jewelers' wax, carved, and chased. See Chasing. It is then lightly buffed and soldered to the back through a drilled hole with a soldering bit. See Pewter Soldering and Welding, step c.

Bill of Material
(Supplementary Project)

Material: All pieces made of soft-spinning brass sheet except the top, which is made of half-hard brass bar and the figure of britannia metal scrap.

Pieces		Thickness	Width	Length
1	Base	20 Ga. (B&S)	4⅜	4⅝
1	Second base	22 Ga.	1⅝	4⅜
1	Third base	22 Ga.	1¼	4⅛
1	Drapery	28 Ga.	5/32	11⅛
1	Drapery	28 Ga.	5/32	10¾
1	Drapery	28 Ga.	7/32	10
2	Tie backs	28 Ga.	1/16	1½
2	Tie backs	28 Ga.	1/16	1
1	Top	1/16	½	12¼
1	Figure — 1-oz. casting			

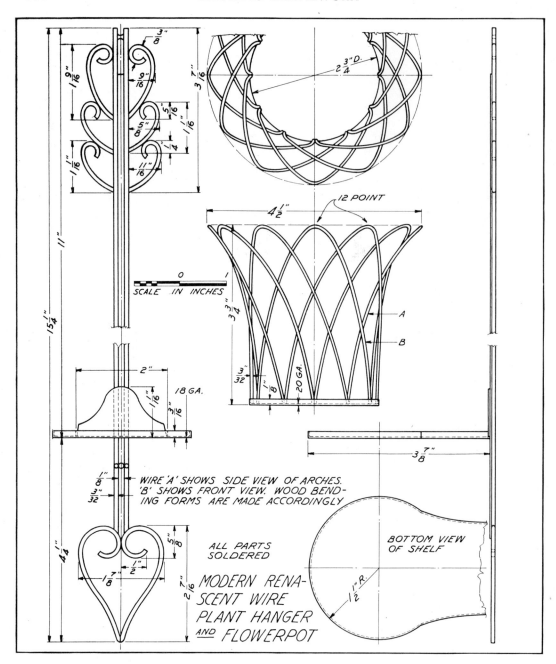

Plate 25.

Plate 25. Wire Basket for Flowers

Bent-wire lighting fixtures, lamps, tables, trays, and flower accessories, like the pot holder shown in Figure 194, are useful in the light interior decorations of the present time. They are naturally transparent and possess all the grace of late Renaissance work.

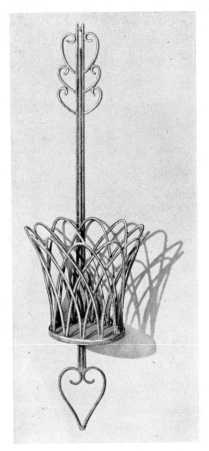

Fig. 194. Wire basket for flowers.

Procedure

1. The base is bent over a round form. See Bending, step 1.

2. The wire is straightened if necessary as directed under Straightening, cut with pliers to the required lengths, and bent. For the flowerpot, bending is done over a wood form which is cut to the shape of the front view marked *B* in the drawing.

The form must be cut slightly narrow to compensate for the back spring of the wire.

3. Each arched piece is pressed a second time over a form to the shape of the outward curvature of the section. See *A* in drawing.

4. An earthen flowerpot is set into the copper base already made and weighted. The base is marked at the intersecting points of the arches. An arch is set into place and held by a turn of string around the pot; another arch is set and the string is wound around it, and so on all around. The pieces then are aligned.

5. The contact points below are soldered. See Soft Soldering, steps 1, 2, 3, and 7, Example 3.

6. The pot is removed and the upper intersections are soldered.

7. The pot holder is made of bent pieces, arranged on a board, and held by means of brads. They are soldered. See Soft Soldering, step 7, Example 3. All of the wire is polished with emery cloth before assembly.

8. The holder base is made as was the flowerpot base. It is soldered from the back.

9. The pieces are washed and painted. See Finishing, Painting Tôle Work.

Bill of Material

Material: All pieces made of half-hard copper wire except the bottom of basket and the shelf, which are made of cold-rolled annealed copper sheet.

Pieces		Thickness	Width	Length
12	Basket	3/32D.		8 15/16
2	Arrow	3/32D.		4¼
2	Feather	3/32D.		2⅝
2	Feather	3/32D.		2
2	Feather	3/32D.		1⅞
2	Shaft	3/32D.		13
1	Shaft	⅛D.		12⅛
1	Bottom of basket	24 oz.	3	3
1	Shelf	32 oz.	5⅛	3⅜

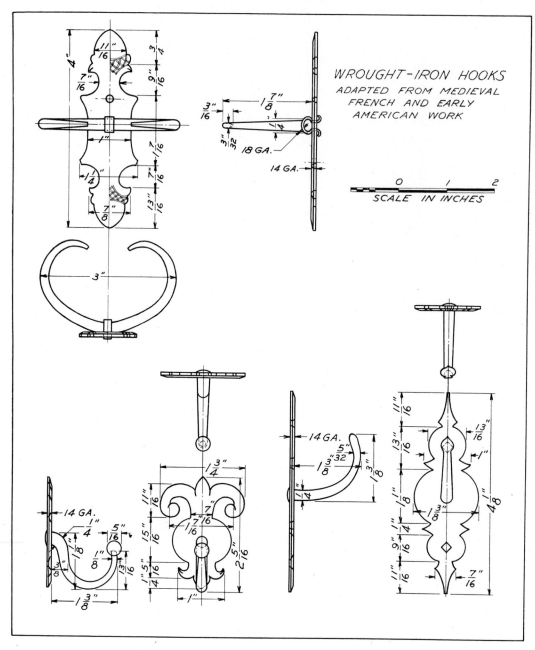

WROUGHT-IRON HOOKS
ADAPTED FROM MEDIEVAL
FRENCH AND EARLY
AMERICAN WORK

Plate 26.

Plate 26. Iron Hooks

Each metal and each design motif is expressive of a period or level in civilization. Iron is characteristic of medieval Europe, and in America, of the simple pilgrim and frontier periods.

The hooks in Figure 195 are typical of iron work during and after the American

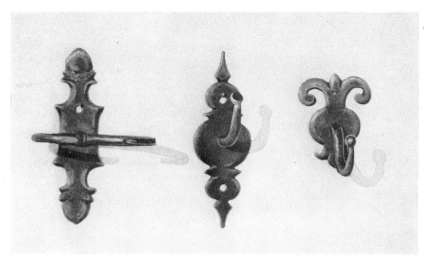

Fig. 195. Iron hooks.

Bill of Material

Pieces	Material	Use	Thickness	Width	Length
1	Mild steel hoop	Back	14 Ga.	$1\frac{1}{4}$	4
1	Mild steel bar — square	Hook	$\frac{1}{4}$	$\frac{1}{4}$	$3\frac{3}{4}$ (Forged to $6\frac{3}{4}$)
1	Sheet iron	Band	18 Ga. (B&S)	3/16	$1\frac{5}{8}$
1	Mild steel hoop	Back	14 Ga.	$1\frac{3}{4}$	2 5/16
1	Mild steel bar — square	Hook	$\frac{1}{4}$	$\frac{1}{4}$	$1\frac{5}{8}$ (Forged to $2\frac{3}{4}$)
1	Iron rivet head	Ball	$\frac{1}{4}$	Head only	
1	Mild steel hoop	Back	14 Ga.	$1\frac{3}{8}$	$4\frac{1}{8}$
1	Mild steel bar — square	Hook	$\frac{1}{4}$	$\frac{1}{4}$	$1\frac{1}{2}$ (Forged to $2\frac{1}{2}$)

Revolution. Examples may be found on Conestoga wagons, shutter fasteners, door latches, and fire-tool handles.

Procedure

1. The stock is cut with a hack saw.

2. A half pattern is sketched on paper and folded over. The pattern is cut out and glued to the iron. See Marking.

3. The iron is placed in a vise and the waste metal is removed. See Cutting, Metals of Medium Thickness, steps 2, 3, or 4.

4. It is filed to the line. See Filing, steps 1, 2, and 3.

5. The holes are drilled, as directed under Drilling, and filed square where so indicated.

6. The paper is washed off and the piece is modeled. See Filing, step 9.

7. A square bar is forged to the length needed. See Forging, steps 1, 2, and 3, Examples *d* and *i*. The end may be forged into a ball or seed form over the edge of an anvil, or it may be left pointed. If no forge is available, the hook may be filed to form.

8. The hook is bent on an anvil or over a form. It also may be hammered into a form similar to, but deeper than, that shown in Figure 82.

9. The excess stock is removed, and the hook is placed in a vise and shouldered, as shown at *A*, Figure 196. The back plate is riveted to the hook. See Riveting.

10. The complete hook then is heated red, cooled, and polished. See Finishing, Antique Iron.

The other hooks may be made in the

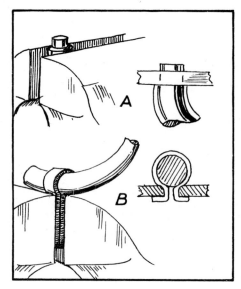

Fig. 196. Securing hooks.

same manner. The one to the left is cross marked with a chisel, and its double hook is secured by a band as at *B*, Figure 196,

and soldered. See Soft Soldering, step 5, Example 7.

Plate 27. More Hooks

The heart-shaped hook in Figure 197 is typical of the work of the German colonists in Pennsylvania. The pattern to the right is of fifteenth-century Spanish origin. Its backplate is one of a type taken from iron nailheads to be found on heavy oak cathedral doors.

Procedure

1. In the first hook, the backplate is laid out on paper, cut, glued to the stock, and sheared out. See Cutting, Metals of Medium Thickness, step 2.

2. Occasionally heart-shaped patterns include a center cutout design. These are cut as in Cutting, Metals of Medium Thickness, step 8.

3. The holes for the rivets and hanging screws are drilled. See Drilling.

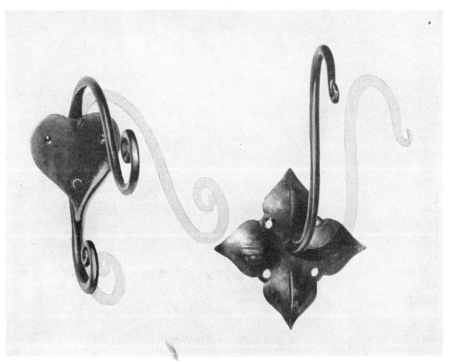

Fig. 197. More hooks.

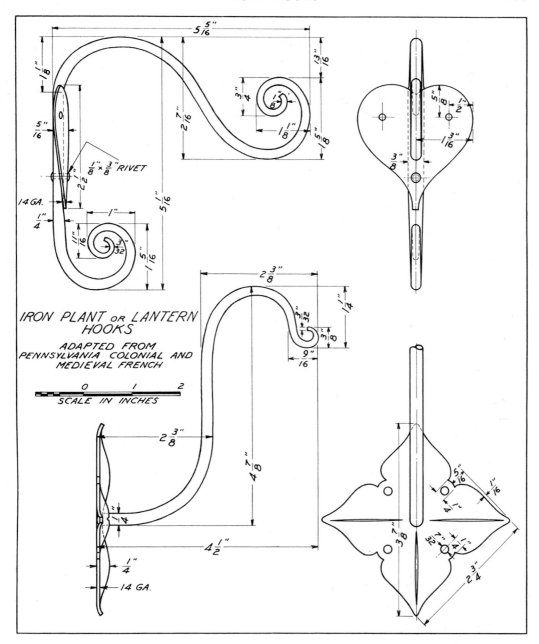

IRON PLANT OR LANTERN HOOKS

ADAPTED FROM PENNSYLVANIA COLONIAL AND MEDIEVAL FRENCH

SCALE IN INCHES

Plate 27.

4. The edges are filed. See Filing, steps 1, 2, and 3.

5. It is modeled. See Filing, step 9.

6. Both ends of the hook piece are tapered, as directed under Forging, steps 1, 2, and 3, Examples *d* and *i,* and the cen-ter is flattened. See Forging, step 3, Example *g.*

7. Its ends are curved. See Forming of Iron, step 1, or Forging, steps 7 and 8*a.*

8. The large curve is formed. See Forming of Iron, step 1, *c* and *d.*

Bill of Material

Pieces	Material	Use	Thickness	Width	Length
1	Mild steel hoop	Back	14 Ga.	2⅜	2½
1	Mild steel bar — square	Hook	¼	¼	12¾ (Forged to 17⅛)
1	Black iron rivet		⅛		½
1	Mild steel hoop (Substitute sheet iron 18 Ga. B&S)	Back	14 Ga.	2¾	2¾
1	Mild steel bar — square	Hook	¼	¼	6 (Forged to 8¾)

9. The holes are drilled in the hook piece and countersunk. Both pieces then are riveted. See Riveting.

10. It is then colored. See Finishing, Antique Iron.

The backplate of the Spanish hook is explained in the text of Plate 28. Its tapered arm is made similar to the other hook in Figure 197, and its fastening is like that of the hook in Plate 26.

Plate 28.   A Medieval Hook

The horse's head shown in Figure 198 is of medieval German origin. The backplate is a typical boss from a cathedral door of the same period.

Procedure

1. The pattern for the hook plate is sketched, cut out, and glued to a square piece of stock.

2. The metal is drilled at the leaf intersections and in the center, as described under Drilling, and is filed to the lines. See Filing, steps 1 to 3.

3. The paper is removed and the piece is modeled. See Filing, step 9.

4. The metal is laid in reverse over an indentation in a block and is embossed. See Low Raising, step 1, and Figures 61, 62, and 68.

5. The veins are filed over each petal with the edge of a half-round file.

6. The hook is forged from a ⅜-in. bar.

Fig. 198. A medieval hook.

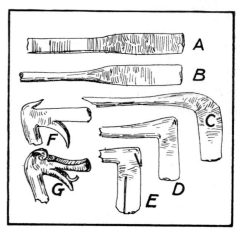

Fig. 199. Steps in the making of a horsehead hook.

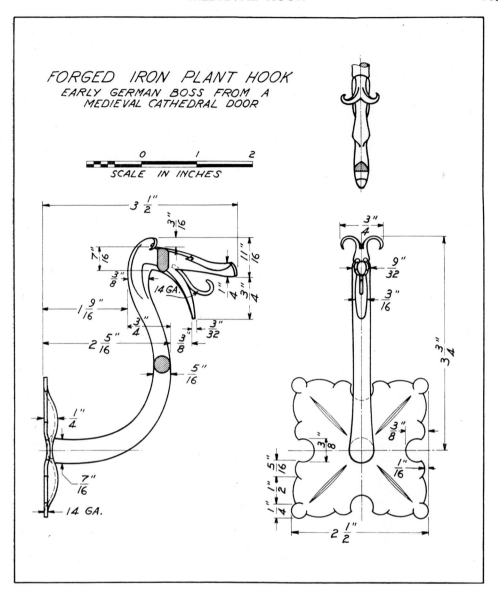

FORGED IRON PLANT HOOK
EARLY GERMAN BOSS FROM A
MEDIEVAL CATHEDRAL DOOR

SCALE IN INCHES

Plate 28.

Bill of Material

Pieces	Material	Use	Thickness	Width	Length
1	Mild steel hoop	Back	14 Ga.	2½	2½
1	Mild steel bar — square	Hook	⅜	⅜	4½ (Forged to 6½)
1	Black iron wire	Tongue	14 Ga.		1¼

a) The bar is drawn out flat and straightened to a ¼ by ½-in. section. See Forging, step 3, Example *g*.

b) It is reheated and the neck is drawn in and rounded to about 5/16 in. in the center of a 6-in. length. See Forging, step 3, Example *e*, and *B*, Figure 199.

c) The head is reheated and set into a vise edgewise almost to the neck, and bent down sharply to a right angle or more while still red, as shown at *C*, Figure 199.

d) It is again reheated and alternately driven, first the neck into the head, and then the head into the neck, on the face of the anvil. The iron is squared as shown in *D*, Figure 199.

e) The head is sawed to form the ears and mouth, as shown at *E*, Figure 199, and the ears are pried up and divided by a saw.

f) It is reheated once more, the ears are bent back and the mouth is bent open wide. See *F*, Figure 199.

g) The nose is hammered down and filed out from the eyebrows, as shown at *G*, Figure 199. The lower jaw is narrowed and filed. The mouth is cleaned and the neck rounded under and back of the head by a file.

h) A hole is drilled in the mouth, a wire is notched and inserted, and the side of the face is hammered to secure the wire. The tongue is formed with round-nose pliers while hot.

i) The neck is bent into a form. See Forging, step 8.

7. The hook is now shouldered as shown in Figure 196, and the backplate is riveted over it.

8. It is colored. See Finishing, Antique Iron, for the proper procedure.

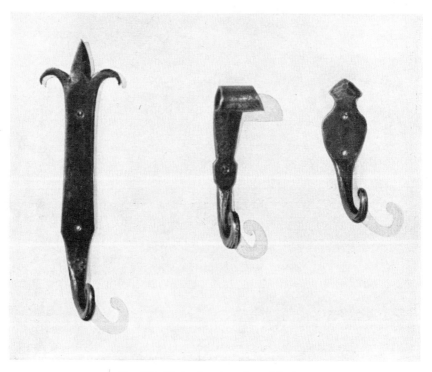

Fig. 200. Early American forged hooks.

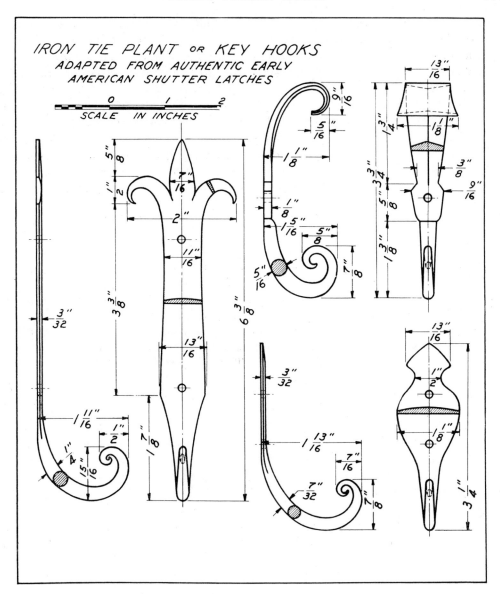

IRON TIE PLANT OR KEY HOOKS
ADAPTED FROM AUTHENTIC EARLY
AMERICAN SHUTTER LATCHES

SCALE IN INCHES

Plate 29.

Bill of Material

Material: Each hook is made of mild steel band.

Pieces	Thickness	Width	Length
1	3/16	½	7 (Forged to 8⅞)
1	3/16	½	6 (Forged to 7¼)
1	12 Ga.	¾	4 (Forged to 5¾)

Plate 29. Early American Forged Hooks

Not long after the early American settlers took possession of our wilderness they discovered, ten miles from Boston, a deposit of bog iron which they reduced, by the simple methods then known, to wrought bar and sheet for local smiths. Oil lamps,

Betty lamps of the type brought from Europe, door and window hardware, fire tools, and so on, which are known to have originated there, are still in existence, and in some instances in use.

The hooks shown in Figure 200 are adapted from shutter fasteners; the one to the right from New York State, dated 1642, and the others from Connecticut and Charleston of a later date. They are essentially forge work but may be made cold by hammering and filing.

Procedure

1. The first problem is to make a round taper out of flat bar. See Forging, steps 1 to 3, *d* and *i.*

2. For the upper part, the bar is spread as directed under Forging, step 3, *g*, flared at the end as explained under Forging, step 3, *a,* or it is shouldered like the one in the center. This is done by file, or it may be forged. See Forging, step 3, *h.* In spreading and flaring, the center of the iron is left crowned and, if possible, the hammer is manipulated so that a distinct center line remains.

3. The hooks are formed by heating the tapered ends red and turning them into volutes with round-nose pliers. Several attempts are necessary as cold pliers quickly cool the small tapered tips, and therefore must be done gradually.

4. The upper volute on the center hook may be bent as described under Forming of Iron, step 1, or for advanced students, as in Forging, step 7.

5. The fleur-de-lis to the left is sawed, bent over a rod, and filed.

6. The design in the hook to the right is filed.

7. The holes are drilled for hanging. See Drilling.

8. The hooks then are colored following the directions in the several steps under Finishing, Antique Iron.

Plate 30. Medieval Brackets for Lights or Plants

Brackets, like the one shown in Figure 201, are the product of feudal France and Spain, where work in metals was of high standard, French ironwork is forceful, simple, and beautifully done. The fleur-de-lis was used extensively in decorative work from early times. Spain also used it, and today excellent examples are found in Spanish church screens, lights, etc.

Procedure

1. A half pattern for the back is sketched on paper, folded, cut out, and glued to the metal stock.

2. The inside cutting is done as described under Cutting, Metals of Medium Thickness, step 8.

3. The outside cutting is done as described under Cutting, Metals of Medium Thickness, steps 3 and 4.

4. The metal is filed to the lines. See Filing, steps 1 to 3.

5. The center holes are drilled. See Drilling.

6. It is modeled. See Filing, step 9.

7. A bar of iron for the bracket is heated and tapered as described under Forging, steps 1, 2, and 3, *d* and *i.* It may be left round or octagonal.

8. The volute is bent while red hot. See Forging, steps 7, 8, or 9. The large curve is bent similarly or as described under Forming, step 1, and Figure 82.

9. The top end is shouldered as shown in *A,* Figure 196.

10. A band is cut, bent around the volute, as shown at *B,* Figure 196, inserted into the backplate, bent out, and soldered. See Soft Soldering, steps 1 to 4, and 5, Example 7. (The arm on the Spanish piece is shouldered and riveted, as shown at *A,* Figure 196.)

11. The top disk is made of sheet iron, as directed under Cutting, Thin Metal, or

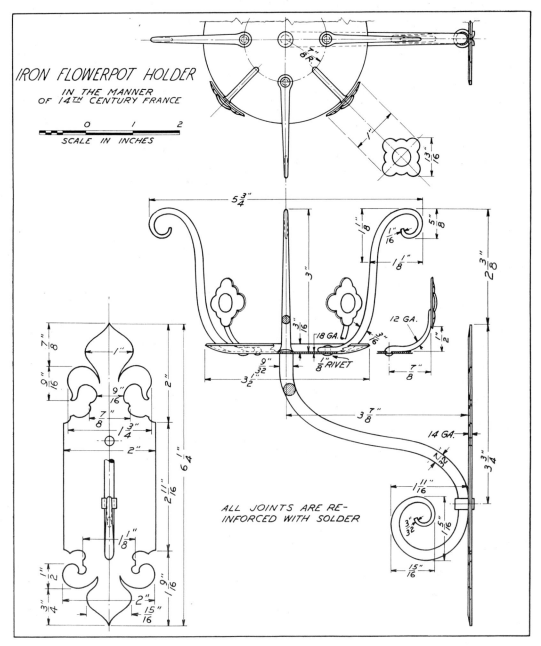

IRON FLOWERPOT HOLDER
IN THE MANNER
OF 14TH CENTURY FRANCE

SCALE IN INCHES

ALL JOINTS ARE RE-
INFORCED WITH SOLDER

Plate 30.

Metals of Medium Thickness, step 2, and are dished at the edges. See Raising, steps 1 or 6.

12. For the Spanish holder, four strips are cut from band iron. See Cutting, Metals of Medium Thickness, step 2.

13. These and the stock for the hoop are hammered. See Forging, step 3, *k*.

14. They are bent to shape. See Forming of Iron, step 1, *d*, Figure 82.

15. All parts are fired. See Finishing, Iron Coloring.

Bill of Material

Pieces	Material	Use	Thickness	Width	Length
1	Mild steel hoop	Back	14 Ga.	2	6¼
1	Mild steel bar — square	Bracket	¼	¼	7½ (Forged to 9¾)
1	Sheet iron, box annealed, one pass, cold rolled	Cup	18 Ga. (B&S)	3½	3½
4	Sheet iron, box annealed, one pass, cold rolled	Flowers	18 Ga. (B&S)	13/16	13/16
1	Sheet iron, box annealed, one pass, cold rolled	Band	18 Ga. (B&S)	¼	1½
4	Mild steel bar — round	Arms	3/16D.	3/16	4 (Forged to 5¼)
4	Black iron wire	Flower stems	12 Ga.		1¾
4	Black iron rivets roundhead		⅛		¼

16. The disk and arms are soldered. See Soft Soldering, step 5, Example 5.

17. The hoop is soldered in the same manner.

18. The unit is riveted to the arm, washed, and finished. See Finishing, Antique Iron.

19. For the French holder, four iron rods are tapered as in Forging, steps 3, *d* and *i*, bent into scrolls as was the bracket in step 8, flared below, and drilled as in Drilling.

20. The rosettes are cut, filed, and modeled by a round punch into the end of a wood block. See Low Raising, step 1. These are soldered to ends of wire. See Soft Soldering, step 5, Example 5. The wires are bent in the vise at their lower ends and curved with pliers.

21. All crown parts are riveted into holes drilled into the disk, and soldered as in Soft Soldering, step 5, Example 7.

22. Finishing is as in step 18, above.

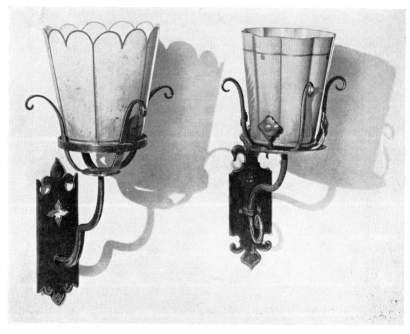

Fig. 201. Medieval brackets for lights or plants.

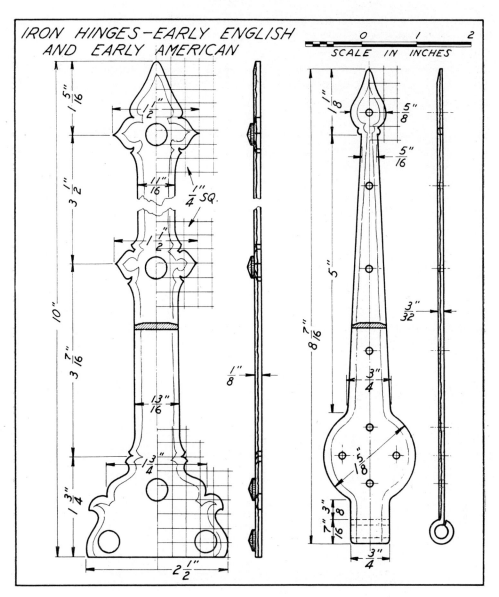

Plate 31.

Bill of Material

Pieces	Material	Use	Thickness	Width	Length
1	Mild steel band	Hinge	12 Ga.	2½	10
5	Black iron rivets or forged screws	Hinge	3/16		As required
1	Mild steel band	Hinge	12 Ga.	1¾	9¼

Plate 31. A Hinge for the Old Oaken Door

Gothic architecture developed in the north of France in the twelfth century. Its best examples are to be found within a limited area around Paris, from which its influence spread. Stone, oak, and iron were its symbols. Natural forms, such as grape, ivy, and oak, to be seen in early work, later developed into conventional types. The upper hinge in Figure 202 is a good example of this type.

In contrast is the Dutch Colonial hinge of 1720, the lower hinge in Figure 202. It is typical of hundreds of its kind found in Pennsylvania and in the New England States.

Procedure

1. A full-sized sketch of half the hinge is made on paper. It is folded, cut out, and glued to the metal.

2. This is placed in a vise and as much as possible is sheared away. See Cutting, Metals of Medium Thickness, step 2. It is filed to the line. See Filing, steps 1 to 3. The edge is drawfiled. See Filing, step 8.

3. The metal is hammered with the flat face of a hammer. The blows are ranged in three general planes, those on top being flat and those along the edges running off to each side at an angle of 5 to 10 deg.

4. The holes are drilled. See Drilling.

5. The piece is colored. See Finishing, Antique Iron.

6. The screws may be heated red, inserted into holes, and hammered to appear forged. A slot also may be cut crosswise in the screwhead to form a Tudor rose.

Plate 32. Paper Knives

These modern conveniences offer an opportunity for the study of period types. Number 1, Plate 32, is an early Jacobean pattern of great simplicity; 2 is early French; 3 is based on the Renaissance baluster while still holding to the French medieval finial; 4 is modern Renascent of the Danish silver type, and 5 is a French Empire pattern in which the palm and the Garrya husk are featured.

Procedure

1. The stock is cut.

2. The design is selected, one side is drawn full size on paper and it is transferred to the other side by folding the sketch to the inside and rubbing the out-

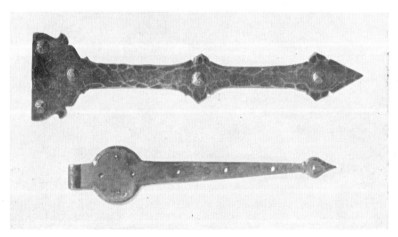

Fig. 202. A hinge for the old oaken door.

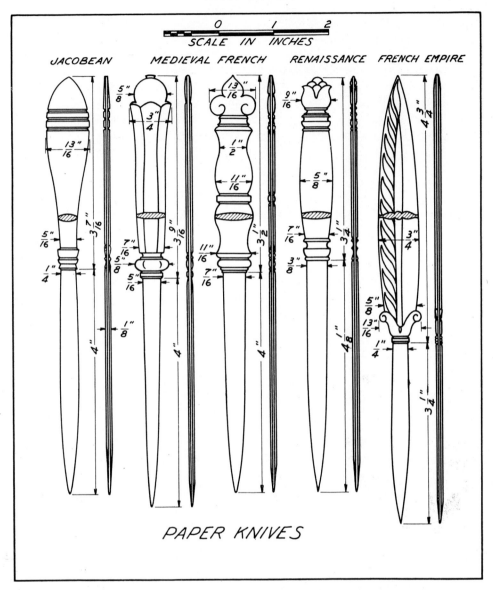

Plate 32.

Bill of Material

Material: All knives are made of 14-gauge mild steel hoop.

Pieces	Width	Length
1	13/16	7 7/16
1	3/4	7 9/16
1	13/16	7½
1	5/8	7⅜
1	3/4	8

side of the paper with a smooth tool. The paper is unfolded, the design touched up, and glued to the iron. It is not necessary to cut out the paper pattern.

3. The rough cutting of the knife is done by shearing. See Cutting, Metals of Medium Thickness, step 2. The design, being quite small and irregular, is rough cut with a hack saw and filed to the lines. See Filing, steps 1 to 3.

4. The metal is cleaned, clamped to a wood block as shown in Figure 15, and modeled. See Filing, step 9.

5. The blade and handle are highly finished. See Finishing, Polishing. The handle then is washed, dried, and colored. See Finishing, Antique Iron.

6. The blade is again brightly polished and waxed.

Plate 33. Nut Cracker

The ironwork of the seventeenth century is influenced by the classic awakening of a hundred years previous, showing the trend toward Grecian forms and formal design. In other words, the ironsmith in his decline tried to do with iron what was being done in bronze. The English nut cracker, shown in Figure 203, combines the Renaissance shell with early forms.

Fig. 203. The nut cracker.

Procedure

1. The pattern for each part of the frame is laid out on paper. It is folded, cut, and glued to metal stock.

2. It is rough cut with a saw and filed to the pattern lines. The holes are drilled as directed under Drilling. Two of them are filed square as shown.

3. The crossbar is filed. See Filing, steps 1 to 3.

4. The shell is cut with a heavy snips and filed. It is then dished over a depression in a block. See Low Raising, step 4, *a*. Hammer blows are light and close together. Radiating lines are filed from the intersection of the scallops down toward a center on the bend. The latter is made over the edge of a block with a mallet.

5. The crossbar and frame are modeled. See Filing, step 9.

6. The frame is bent at points indicated on the drawing, the shell piece is riveted to the bottom, and the crossbar, having been shouldered at each end as shown, is pressed home and riveted. See Riveting.

7. The center hole in the crossbar is tapped. See Tapping.

8. The thread on the bolt, which usually extends only part way, is cut to a point directly under the head. The latter is then heated red, flattened, and widened out, and the design is filed in. See Filing, step 3. The lower end is shouldered, as shown at *A*, Figure 196, to which a small, drilled, filed, and cupped iron square is loosely riveted after the bolt is screwed through

Bill of Material

Pieces	Material	Use	Thickness	Width	Length
1	Mild steel hoop	Frame	14 Ga.	3/4	6 1/2
1	Mild steel hoop	Swivel nut	14 Ga.	9/16	9/16
1	Sheet iron, box annealed, one pass, cold rolled	Cup	18 Ga. (B&S)	2 3/16	1 11/16
1	Mild steel bar	Crossarm	1/4	1/2	2
1	Machine bolt	Screw	1/4		2
1	Black iron rivet roundhead		1/8		1/4

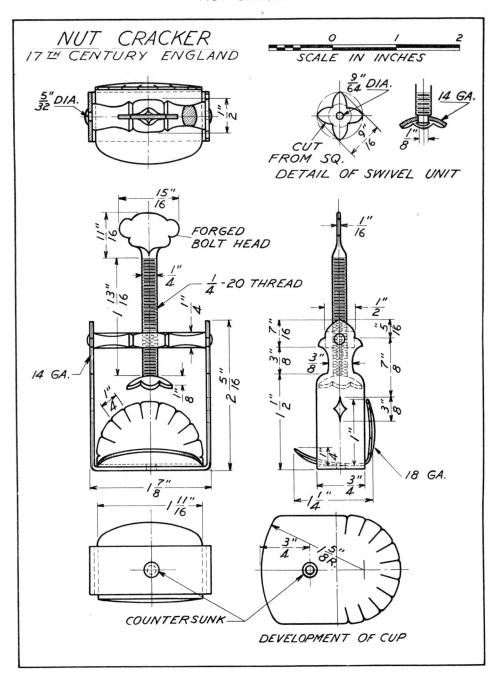

Plate 33.

the crossbar. The bar is turned out for this operation, and then turned back and tightened.

9. The whole piece is finished. See Finishing, Antique Iron, for the proper procedure in doing this work.

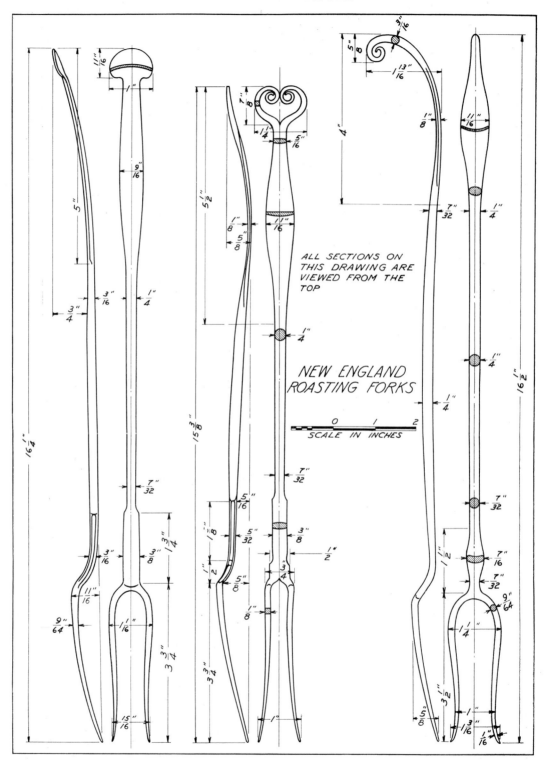

ALL SECTIONS ON
THIS DRAWING ARE
VIEWED FROM THE
TOP

*NEW ENGLAND
ROASTING FORKS*

SCALE IN INCHES

Plate 34.

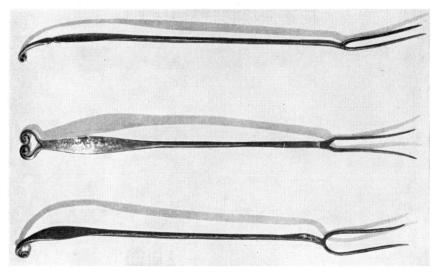

Fig. 204. Colonial fireplace forks.

Bill of Material

Material: All forks are made of ¼-in. square mild steel bars.

Pieces	Length
1	15 (Forged to 16¼)
1	15¼ (Forged to 17⅜)
1	17 (Forged to 18⅞)

Plate 34. Colonial Fireplace Forks

In the rural homes of England and the isolated American colonies, forks like the

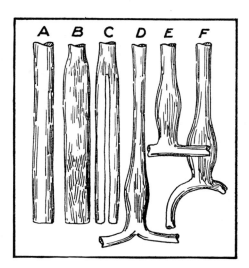

Fig. 205. Steps in forging a fork.

ones shown in Figure 204 were found hanging at the fire. They are simple in design but of very fine workmanship.

Procedure

1. A rod is heated and drawn out flat for 3½ in. at its end. See Forging, steps 1, 2, and 3, g. It should measure about 5/32 by ⅜ in. on the flat section.

2. The metal of the handle is spread at the wide section above the prongs as shown, and at the spreading of the upper handle. See Forging, step 3, f.

3. The handle between the two points mentioned above is drawn in, the smallest diameter being at 3 in. above the prongs. See Forging, step 3, e.

4. The upper tip of the handle is tapered round to a point 3/32 in. in diameter. See Forging, step 3, d and i.

5. Each section should flow into the other and each surface treatment should lead gracefully into another.

6. The prong end now is made into a fork.

a) It is set into a vise and split equally with a saw. See C, Figure 205.

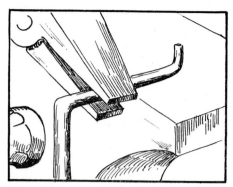

Fig. 206. Forging the handle of door knocker.

b) The piece is heated red, placed vertically in a vise, and bent down at right angles toward each side, as shown at *D*, Figure 205.

c) It is reheated and set into a vise, then hammered down at the intersecting point, as shown at *E*, Figure 205, until the end of the saw cut is worked out.

d) Each prong now is drawn out, tapered, and rounded, as directed under Forging, step 3, *d* and *i*, or they are filed. See Filing, steps 1 to 3.

e) The prongs then are bent over the horn of an anvil to the pattern, as shown

at *F*, Figure 205. A pipe in the vise may substitute for the horn.

f) The prongs are set into the vise to the top of the arch, and the handle is bent down 45 deg.

g) The fork is reversed in the vise and bent at the point given in the plate by hammer and blunt tool, as shown in Figure 85.

7. The tapered top is heated red and bent to a volute. See Forging, step 8, *a*, or 9.

8. The spread areas on the handle are embossed upward. See Low Raising, step 1.

9. The prongs are curved and aligned as required and the entire piece is aligned.

10. It is then colored. See Finishing, Antique Iron.

Plate 35. Two Door Knockers

Knockers were widely used in Europe and its colonies, and designs varied endlessly from iron-chiseled rings and grotesque figures in Spain to brass urns in England and America. Many excellent iron knockers were used in this country. Those shown in Figure 207 were used in Connecticut in the early eighteenth century.

Fig. 207. Two door knockers.

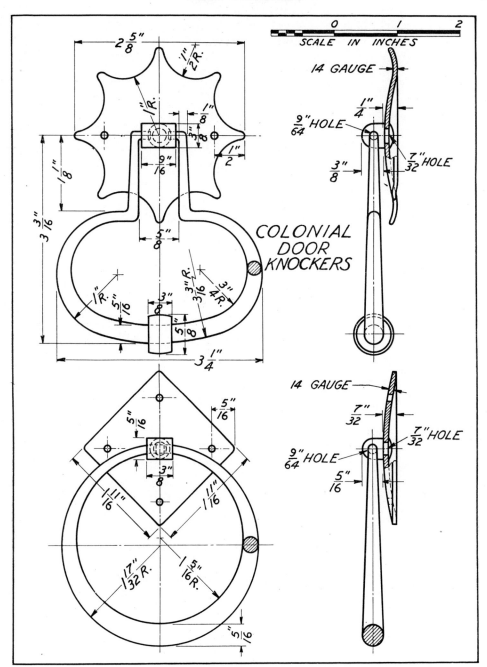

Plate 35.

Procedure

1. The pattern for the backplate is sketched on paper, folded, cut out, and glued to the metal stock.

2. The cutting is done as described under Cutting, Metals of Medium Thickness, step 3 or 4.

3. It is filed to the line and modeled.

Bill of Material

Pieces	Material	Use	Thickness	Width	Length
1	Mild steel hoop	Back	14 Ga.	2⅝	2⅝
1	Mild steel bar — square	Handle	5/16	5/16	6 (Forged to 10¼)
1	Mild steel bar — square	Bearing	½	½	⅜
		Forged to	⅜	7/16	9/16
1	Mild steel bar — round	Knocker	¼ D.		1⅜
1	Mild steel hoop	Back	14 Ga.	1 11/16	1 11/16
1	Mild steel bar — round	Ring	5/16 D.		5 (Forged to 8¾)
1	Mild steel bar — square	Bearing	⅜	⅜	7/16
		Forged to	5/16	⅜	½

See Filing, steps 1 to 3, and 9.

4. It is drilled, and countersunk on the back. See Drilling.

5. A bearing piece is cut from a bar and drilled. It is shouldered as shown at *A*, Figure 196, and filed round on the front as shown in the drawing.

6. The backplate is embossed, as described under Low Raising, step 1, and lightly planished. See Planishing, step 2, *a*.

7. The bearing piece is riveted. See Riveting.

8. A bar now is heated and tapered round at both ends. See Forging, steps 1, 2, and 3, *d* and *i*. The tapers end at a center point.

9. At this point a notch is filed around the bar.

10. A ¼-in. bar, hammered to oval section, is heated and bent into a ring. See Forging, step 8, *a*. It is cut off to the proper length so that it may be slipped over the notch later.

11. The tapered rod now is bent sharply at four points as indicated in the drawing, and its inner bends are squared, as shown in Figure 206. To do this, (*a*) it is heated red hot and held in large tongs against the anvil body, as shown, and driven lightly upon the rod back of it, the angle of the bend being maintained at a constant 90 deg.

b) It is reheated, reversed in the tongs, and the opposite side is hammered.

c) The hammering is alternated until the corner is square.

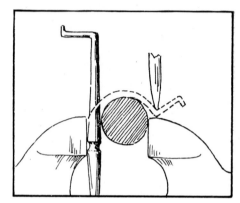

Fig. 208. Bending pendant of knocker.

d) The metal running into the corner is rounded in.

12. The pendant is curved, one side at a time, over a 1¼-in. bar or a 1-in. pipe. Both are set into a vise as shown in Figure 208. The bending is done by block and hammer as far as possible, after which the unit is revolved and driven down by a blunt tool and hammer as shown in Figure 208.

13. The ring, held with tongs, now is heated red, slipped over the notch, and pressed into place with the same tongs to shrink tight on cooling.

14. The pendant then is aligned and snapped into the bearing.

15. The project is finished. See Finishing, Antique Iron.

The operation of squaring may be omitted altogether and tapering may be produced by filing if a forge is not available.

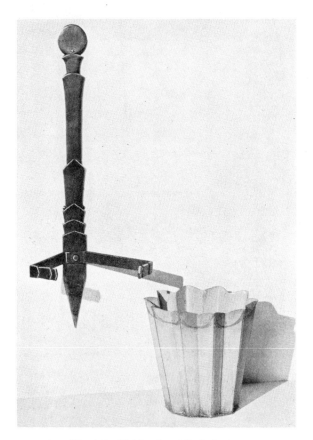

Fig. 209. Holder for potted plants.

Bill of Material

Material: Mild steel band is used for the back and the holder.

Pieces		Thickness	Width	Length
1	Back	12 Ga.	1	13⅝
1	Holder	12 Ga.	½	9⅞
1	Black iron rivet	⅛		⅜

Plate 36. Holder for Potted Plants

Modern metalwork does not possess the rugged texture of the old but complies with the steel age in having a high smooth finish. The plant holder shown in Figure 209 is designed to fit the modern home.

Procedure

1. The pattern is drawn full size on paper, folded, cut out, and glued to the iron stock.

2. The latter is put into a vise and the corners of the design are cut into by a saw. The waste iron is sheared out as directed under Cutting, Metals of Medium Thickness, step 2, and it is filed to the line. See Filing, steps 1 to 3.

3. The flowerpot-holder arms are cut and filed to pattern.

4. Both pieces are modeled. See Filing, step 9.

5. The holder arms are bent by block

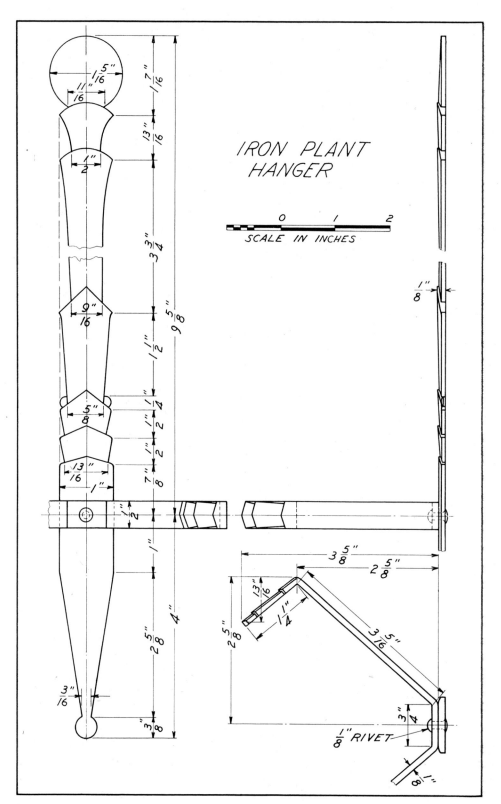

IRON PLANT HANGER

SCALE IN INCHES

Plate 36.

and hammer to the angles shown, the vise having copper jaws, as shown at *B*, Figure 16.

6. Holes in both pieces are drilled as directed under Drilling, and riveted. See Riveting.

7. The holder is finished. See Finishing, Antique Iron.

Plate 37. Modern French Plant Holders

This style is not wholly modern but attempts to hold to the Renascent. It uses the old forms in a new way.

Procedure

1. The pattern of the holder to the left in Figure 210 is drawn full size on paper, folded, cut out, and glued to iron stock.

2. It is cut as described under Cutting, Metals of Medium Thickness, step 2, and filed to the line. See Filing, steps 1 to 3.

3. The applied scrolls and the holder arms also are cut and filed. If wide 14-gauge stock is not available for the former, the design may be pinched together and cut from narrower stock, the ends being bent down after cutting and filing.

4. All pieces are modeled. See Filing,

Fig. 210. Modern French plant holders.

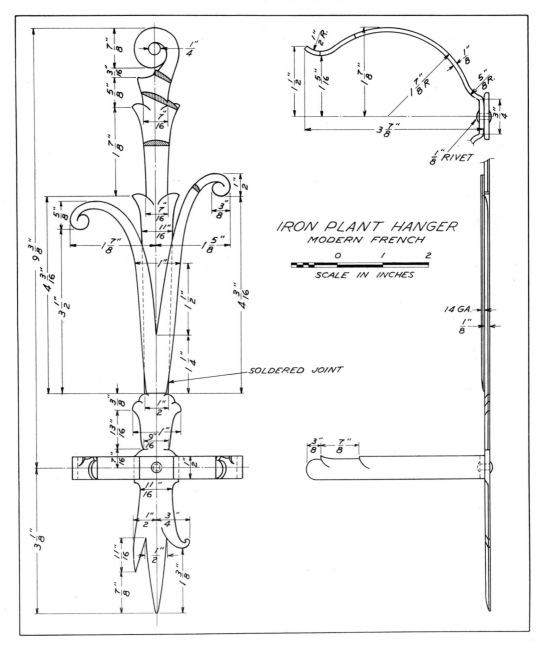

IRON PLANT HANGER
MODERN FRENCH

SCALE IN INCHES

SOLDERED JOINT

14 GA.

Plate 37.

Bill of Material

Material: The back and holder are made of mild steel band and the scroll of mild steel hoop.

Pieces	Thickness	Width	Length
1 Back	12 Ga.	1	12½
1 Scroll	14 Ga.	2½	5
1 Holder	12 Ga.	½	10
1 Black iron rivet	⅛		⅜

step 9. The scroll is finished in this way only on its outer edge.

5. The holder arm is bent as follows:

a) The sharp bends are made in a vise by hammer to a 45-deg. angle.

b) The piece is set in a vise with a 1-in.

pipe tangent ⅝ in. from the sharp bend. It is bent over the pipe by a blunt chisel and hammer, as shown in Figure 208, until it conforms to the design.

c) The tips are also bent over a pipe by a hammer.

d) The large curve is bent into forms, as directed under Forming, step 1, *d* and Figure 82, or over large pipe as in *c*.

6. Holes are drilled. See Drilling.

7. All pieces are heated red. See Finishing, Antique Iron.

8. The contact surfaces on the backpiece and the scroll are filed bright. They are then tinned and soldered. See Soft Soldering, steps 1 to 4, and 6, Example 1.

9. The arm is riveted to the back. See Riveting.

10. It is polished. See Finishing, Antique Iron.

The holder to the right in Figure 210 is made in much the same manner. The flower is cut by shears and file, and is soldered to the top. See Soft Soldering, step 6, Example 2. The lower part of the iron backpiece and its upper leaf tips are bent in addition to being cut, and the bracket is soldered to the back as was the scroll, step 8, above. The bent pot-holder ends are turned over a form. See Forming of Iron, step 1.

Plate 38. Empire Wall-Plant Holder

The plant holder in Figure 211 is another example of modern compromise between classic and present-day styles, its simplicity making it useful in modern decoration.

Procedure

1. A round rod for the shaft is cut, heated, and drawn to a slight taper at each end. See Forging, steps 1, 2, and 3, *d* and *i*.

2. The surface not forged is hammered and worked back to the forging so that the texture blends into one. The rod is aligned.

3. A bow is made of round rod, tapered at each end, and rounded throughout

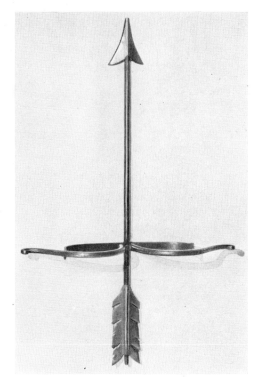

Fig. 211. Empire wall-plant holder.

except at the middle. See Forging, step 3, *d* and *i*. It is spread at the center as directed under step 5 following. If forging is not possible, a flat rod, flared at each end and drawn in cold back of the flare, is satisfactory. See Forging, step 3, *e*. Both ends of the bow are bent into scrolls. See Forging, steps 7 and 8.

4. A back bow is made as shown and flared at each end. See Forging, step 3, *a*.

5. The shaft is heated at its intersection with the bow, and a square rod is laid over it and struck to spread the shaft for an adequate cross bearing.

6. The front bow is bent sharply up at both sides of the center, the latter being held in a slot in a ⅜-in. bar, bringing each section up almost 90 deg. See Forming, step 3.

7. Each arm is bowed. See Forming of

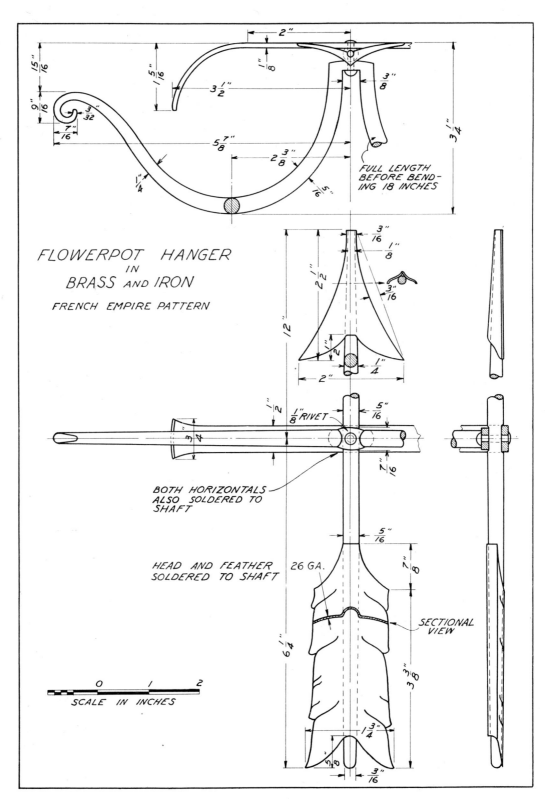

FLOWERPOT HANGER
IN
BRASS AND IRON

FRENCH EMPIRE PATTERN

FULL LENGTH
BEFORE BEND-
ING 18 INCHES

BOTH HORIZONTALS
ALSO SOLDERED TO
SHAFT

HEAD AND FEATHER   26 GA.
SOLDERED TO SHAFT

SECTIONAL
VIEW

$\frac{1}{8}''$ RIVET

0   1   2
SCALE IN INCHES

Plate 38.

Bill of Material

Pieces	Material	Use	Thickness	Width	Length
1	Mild steel bar — round	Shaft	5/16D.	5/16	16½ (Forged to 18¼)
1	Mild steel bar — round	Bow	¼D.	¼	14¼ (Forged to 18⅛)
1	Mild steel band	Back	12 Ga.	½	8¼
1	Black iron rivet		⅛		¾
1	Brass sheet — soft spinning	Arrowhead	22 Ga. (B&S)	2⅜	2½
1	Brass sheet — soft spinning	Feather	22 Ga. (B&S)	2	4¼

Iron, step 1, *d,* and Figures 82 and 83. The back bow is bent as shown.

8. The three parts are heated, as explained under Finishing, Antique Iron, drilled, as directed under Drilling, and riveted. See Riveting.

9. The arrow point and feather are cut by shears from a piece of brass, and filed. See Filing, steps 1 to 4. They are grooved to fit over the shaft by being driven down on the shaft by a slotted wood block and hammer.

10. The edge of the feather is chased as in *B,* Figure 159.

11. The parts are soldered. See Soft Soldering, steps 1 to 4, and 6, Example 1.

12. The whole piece is finished. See Finishing, Antique Iron; and for the brass, Polishing, and Preserving Metals, step 3.

Plate 39. Swinging Plants

The plant holder in Figure 212, like the one in Plate 37, is an adaptation of French pre-Renaissance form.

Procedure

1. The back unit is made like the one for Plate 37, steps 1 to 4.

2. The bottom scrolls are bent. See Forging, step 9.

3. The holes are drilled for the bearings. See Drilling.

4. The bearing stock also is drilled and filed to within 1/16 in. of the hole. See Filing, steps 1 to 3. It is cut off and shoul-

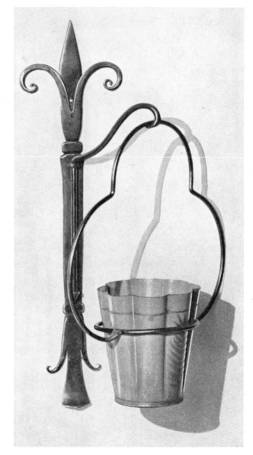

Fig. 212. Swinging plants.

dered on the back, as shown at *A,* Figure 196, inserted, and riveted. See Riveting.

5. The rods for the pot frame and swinging arm are cut. The arm is flared at one end, as directed under Forging, step 3, *a,*

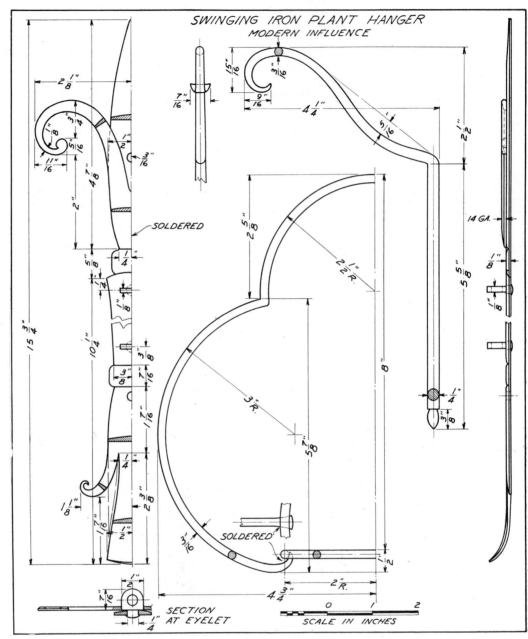

Plate 39.

Bill of Material

Pieces	Material	Use	Thickness	Width	Length
1	Mild steel band	Back	12 Ga.	1	15¾
1	Mild steel hoop	Scroll	14 Ga.	2½	4½
2	Mild steel band	Bearings	12 Ga.	½	⅝
1	Mild steel bar — round	Arm	¼ D.	¼	10 (Forged to 11¾)
1	Mild steel bar — round	Hoop	3/16 D.	3/16	25½
1	Mild steel bar — round	Hoop	3/16 D.	3/16	12⅝

and drawn to a point below. See Forging, step 3, *c* and *d*. It may also be filed as shown in the drawing.

6. The flared end is curled down, as explained under Forming of Iron, step 1, the sharp bend being made in a vise, and it is curved above this bend in forms. See Forming of Iron, step 1, *d*.

7. The pot frame is made as follows: The large rod is flared at both ends and bent as required over a rod. The sharp bends are made in a vise with a hammer. The large curves bent as described under Forming of Iron, step 1, *d*. The ring is bent over a round form, or as described in the foregoing, cut off, and aligned. The contact points are filed bright and the parts are

snapped together and soldered. See Soft Soldering, steps 1 to 4, and 5, Example 6.

8. The backplate, scroll, and arm are fired. See Finishing, Antique Iron.

9. The scroll is soldered to the backplate. Both are filed bright on their contact surfaces, and then tinned. See Soft Soldering, steps 1 to 4, and 6, Example 1.

10. All parts are finished. See Finishing, Antique Iron.

Plate 40. Sixteenth-Century French Brackets

This is a transitional piece made during the decline of the iron period. Here Gothic forms are mixed with those borrowed from Renaissance bronze turnings.

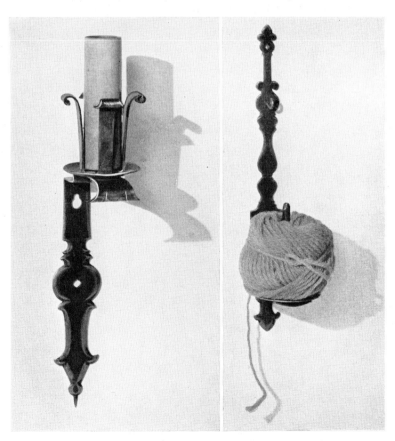

Fig. 213. Sixteenth-century French brackets.

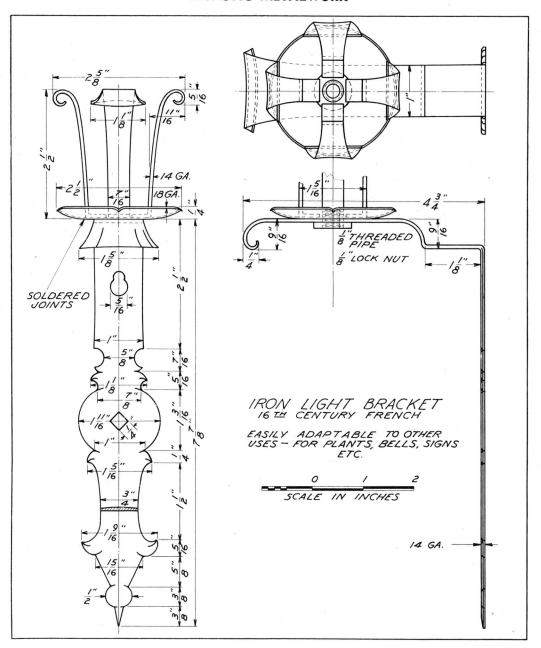

IRON LIGHT BRACKET
16 TH CENTURY FRENCH

EASILY ADAPTABLE TO OTHER
USES — FOR PLANTS, BELLS, SIGNS
ETC.

SCALE IN INCHES

Plate 40.

Procedure

1. The back units of the projects in Figure 213 are made as described under Plate 37, steps 1, 2, and 4.

2. The holes are drilled as directed under Drilling, and filed as shown in the drawing.

3. The yarn holder has a simple L-shaped front bracket holding the disk. To these is riveted the shouldered rod. See *A*, Figure 196. The bracket is soldered to the back. See Soft Soldering, steps 1 to 4, and 6, Example 1.

Bill of Material

Pieces	Material	Use	Thickness	Width	Length
1	Mild steel hoop	Back	14 Ga.	1 11/16	13¼
4	Mild steel hoop	Crown	14 Ga.	1⅛	3¾
1	Sheet iron, box annealed, one pass, cold rolled	Cup	18 Ga. (B&S)	2½	2½
1	Threaded iron pipe nipple	Fixture base	⅛		½
1	Iron lock nut	Lock	⅛		
1	Candle socket	Light			4
1	Socket cover	Light	1¼		4
1	Cord				8 ft.
1	Plug				

4. The front tip of the light bracket is flared, as described under Forging, steps 1, 2, and 3, *a*, and bent. See Forming of Iron, step 1. The veins are filed.

5. The sharp bends are made by vise and mallet, and the return bend on the top is made over a pipe with a blunt tool, as shown in Figure 208. The curled end is turned down in this operation.

6. A disk is cut with a shears, and is filed. It is dished as explained under Low Raising, step 4, *a*, and fluted with a chisel, as shown at *B*, Figure 159. It is then drilled.

7. The stock for the socket prongs is heated and flared. See Forging, steps 1, 2, and 3, *a*. It is tapered at the bottom, as directed under Forging, step 3, *b*, or filed to taper toward the base. The prongs are cut off and curved on top. See Forming of Iron, step 1. They are then sharply bent below and aligned.

8. All the parts are heated red. See Finishing, Antique Iron.

9. The prongs and disk are filed bright at contact points and tinned and soldered to the disk. See Soft Soldering, step 5, Example 5.

10. All parts are finished. See Finishing, Antique Iron.

11. They are assembled over a pipe nipple, the fixture drawing both parts together against the lock nut. See Wiring.

A disk for a flowerpot may be substituted for the light socket.

Plate 41. Modern Italian Holders

The holders in Figure 214, combining forms of the Italian Renaissance with those of today, are designed to grace the bare stone or plaster walls of formal settings. The method of surface treatment, seen in the arm of the project to the left, is quite different from that in other projects, any variation of which may be used on tables and stands in place of twists and peening.

Procedure

1. The backplate of the bracket to the left in Figure 214 is made as explained in Plate 37, steps 1, 2, and 4.

2. The lower leaf and the flower-cup design are embossed. See Raising, step 1.

3. The marks in the scallops are center punched.

4. The disk is shaped as described under Raising, step 4, *a*. Its scallops are laid out and filed, and drilled for the rivets, and for a cord if it is to be used as a light.

5. The bar is laid out and filed as follows:

a) A saw cut of four strokes is made at each intersection and is carried around the four sides. The cuts are filed by a square file set on edge, four strokes in each cut.

b) All sharp edges and points are rounded by a fine, half-round file used with a rolling motion, and in a direction away from the cuts. See Filing, step 3.

c) On the long upper form a husk is produced by filing the arrises to the re-

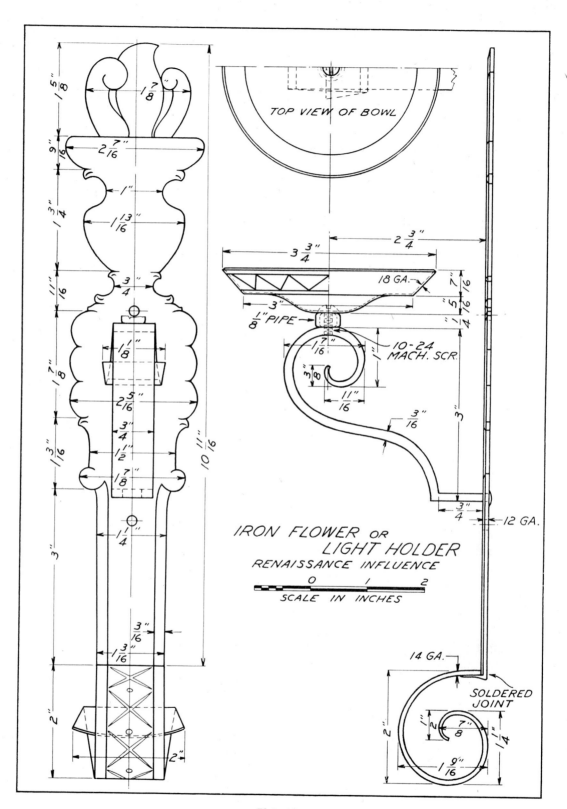

TOP VIEW OF BOWL

18 GA.

$\frac{1}{8}$"PIPE

10-24 MACH. SCR.

12 GA.

14 GA.

SOLDERED JOINT

IRON FLOWER OR
LIGHT HOLDER
RENAISSANCE INFLUENCE

0   1   2

SCALE IN INCHES

Plate 41.

Bill of Material

Pieces	Material	Use	Thickness	Width	Length
1	Mild steel band	Back	12 Ga.	2 7/16	11⅛
1	Mild steel hoop	Scroll	14 Ga.	2	6¼
1	Mild steel band	Arm	3/16	¾	8 (Forged to 8⅜)
1	Sheet iron, box annealed, one pass, cold rolled	Bowl	18 Ga.	4	4
1	Black iron pipe	Collar	⅛		¼
1	Machine screw		10–24		½

quired shape. The faces then are hammer marked.

6. The bar is bent hot over an anvil horn, cooled, cut off, shouldered at both ends, as shown at *A*, Figure 196, inserted into the back, and riveted. See Riveting.

7. It is then finished. See Finishing, Antique Iron.

The bracket to the right is similarly made. Its bottom volute, flame, and disk edge are cut by a chisel prior to bending. See Cutting, Metals of Medium Thickness, step 6. The ends of the volutes are flared, as described under Forging, step 3, *a*, and bent as described under Forming of Iron,

step 1. The sharp bend in the arm is made by the process in Forming, step 3. The back is shouldered as in *A*, Figure 196, and the top is drilled and tapped. See Tapping. The arm is then riveted to the backplate. The disk is pressed as directed under Low Raising, step 6, and shaped. See Raising, step 4, *a*. It is attached by machine screw through an intermediate piece in the form of a short collar made of ⅛-in. pipe as shown.

All parts are then brought to red heat in the furnace, the bottom scroll is soldered to the back as in step 9, Plate 40, and the project is finished as in Finishing, Antique Iron.

Fig. 214. Modern Italian holders.

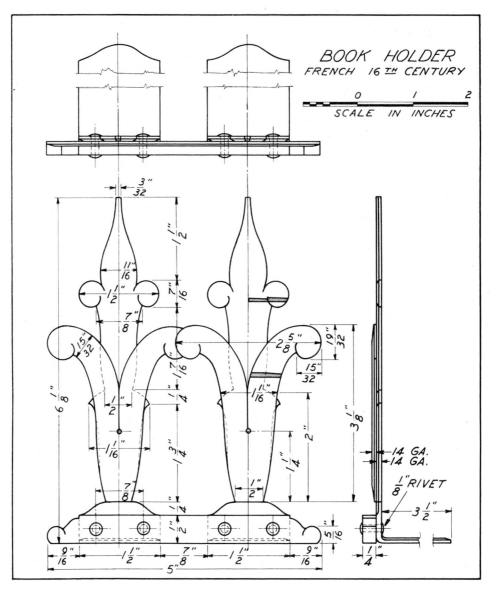

Plate 42.

Bill of Material

Material: The back and scrolls are made of mild steel hoops and the crossbar of a mild steel bar.

Pieces		Thickness	Width	Length
2	Back	14 Ga.	1½	9⅝
2	Scrolls	14 Ga.	2½	3¼
1	Crossbar	¼	½	5
4	Black iron rivets	⅛		½

Plate 42. Early French Book Ends

Constant warfare between rival dukes in medieval France developed a group of skilled craftsmen from whose hands came not only armor and implements, but decorative pieces that surpassed the work of any other land. The book ends in Figure 215 belong to this period of ironwork.

Fig. 215. Early French book ends.

11. The scroll pieces are filed to taper below as wedges.

12. The contact points on the vertical pieces are filed bright and the pieces are soldered. See Soldering, steps 1 to 4, and 6, Example 1.

13. The book ends are finished. See Finishing, Antique Iron.

The applied scrolls may be omitted, if desired, since the vertical ones make satisfactory book ends.

Plate 43. Another Book End

The book ends in Figure 216 represent the Renaissance period of transitional French ironwork of the sixteenth century.

Procedure

1. The patterns for the vertical and applied scrolls are drawn on paper. They are then folded, cut out, and traced on four sets of paper patterns. These patterns are glued to the iron.

2. The metal is cut. See Cutting, Metals of Medium Thickness, steps 2 and 3.

3. It is filed to the line. See Filing, steps 1 to 3.

4. It is modeled. See Filing, step 9.

5. The base pieces are cut, laid out, rough cut, filed, and modeled.

6. The holes are laid out on the base pieces and drilled. See Drilling.

7. The bending lines for the vertical scrolls are carefully marked. The scrolls then are set in a vise, checked with a square, and bent with block and hammer.

8. The scrolls, backed with a wood block, are clamped to the front bar already drilled, aligned, set upon the drill table, and drilled.

9. The holes in the front bar are countersunk and the pieces are riveted. See Riveting.

10. All of the parts are heated. See Finishing, Antique Iron.

Procedure

1. The processes for Plate 42, steps 1 to 10, are applicable here, except that holes are drilled in the upper part of the uprights and filed square. Cutting, Metals of Medium Thickness, step 3 or 4, is used in place of step 2. The top and bottom units are embossed, as directed under Raising, step 1, and the base piece is notched as was the bar in Plate 41, step 5, *a.*

2. The book ends are finished as described under Finishing, Antique Iron.

Fig. 216. Another book end.

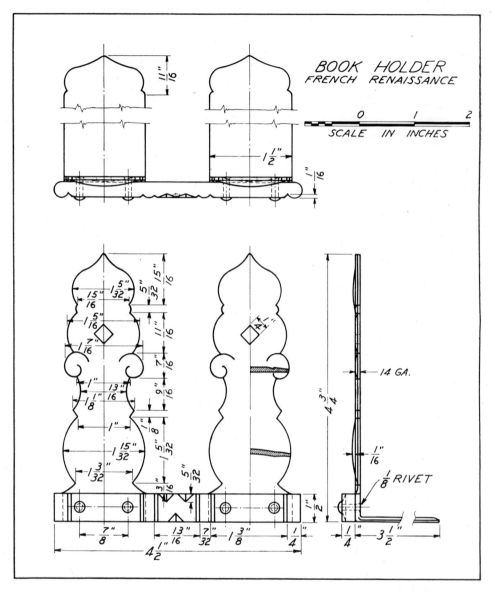

Plate 43.

Bill of Material

Material: The back is made of mild steel hoops and the crossbar of a mild steel bar.

Pieces		Thickness	Width	Length
2	Back	14 Ga.	1½	8¼
1	Crossbar	¼	½	4½
4	Black iron rivets	⅛		½

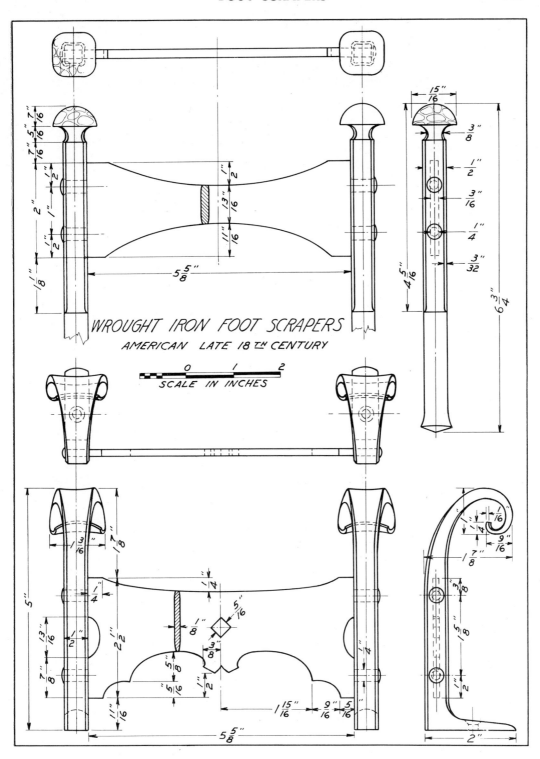

WROUGHT IRON FOOT SCRAPERS

AMERICAN LATE 18TH CENTURY

SCALE IN INCHES

Plate 44.

Fig. 217. Boot scrapers.

Bill of Material

Material: All pieces are made of mild steel bars.

Pieces		Thickness	Width	Length
2	Posts	1/2	1/2	7
1	Crosspiece	3/16	2	7
2	Posts	1/2	1/2	7 (Forged to 9 1/8)
1	Crosspiece	12 Ga.	2 1/2	7

Plate 44. Boot Scrapers

In the early American period, when most streets and highways were dirt roads, boot scrapers were a real necessity. Many interesting scrapers were produced. The one to the left in Figure 217 is from Germantown, Pennsylvania, and the other is a rare example from New Orleans. Though they would seem to require forging, similar effects may be produced by cold hammering and filing.

Procedure

1. When scrolls are used at the ends of the posts, the iron bar is flared. See Forging, steps 1, 2, and 3, *a*. It is then bent. See Forging, steps 7 and 8, *a*.

2. If a knob is used, the iron is upset and forged over a fuller. See Forging, step 5.

3. The post arrises are hammered until the corner surfaces are 1/8 in. wide.

4. The holes are drilled. See Drilling.

5. The cross members are laid out and cut. See Cutting, Metals of Medium Thickness, steps 2 and 3. They are then filed as directed under Filing, steps 1 to 3, and modeled. See Filing, step 9. The shoulders are cut and filed to fit the holes in the posts, as shown at *A*, Figure 196.

6. The posts are assembled and riveted.

7. The piece is finished. See Finishing, Antique Iron.

Plate 45. Early English Light

This project introduces a series of plates devoted to the construction of simple and typical iron lamps. They are selected from a field remarkable for its variety of design covering a period of seven centuries. The lamp shown in Figure 218 is of eighteenth-century English origin, and was widely used there and in the American colonies.

Procedure

1. A disk is cut, as directed under Cutting, Thin Metal, if a heavy shears is used, or Metals of Medium Thickness, step 2. It is filed as explained under Filing, steps 1, 2, and 4, shaped as directed under Low Raising, step 6, and drilled. See Drilling.

2. The foot stock is pointed as described under Forging, steps 1, 2, and 3, *c*, and shouldered as directed under Forging, step 3, *h;* or it is filed and cut off.

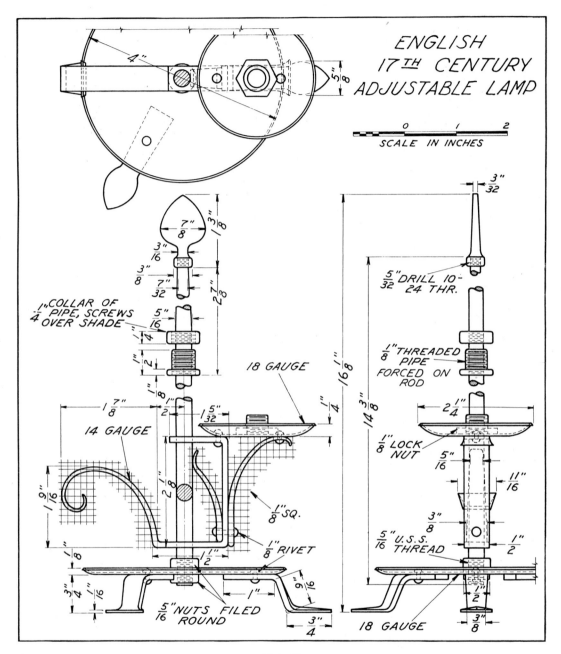

Plate 45.

3. The feet are bent as directed under Forming of Iron, step 2, drilled, and riveted. See Riveting.

4. A rod is drawn out as explained under Forging, step 3, *d* and *i*, and the hammer-

ing is continued down to its base. The rod may be filed if it is not forged.

5. The rod is threaded top and bottom, as directed under Threading, a filed nut is screwed to the top of the lower thread, and

Bill of Material

Pieces	Material	Use	Thickness	Width	Length
1	Sheet iron, box annealed, one pass, cold rolled	Base	18 Ga. (B&S)	4	4
1	Sheet iron, box annealed, one pass, cold rolled	Drip cup	18 Ga. (B&S)	2¼	2¼
3	Mild steel hoop	Feet	14 Ga.	½	2 5/16
1	Mild steel hoop	Frame	14 Ga.	½	8⅜
1	Mild steel hoop	Cup bracket	14 Ga.	½	3
1	Mild steel hoop	Spring	14 Ga.	⅜	2
1	Mild steel bar — round	Post	5/16D.	5/16	14⅜
2	Black iron nuts	Post lock	5/16 USS		
5	Black iron rivets		⅛		⅜
1	Black iron rivet	Spring	⅛		½
1	Black iron pipe	Shade rest	¼		⅛
1	Black iron pipe	Shade lock	¼		¼
1	Iron lock nut	Fixture base	⅛		
1	Iron threaded pipe nipple	Fixture base	⅛		½
1	Iron threaded pipe nipple	Shade lock	⅛		½
1	Mild steel bar — square	Finial	⅜	⅜	1
1	Candle socket	Light			4
1	Socket cover — fiber	Light	1¼ O.D.		4
1	Cord				8 ft.
1	Plug				

then the rod is set into the base and locked into place with another nut below.

6. A small disk is laid out and cut, filed, and dished. See Low Raising, step 4, *a*. A hole is drilled smaller than necessary, enlarged with a punch, and tapped. See Tapping. A second method of fastening the fixture is shown in the drawing. A lock nut is soldered to the disk.

7. The metal for the bracket is cut, and both pieces to be curled are flared as directed under Forging, step 3, *a*, and bent over forms. See Forming of Iron, step 1, and Figures 84 and 85.

8. The holes are drilled.

9. The bending lines are laid out and bending is done in a vise by a hammer, the scroll facing upward. The last bend is done in a slotted iron bar. See Figure 86.

10. The unit is riveted below and above, aligned, and slipped over the stem.

11. The finial piece is worked on a bar long enough to handle, pointed, notched with a file, cut off, drilled, and tapped.

12. A ⅛-in. pipe nipple is filed to force fit the stem, and the two threaded rings, made of ¼-in. pipe, one below for shade rest and one for shade lock, are screwed on.

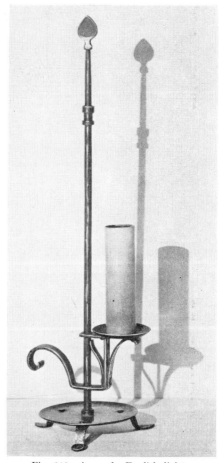

Fig. 218. An early English light.

13. The lamp is finished. See Finishing, Antique Iron.

14. A nipple is screwed into the disk and finally the lamp is wired. See Wiring.

Plate 46. Crusader's Lamp

The thirteenth-century lamp shown in Figure 219 is the type of lamp used at the time of the Crusades.

Procedure

1. The lamp base is made in the same manner as the one in Plate 45, steps 1 to 3, with a slight variation in the feet.

2. A ½-in. pipe is heated and drawn in. See Forging, step 4. A ring is cut off the end thus forged with a pipe cutter or a saw. See Cutting, Pipe Cutting, and Cutting of Tubing.

3. A 1-in. pipe also is drawn in and cut as indicated. Its bottom corner is filed round.

4. Its upper inside burr is filed off as shown in the drawing. A disk of 18-gauge iron or a ⅜-in. iron washer is forced into the ring, rested upon the lower inside burr, and soldered. See Soft Soldering, steps 1 to 4, and 5, Example 7.

5. The disk is drilled or the washer is filed to fit over a ⅛-in. pipe.

6. A nut is forged round. See Forging, step 8, c.

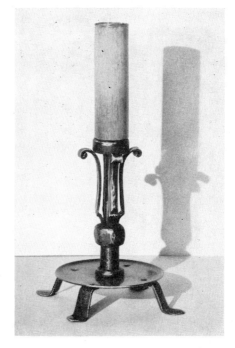

Fig. 219. A crusader's lamp.

7. A piece of ⅜-in. pipe is cut and squared top and bottom. See Filing, step 10.

8. A piece of ⅛-in. pipe is cut and both ends are threaded. See Threading.

9. The socket prongs are forged. See Forging, steps 1, 2, and 3, k.

10. They are heated red and rolled. See Forging, step 9; also Figure 229.

11. The sharp bend is made in a vise by

Bill of Material

Pieces	Material	Use	Thickness	Width	Length
1	Sheet iron, box annealed, cold rolled, one pass	Base	18 Ga. (B&S)	4	4
4	Mild steel hoop	Feet	14 Ga.	½	2⅝
4	Mild steel hoop	Crown	14 Ga.	½	4¼
1	Black iron pipe	Lower ring	¾		¼
1	Black iron pipe	Stem	⅜		⅞
1	Black iron pipe	Top ring	1		½
1	Black iron pipe	Core	⅛		4¾
2	Iron lock nuts	Top and bottom locks	⅛		
1	Iron washer	Top disk	⅜ I.D.		
1	Black iron nut	Center ball	¾ Thread		
4	Black iron rivets		⅛		⅜
1	Candle socket	Light			4
1	Socket cover — fiber	Light	1¼ O.D.		4
1	Cord				8 ft.
1	Plug				

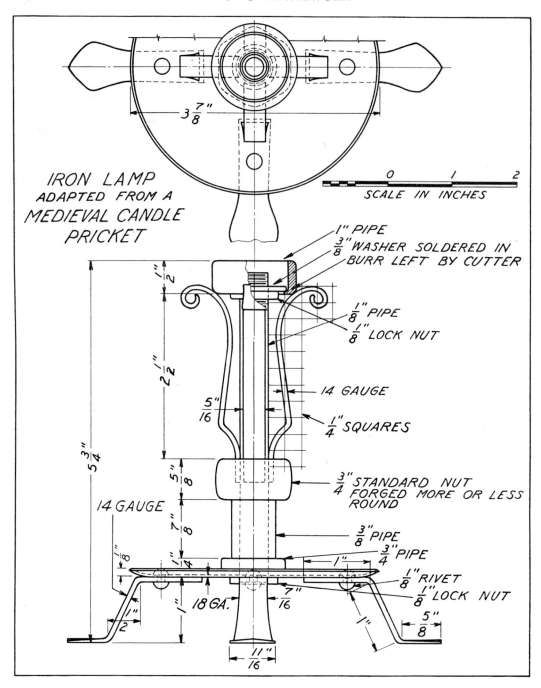

IRON LAMP
ADAPTED FROM A
MEDIEVAL CANDLE
PRICKET

SCALE IN INCHES

Plate 46.

a hammer or by the process in Forming, step 3, and Figure 86, and the final shape with dies. See Forming of Iron, step 1, *d*, and Figure 82, or Forming, step 4, and Figure 87. They are filed below to fit between the nut and the 1/8-in. pipe.

12. All pieces are now fired. See Finishing, Antique Iron.

13. The ⅛-in. pipe is filed bright back of the nut. The prongs are also filed bright on their bottom inside and outside surfaces contacting the pipe and nut.

14. A lock nut, the base, the small ring, the ⅜-in. pipe length, and the nut are slipped down over the ⅛-in. pipe. The prongs are arranged and pressed down, and the top ring is placed over them and held with a temporary lock nut.

15. When all is aligned, the prongs are soldered to the pipe. See Soft Soldering, steps 1 to 4, and 5, Example 7.

16. The lamp is finished as described under Finishing, Antique Iron, and it is wired. See Wiring.

Plate 47. A Lamp of the Transition

The lamp in Figure 220 is composed of forms inspired by the Roman balustrade and acanthus husk and these are set upon a rugged iron base. Thus, the sixteenth-century piece is adapted from forms in common use during the period of growing classic influence in the early Renaissance.

Procedure

1. A disk is laid out and cut. See Cutting, Thin Metal. The scallops, however, are cut

Fig. 220. A lamp of the Transition.

with a saw and a file. See Filing, steps 1, 2, and 3.

2. It is set in a vise between short lengths of 2½-in. pipe and bent down over them. See Bending, step 1. It is curved outward over a pipe with a hammer.

3. The holes are drilled. See Drilling.

4. The foot stock is forged. See Forging,

Bill of Material

Pieces	Material	Use	Thickness	Width	Length
1	Sheet iron, box annealed, one pass, cold rolled	Base	18 Ga. (B&S)	3¾	3¾
1	Sheet iron, box annealed, one pass, cold rolled	Drip cup	18 Ga. (B&S)	2⅝	2⅝
3	Mild steel hoop	Feet	14 Ga.	½	2½
1	Mild steel band	Handle	12 Ga.	½	7⅞
1	Black iron pipe	Core	⅛		5⅞
1	Black iron pipe	Stem	⅜		4 5/16
1	Black iron pipe	Lower ball	½		9/16
1	Black iron pipe	Lower ring	¾		¼
1	Iron washer	Stem disk	½ I.D.		
1	Iron washer	Stem disk	⅜ I.D.		
2	Iron lock nuts	Top and bottom lock	⅛		
4	Black iron rivets		⅛		⅜
1	Candle socket	Light			4
1	Socket cover — fiber	Light	1¼ O.D.		4
1	Cord				8 ft.
1	Plug				

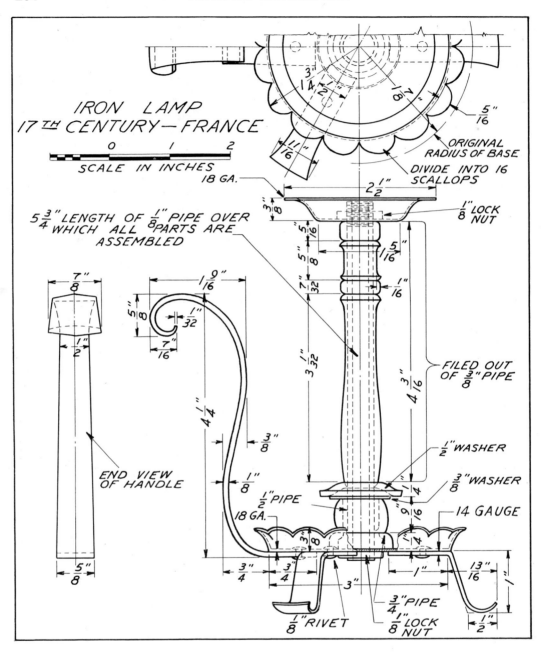

IRON LAMP
17TH CENTURY—FRANCE

SCALE IN INCHES

Plate 47.

steps 1, 2, and 3, *a*. The feet are cut off by a saw, curved, as directed under Forming of Iron, step 2, and bent sharply above by a vise and hammer. They are drilled and riveted to the base. See Riveting.

5. The handle stock is flared and drawn in behind the flare. See Forging, step 3, *e*. It is spread below as indicated in the drawing. See Forging, step 3, *f*.

6. The handle is curled and formed. See

Forming of Iron, step 1. It is then drilled and riveted.

7. A top disk is cut and shaped, as directed under Raising, step 4, *a,* and drilled.

8. The stem is made as follows: (*a*) A ¾-in. pipe is drawn in, as directed under Forging, step 4, and the forged end is cut off by a pipe cutter or saw. See Cutting, Pipe Cutting, and Cutting Tubing, thus making a ring.

b) A ring of ½-in. pipe is made in the same manner, though 9/16 in. long, and its bottom corner is filed round.

c) A ½-in. washer is dished. See Raising, step 4, *a.*

d) A ⅜-in. pipe is drawn in below as shown at *A,* Figure 221. It is heated red hot and drawn in a trifle as shown at *B,* Figure 221. It is filed deeper, first to somewhat of a square section, then octagonal, and finally round. It is notched with a saw all around at intersecting points as shown at *C,* Figure 221, and filed to depth with the edge of a square file. It is filed by a round file to a concave, first in a square section, then octagonal, and finally round, as shown at *D,* Figure 221, and the small sections are rounded as shown at *E.* Both concave curves sweep gradually in their long sections as shown at *X,* but they turn out quite sharply at their ends, as shown at the arrow.

9. All parts are fired. See Finishing, Antique Iron.

10. With a lock nut below, the base and stem parts are slipped over a ⅛-in. pipe length, previously threaded at both ends. See Threading. They are locked above by the candle socket. See Wiring.

11. The lamp is finished as explained under Finishing, Antique Iron, and then wired. See Wiring.

Plate 48. A Lamp for a Knight

The lamp in Figure 222, with its ornamental horse, brings to light the gallant days when knighthood was at its height.

Procedure

1. An iron bar is heated red hot and forged on the side of the body, drawn in at the neck, as directed under Forging, steps 1, 2, and 3, *e,* and spread slightly at the head. See Forging, step 3, *f.* It is then cut, bent, and filed at the head in the same manner as the one described in Plate 28, step 6, and as shown in Figure 199. In this horse's head, however, the stock is heavier to begin with. It is flattened out to about 7/16 by ⅝ by 1⅝ in.

2. The end is reheated and the neck is

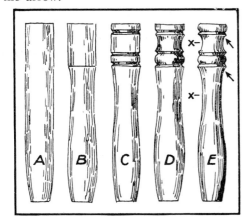

Fig. 221. Steps in making lamp standard.

Fig. 222. A lamp for a knight.

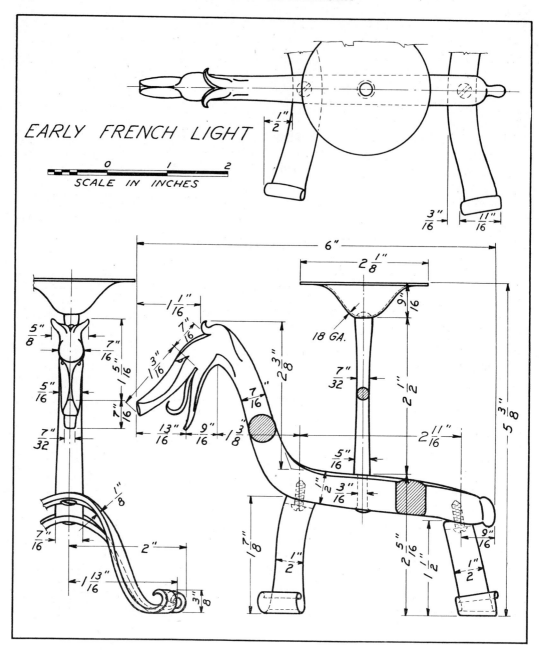

EARLY FRENCH LIGHT

SCALE IN INCHES

Plate 48.

bent over the tip of the anvil horn, both under the chin and where it leaves the body.

3. The body is rounded over the top and the texture of the surface is unified. The tail is forged over the edge of the anvil and filed as shown. See Forging, step 3, *h*.

4. Two bands of iron are flared. See Forging, step 3, *a*. Then they are curled and formed. See Forming of Iron, step 1.

Bill of Material

Pieces	Material	Use	Thickness	Width	Length
1	Mild steel bar — square	Body	½	½	6½ (Forged to 7¾)
2	Mild steel band	Legs	12 Ga.	½	6¾
1	Mild steel bar — round	Stem	5/16D.	5/16	3⅜
1	Sheet iron, box annealed, cold rolled, one pass	Cup	18 Ga. (B&S)	2¼	2¼
	For lamp add				½
1	Iron-threaded pipe nipple	Fixture base	⅛		
1	Candle socket	Light			2
1	Socket cover — fiber	Light	1¼ O.D.		2
1	Cord				8 ft.
1	Plug				

Next they are set vertically in a vise, scrolls up, and are twisted to face about 10 deg. forward. The same is done in reverse on the rear scrolls.

5. Both scrolls are drilled, as directed under Drilling, and countersunk. The body is drilled and tapped for the legs, as explained under Tapping, and drilled for the socket holder. The legs are attached and soldered. See Soft Soldering, step 5, Example 7.

6. A disk is shaped as described under Raising, step 4, *a*. It is drilled for riveting and wiring, that is, a ¼-in. hole is drilled beside the rivet hole for wire outlet.

7. A rod is forged as explained under Forging, step 3, *e*, shouldered as shown at *A*, Figure 196, and inserted and riveted. See Riveting.

8. A ⅛-in. pipe nipple is soldered into the cup by the preceding process.

9. The lamp is finished as directed under Finishing, Antique Iron, and wired. See Wiring.

Plate 49. French Craftsman's Lamp

Predominating scrolls have been avoided in this course. They have been overemphasized in recent work in this field. In the lamp in Figure 223 will be found a happy blending of scrolls with seventeenth-century French forms. They are not forged.

Procedure

1. A disk is laid out and cut. See Cutting, Thin Metal.

2. It is dished as described under Raising, step 4, *a*, and drilled for ⅛-in. pipe. See Drilling.

3. The foot stock is heated and flared as explained under Forging, steps 1, 2, and 3, *a*, and the remaining stock is narrowed. See Forging, step 3, *k*.

4. The scrolls are bent. See Forming of Iron, steps 1, *a* to *d*. The sharp bend is made in a slotted bar by a hammer, Figure 86. The large curves are obtained by ham-

Fig. 223. A French craftsman's lamp.

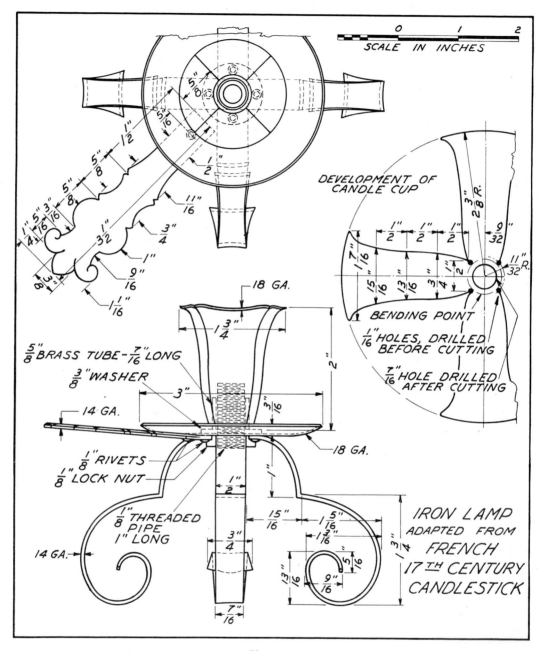

Plate 49.

mering into forms. See Forming of Iron, step 1, *d,* and Figure 82.

5. The legs are bent, drilled, and riveted. See Riveting.

6. The handle design is drawn on paper, folded, cut out, and glued to the iron stock. This is cut as directed under Cutting, Metals of Medium Thickness, steps 1 to 5, filed as explained under Filing, steps 1, 2, and 3, and modeled. See Filing, step 9.

Bill of Material

Pieces	Material	Use	Thickness	Width	Length
4	Mild steel hoop	Legs	14 Ga.	½	6⅜
1	Mild steel hoop	Handle	14 Ga.	1 1/16	3½
1	Sheet iron, box annealed, cold rolled, one pass	Cup	18 Ga. (B&S)	4¾	4¾
1	Sheet iron, box annealed, cold rolled, one pass	Disk	18 Ga. (B&S)	3	3
1	Iron-threaded pipe nipple	Fixture base	⅛		1
1	Iron lock nut	Lower lock	⅛		
1	Iron washer	Cup base	⅜ I.D.		
5	Black iron rivets		⅛		⅜
1	Candle socket	Light			4
1	Socket cover — fiber	Light	1¼ O.D.		4
1	Cord				8 ft.
1	Plug				

7. It is drilled and riveted on.

8. The socket cup is laid out on paper, folded, cut, and glued to the stock.

9. The metal is drilled, cut with a shears, and filed.

10. It is shaped in a groove to the arc required, as described under Raising, step 1, the petals making a round cup encircling the electric socket, its top edge is flared, as directed under Flaring, step 2, and each petal is bent up over a short ⅜-in. pipe pressed against its bottom in a vise. The cup is adjusted so that petal joints are parallel.

11. All parts not black are fired. See Finishing, Antique Iron.

12. The lamp is assembled over a 1-in. length of ⅛-in. threaded pipe over a lock nut, to which is added the assembled disk and a ⅜-in. washer. The cup is slipped over it, and a fixture is screwed on from above.

13. The lamp is finished as described under Finishing, Antique Iron, and is wired. See Wiring.

Plate 50. Romanesque Lamp

The twelfth-century lamp shown in Figure 224 is similar to the thirteenth-century lamp in Figure 219 which is a type of lamp used at the time of the Crusades.

Procedure

1. A disk is laid out, cut as directed un-der Cutting, Thin Metal, or Metals of Medium Thickness, step 2, and bent up. See Low Raising, step 6. The edge design is laid out and cut with a chisel, as explained under Cutting, Metals of Medium Thickness, step 6, and is filed to the line. See Filing, steps 1 to 3.

2. The foot stock is forged as directed under Forging, steps 1, 2, and 3, a, and is

Fig. 224. Romanesque lamp.

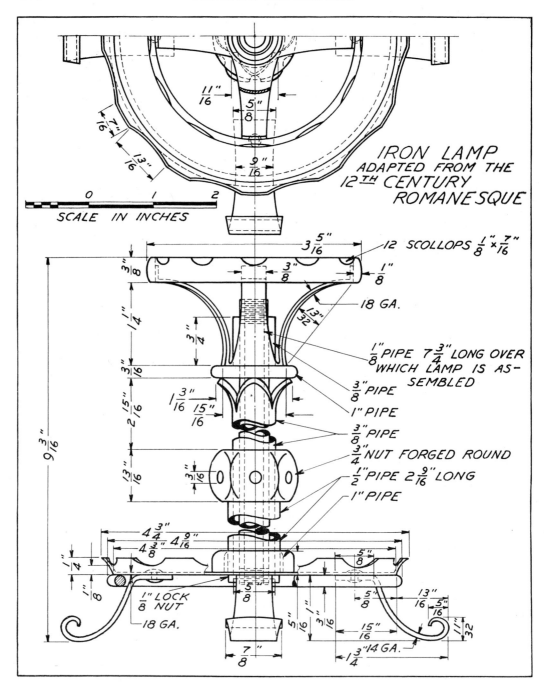

Plate 50.

cut. It is curled up as explained under Forming of Iron, step 1, and is bent sharply in the vise with a hammer. See Figure 85.

3. The feet and base are drilled as described under Drilling, and riveted. See Riveting.

Bill of Material

Pieces	Material	Use	Thickness	Width	Length
4	Mild steel hoop	Feet	14 Ga.	3/4	3
1	Sheet iron, box annealed, cold rolled, one pass	Disk	18 Ga. (B&S)	5	5
4	Sheet iron, box annealed, cold rolled, one pass	Crown arms	18 Ga. (B&S)	11/16	2 1/4
1	Mild steel bar — round	Base ring	3/16 D.		14 3/8
1	Mild steel band	Crown	12 Ga.	3/8	10
1	Black iron pipe	Lower ring	1		5/16
1	Black iron pipe	Lower stem	1/2		2 9/16
1	Black iron pipe	Upper stem	3/8		3 1/16
1	Black iron pipe	Upper ring	1		3/16
1	Black iron pipe	Top collar	3/8		3/4
1	Black iron pipe	Core	1/8		7 3/4
1	Black iron nut	Center ball	3/4 Thread		
1	Iron lock nut	Lower lock	1/8		
4	Black iron rivets		1/8		3/8
1	Candle socket	Light			4
1	Socket cover — fiber	Light	1 1/4 O.D.		4
1	Cord				8 ft.
1	Plug				

4. A ring is bent cold into a circle over a form. It is cut off, aligned, and slipped into place under the disk and soldered at several points. See Soft Soldering, step 5, Example 7.

5. A 1-in. pipe is drawn as described under Forging, step 4, and cut off as a ring. See Cutting, Pipe Cutting, and Cutting Tubing. A second one is cut in the same manner and filed round on its lower edge (upper ring).

6. A 5/8-in. nut is forged as directed under Forging, step 8, c, and each side face is shallow drilled as shown.

7. A length each of 1/8-, 3/8-, and 1/2-in. pipe is cut to the dimensions given. The first is threaded at both ends as explained under Threading, and the other two are heated red and drawn in over an area a little above their centers. This is done over the base of an anvil horn, or they are filed slightly concave and hammered. The upper pipe is cut at its top end by a hack saw. It is then filed and flared as in F, Figure 230.

8. The four arms are cut and their upper ends are bent up at right angles. Their horizontal and vertical curves are bent at the same time between hardwood dies, the lower over an arched block with a groove filed over its top in the direction of the arc, and the upper one in the opposite direction with its edges filed round.

9. The crowning ring stock is forged as described under Forging, step 3, k, bent around a 3-in. form as explained under Bending, step 4, and decorated by a file along its outer edge. A small disk for the base of the arms is also cut and drilled to fit over 1/8-in. pipe.

10. All parts not black are fired. See Finishing, Antique Iron.

11. The crown parts are filed bright at contact points and the arms are soldered to the disk. See Soft Soldering, steps 1 to 4, and 5, Example 5. The crowning ring is soldered to the arms as described under Soft Soldering, step 5, Example 6, the joint in the ring is soldered with one of the arms.

12. With a lock nut at the lower end of the 1/8-in. pipe, the base, ring, stem parts, upper ring, and crown are slipped on, a 3/4-in. length of 3/8-in. pipe is set over the crown, and all are locked with the candle socket.

13. The lamp is finished as directed under Finishing, Antique Iron, and wired as explained under Wiring.

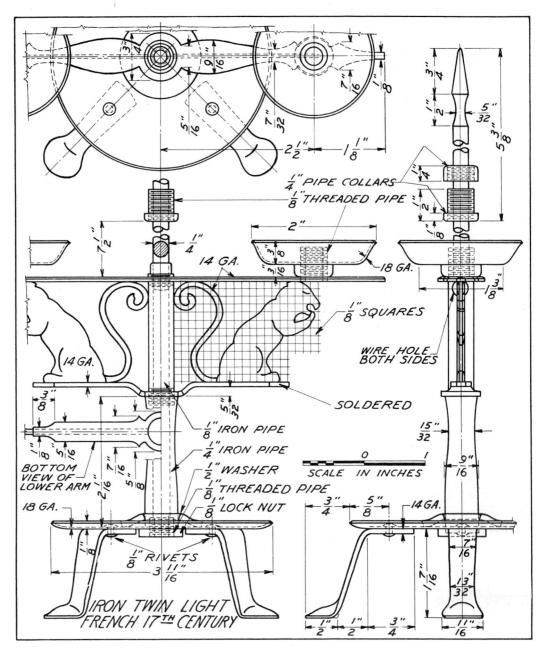

Plate 51.

Plate 51. Twin Lights

The lamp in Figure 225 shows in a marked degree the French understanding and able handling of Italian art of the sixteenth century.

Procedure

1. The lamp base is made in the same manner as the one in Plate 45, steps 1 to 3. The feet, however, are rounded and embossed. See Low Raising, step 1.

Bill of Material

Pieces	Material	Use	Thickness	Width	Length
1	Sheet iron, box annealed, cold rolled, one pass	Base	18 Ga. (B&S)	3¾	3¾
2	Sheet iron, box annealed, cold rolled, one pass	Drip cups	18 Ga. (B&S)	2⅜	2⅜
4	Mild steel hoop	Feet	14 Ga.	½	2⅞
1	Mild steel hoop	Lower arm	14 Ga.	⅝	4 5/16
1	Mild steel hoop	Upper arm	14 Ga.	¾	7¼
2	Mild steel hoop	Lions	14 Ga.	1⅝	1¾
2	Black iron wire	Tails	14 Ga.D.		3⅜
1	Iron washer	Stem base	½ I.D.		
1	Iron lock nut	Lower lock	⅛		
4	Black iron rivets		⅛		⅜
1	Black iron pipe	Lower stem	¼		2 1/16
1	Black iron pipe	Upper stem	⅛		2⅛
2	Black iron pipe	Cup collars	¼		3/16
1	Black iron pipe	Shade rest	¼		⅛
1	Black iron pipe	Shade lock	¼		¼
1	Iron threaded pipe nipple	Lower lock	⅛		⅜
1	Iron threaded pipe nipple	Shade lock	⅛		½
2	Iron threaded pipe nipples	Fixture base	⅛		½
1	Mild steel bar — round	Stem	¼D.	¼	13⅛
2	Candle sockets	Lights			4
2	Socket covers — fiber	Lights	1¼ O.D.		4
1	Cord				10 ft.
1	Plug				

2. A ½-in. washer is dished. See Low Raising, step 4, *a*.

3. A ¼-in. pipe is filed to appear drawn in as a husk, squared at the top and bottom as described under Filing, step 10, and tapped. See Tapping.

4. A ⅛-in. pipe for the space between the arms is cut and threaded at both ends. See Threading. It is filed slightly concave, and cut in on both sides at the top by file and drill for wire outlets as indicated in the drawing.

5. A rod is drawn out as described under Forging, steps 1, 2, and 3, *e* and *i*, and the hammering is continued to the lower end which is forged or filed to a force fit into the end of the ⅛-in. pipe. Its top is drawn to a point as directed under Forging, step 3, *c*, under which a neck is forged over the horn with a cross-peen hammer; it may also be filed in.

6. The two bars are laid out on paper, cut, and glued to the iron stock which is drilled and tapped. It is then cut as described under Cutting, Metals of Medium Thickness, steps 2 and 3, and filed as directed under Filing, steps 1, 2, 3, and 9. The lower bar is bent as indicated in the drawing, using the method in Figure 86.

7. The two lion figures are laid out, and cut and filed as described in the foregoing. They are modeled on both sides. See Filing, step 9.

8. The tails are made of wire bent by round-nose pliers.

9. Two rings are cut off tapped ¼-in. pipe and rounded on all edges. These are to lie under the drip cups.

10. Two disks are dished as explained under Raising, step 4, *a*, and drilled.

11. A ⅛-in. pipe nipple is filed to fit tight on the rod, and two tapped ¼-in. pipe rings are screwed on, one below for the shade rest, and the other above for the shade lock.

12. All pieces not black are fired. See Finishing, Antique Iron.

13. The parts to be soldered are filed bright on their contact points.

14. A nipple and lock nut are screwed from under the base into the ¼-in. pipe husk, and the washer is slipped over the

Fig. 225. Twin lights.

latter and soldered on. See Soft Soldering, step 5, Example 7. The lower arm is screwed to the ⅛-in. pipe, and both are screwed into the top of the ¼-in. pipe husk. The wires are now drawn up through the bottom. See Wiring, Example 3. Two are led out of the opening to the left and two to the right. The upper arm is screwed into place and the figures and tails are set between the lower and upper arms and held with clips. The wires are covered with damp paper, and the figures are soldered on as described under Soft Soldering, step

5, Example 7. The flame should be directed away from the wires. A pipe nipple is screwed into each arm, and the rings are screwed down over them. The wires are now brought over and up through the nipples one on each side of the figure. They are drawn tight, the disks are set over the nipples, and the candle sockets are screwed over them. To these the wires are attached. The upper stem is driven home.

15. The lamp is finished as directed under Finishing, Antique Iron, and the wiring is completed. See Wiring.

Plate 52.   Medieval French and Spanish Lamps

During the fourteenth century, in Spain and in France, the lily was one of the most familiar forms in decoration. Those in the lamps in Figure 226 were adapted from cathedral screens of that period, one from France and the other from Spain. Both countries produced excellent ironwork for many centuries.

Procedure

1. The base is made in the same manner as the one in Plate 45, steps 1 and 3. The disk is hammered at its edges and the feet are drawn narrower, however, as described under Forging, steps 1, 2, and 3, *b*.

2. A ¾-in. pipe is drawn in as explained under Forging, step 4, and it is cut into a lower ring. See Cutting, Pipe Cutting, and Cutting Tubing.

3. A ⅜-in. and a ½-in. length of pipe are made in the same manner except that they are longer and rounded below. See drawing.

4. A ⅜-in. pipe is drawn in as shown at *A*, Figure 227, and cut off. It is cut four ways by a hack saw, following lines as exactly as possible, as shown at *B*, Figure 227. The petals are cut out of paper and glued over each prong. The top is rough cut to shape by a hacksaw, and the petals

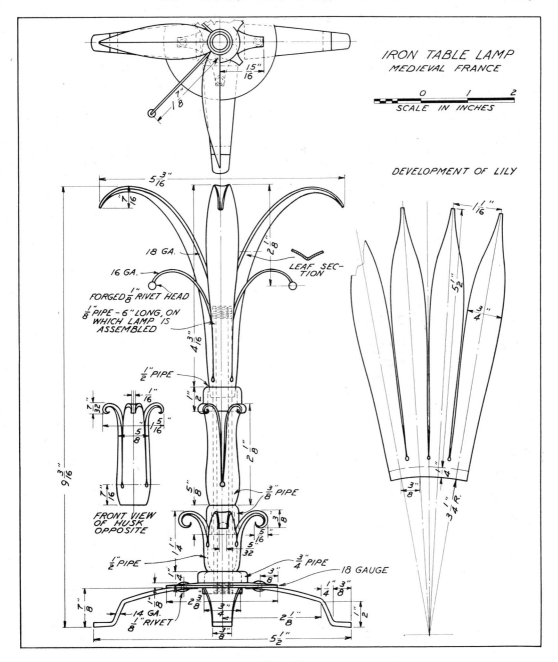

Plate 52.

are bent out as shown at *C*, Figure 227. They are filed to the line and tapered in thickness, as shown at *D*, Figure 227. The lower end of the saw cut is drilled. Each outer petal face is filed on each side of a center ridge, as shown at *E*, Figure 230.

Bill of Material

Pieces	Material	Use	Thickness	Width	Length
1	Sheet iron, box annealed, cold rolled, one pass	Base	18 Ga. (B&S)	2⅜	2⅜
1	Sheet iron, box annealed, cold rolled, one pass	Flower petals	18 Ga. (B&S)	3 5/16	5¾
4	Mild steel hoop	Feet	14 Ga.	¾	2⅝
4	Black iron rivets		⅛		⅜
1	Iron lock nut	Lower lock	⅛		
1	Black iron pipe	Lower ring	¾		¼
1	Black iron pipe	Lower husk	½		2¼
1	Black iron pipe	2nd Husk base	⅜		⅝
1	Black iron pipe	2nd Husk	⅜		2⅞
1	Black iron pipe	Top ball	½		½
1	Black iron pipe	Core	⅛		6
4	Black iron wire	Stamens	16 Ga.		3½
4	Black iron rivet heads only	Stamens ends	⅛		
1	Candle socket	Light			4
1	Socket cover — fiber	Light	1¼ O.D.		4
1	Cord				8 ft.
1	Plug				

5. Another husk is made of ½-in. pipe, and both are curled hot with a round-nose pliers as shown at *E*, Figure 227.

6. The crowning lily is drawn full size on paper, glued to metal and cut. See Cutting, Thin Metal. The end of each cut is drilled.

Fig. 226. Medieval French and Spanish lamps.

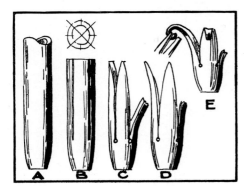

Fig. 227. Five steps in forming husk.

7. Each petal is bent down the center in a vise, by a hammer and wood block. See Folding, step 4. They are annealed and curved outward over a grooved block rounded to the exact side profile of the leaf by means of a second block cut in reverse and filed V from a line down its center. This is driven into the leaf after preliminary shaping by a hammer.

8. The rivet heads are rounded over the edge of an anvil, cut off with pliers, drilled, and soldered to the end of the wires. See Soft Soldering, step 5, Example 7.

9. All parts not black are fired. See Finishing, Antique Iron.

10. All parts to be soldered are filed bright on their contact points.

11. A ⅛-in. pipe is threaded at both ends. See Threading. A lock nut is screwed on its end, the base and stem parts are slipped over it, and the lily petals are trimmed, shaped over ⅛-in. pipe, and forced into the interval between the ring and the pipe, and soldered. See Soft Soldering, step 5, Example 7. The lower lock nut is screwed up tight.

12. The wires with rivet heads are forced into the interval between leaves and pipe and bent outward as shown.

13. The lamp is then finished as directed under Finishing, Antique Iron, and wired as explained under Wiring.

Fig. 228. A French Gothic lamp.

Plate 53. French Gothic Lamp

Little need be added to the material already given in the text for Plates 30, 31, 42, and 46, on the subject of feudal ironwork, of which the lamp in Figure 228 is an excellent though late example. It dates back to the fourteenth century.

Procedure

1. A base unit is made like the one in Plate 45, steps 1 to 3. Before the feet are bent, however, they are hammered along their edges to effect a chamfer, and a diamond pattern is chiseled into them. See Cutting, Metals of Medium Thickness, step 6.

2. A length of ⅜-in. pipe is cut, grooved for its entire circumference at the intervals shown in the drawing with a square file. The intervening sections are filed a trifle

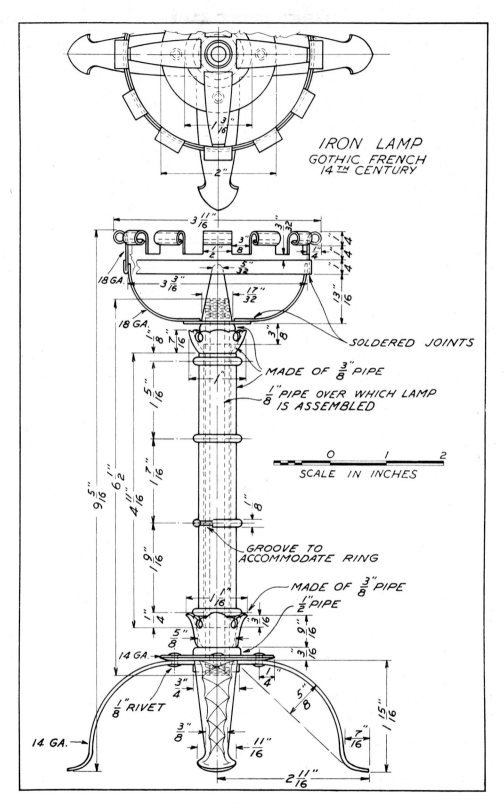

IRON LAMP
GOTHIC FRENCH
14TH CENTURY

SOLDERED JOINTS

MADE OF $\frac{3}{8}$" PIPE

$\frac{1}{8}$" PIPE OVER WHICH LAMP
IS ASSEMBLED

SCALE IN INCHES

GROOVE TO
ACCOMMODATE RING

MADE OF $\frac{3}{8}$" PIPE

$\frac{1}{2}$" PIPE

18 GA.

18 GA.

14 GA.

$\frac{1}{8}$" RIVET

14 GA.

Plate 53.

Bill of Material

Pieces	Material	Use	Thickness	Width	Length
4	Mild steel hoop	Feet	14 Ga.	¾	3½
1	Mild steel hoop	Base	14 Ga.	2	2
4	Black iron rivets		⅛		⅜
1	Iron lock nut	Lower lock	⅛		
1	Black iron pipe	Core	⅛		6½
1	Black iron pipe	Lower ring	½		3/16
1	Black iron pipe	Lower husk	⅜		⅝
1	Black iron pipe	Stem	⅜		4 11/16
1	Black iron pipe	Upper husk	⅜		½
1	Black iron pipe	Upper ball	⅜		⅜
4	Black iron wire	Stem rings	12 Ga. (B&S)		2⅜
1	Sheet iron, box annealed, cold rolled, one pass	Crown base	18 Ga. (B&S)	1 3/16	1 3/16
4	Sheet iron, box annealed, cold rolled, one pass	Crown arms	18 Ga. (B&S)	17/32	2
1	Sheet iron, box annealed, cold rolled, one pass	Crown	18 Ga. (B&S)	1½	10¼
1	Candle socket	Light			4
1	Socket cover — fiber	Light	1¼ O.D.		4
1	Cord				8 ft.
1	Plug				

concave to simulate wear. It is heated red and cooled.

3. A wire is wound fully four times around a ⅝-in. rod and cut at right angles. The resulting four rings are aligned and snapped into the pipe grooves and soldered at their joints. See Soft Soldering, step 5, Example 7.

4. Two rings of the heights shown are made of ⅜- and ½-in. pipe, first drawn in as described under Forging, step 4, and cut. See Cutting, Pipe Cutting, and Cutting Tubing. The ⅜-in. pipe is filed round on its second corner.

5. A disk and four arms are cut. The disk is drilled to fit a ⅛-in. pipe, and the

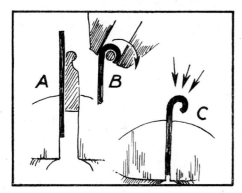

Fig. 229. Making the dentils.

arms are bent into a hardwood form with a ball-peen hammer. See Forming of Iron, step 1, d. The arms are soldered to the disk. See Soft Soldering, step 5, Example 5.

6. The notched crown is made as follows: (a) The notches are laid out on a sheet of iron stock, cut with a heavy shears to depth, and removed with a narrow cold chisel. See Cutting, Metals of Medium Thickness, step 6.

b) The piece is carefully straightened on an anvil.

c) The hem is bent in a vise by a hammer.

d) The tip of each dentil is rolled over a form as directed under Forming of Iron, step 1, and as shown at A, Figure 229. It is closed by rolling over a rod with heavy pliers, as shown at B, Figure 229, or it is hammered in a vise, as shown at C, Figure 229. The last process requires keen judgment in the placement and weight of hammer blows. The part is heated red to blacken it. Last, it is turned into a ring over pipe as explained in Bending, step 4.

7. The crown is filed at the points of contact with its arms and soldered. See Soft Soldering, step 5, Example 6.

8. The two short husks are made as

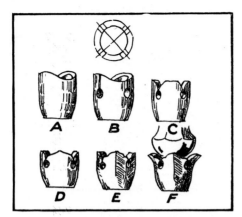

Fig. 230. Six steps in making short husks.

follows: (*a*) A ½-in. pipe is drawn in at the end. See Forging, step 4; *A*, Figure 230.

b) Four holes are drilled as indicated in the drawing, and as shown at *B*, Figure 230. The pipe is then cut off to required length.

c) Notches are filed over each hole with a square file, as shown at *C*, Figure 230.

d) The leaf design is filed over each petal, as shown at *D*, Figure 230.

e) The face of each leaf is filed, as shown at *E*, Figure 230.

f) The top is flared with a ball-peen hammer, as shown at *F*, Figure 230.

9. All parts not black are heated red hot.

10. A ⅛-in. pipe is threaded at both ends. See Threading.

11. With a lock nut at the bottom, the base, ring, lower husk, stem, upper husk, upper ring, and crown are slipped over the pipe and are locked by the fixture.

12. The lamp is finished. See Finishing, Antique Iron.

13. It is wired. See Wiring.

Plate 54. A Georgian Scale

This project will serve as a practical desk, kitchen, or laboratory necessity.

Procedure

1. The base is laid out and cut. See Cutting, Thin Metal.

2. It is shaped by a hammer as described under Low Raising, step 4, *a*, and lightly planished. See Planishing, steps 1 and 2, *a*.

3. The rivet heads for the feet are cut and soldered. See Soft Soldering, step 5, Example 4.

Fig. 231. A Georgian scale.

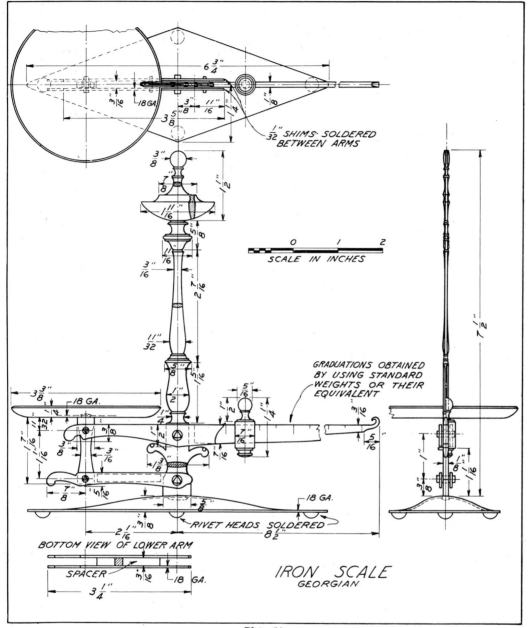

Plate 54.

4. The stem design is laid out on paper, cut out, glued to the iron stock and cut. See Cutting, steps 2, 3, and 4. It is filed as explained under Filing, steps 1, 2, and 3, and both sides are modeled as directed under Filing, step 9.

5. The arms are cut in the same manner and filed. The end of the long arm is heated red and curled. See Forging, step 9.

6. A disk is cut, filed, and dished. See Raising, steps 4, a and 6, a.

7. The base, disk, stem, and arms are

Bill of Material

Pieces	Material	Use	Thickness	Width	Length
1	Sheet iron, box annealed, cold rolled, one pass	Base	18 Ga. (B&S)	2½	6¾
1	Sheet iron, box annealed, cold rolled, one pass	Plate	18 Ga. (B&S)	3½	3½
2	Sheet iron, box annealed, cold rolled, one pass	Lower arms	18 Ga. (B&S)	⅜	3¼
2	Sheet iron, box annealed, cold rolled, one pass	Upper arms	18 Ga. (B&S)	½	3⅝
1	Mild steel band	Post	12 Ga.	1 11/16	7 11/16
1	Mild steel band	Arm	12 Ga.	7/16	8⅛
1	Mild steel band	Plate stem	12 Ga.	⅜	1 9/16
1	Mild steel band	Spacer	3/16	3/16	1⅜
4	Black iron rivets	Feet	3/16	Heads only	
2	Black iron rivets	Bearings	3/16		7/16
2	Black iron rivets	Bearings	⅛		7/16
2	Black iron wire	Stops	14 Ga.		7/16
1	Mild steel bar — round	Weight	½D.		1¼

drilled, accuracy being required. For example, the pair of upper arm pieces are drilled while clamped together. Next, one hole in the lower arms is drilled while held in like manner. Last, all four arms are clamped together, a rivet holding them in line while the second holes are drilled into the lower arms through those in the upper. See Drilling.

8. Into both the main stem and the disk stem holes four arm bearing pins are set. These are held underneath in a vise while the upper end extending about 3/16 in. is filed to a triangular section, the top edge of which is to bear the balancing arms. (Notice, however, that the point at the end of the upper arm faces down.) The end just filed, remaining round in section within the stem, is set with a center punch so that it cannot move. The reverse side is filed in the same manner being held within copper vise jaws.

9. A spacing bar is cut for the lower arms, and all parts are fired. Contact surfaces are filed bright.

10. The arms are soldered while being held on temporary rods through the bearing holes, the rods resting on two blocks of equal height, one on each side, and held immovable by brads. The center of the assembly is then clamped tightly and flux and solder are applied and melted in. See Soft Soldering, steps 5 and 7.

11. The main and disk stems are shouldered, as shown at *A*, Figure 196, and riveted.

12. The arms are bent open and back into position over the bearings.

13. A weight is slotted by a saw to fit over the arm, which, when set to its inside limit, balances the scale. If it does not balance, metal is removed or added to it, as for instance a knob as shown. The weight is fired. See Finishing, Antique Iron.

14. Graduations are scribed and lightly stamped in by a chisel. They may not be filed or cut. The type of graduations depends upon the use of the scale. Small envelopes, containing salt or some similar commodity, weighed at a drug or grocery store, serve as bases for these marks.

15. An additional weight may be hung at the end of the arm.

16. The scale is finished. See Finishing, Antique Iron.

Plate 55.   Iron Flower Brackets

Late in the seventeenth century iron was used in the production of beautiful grilles, gates, and lantern brackets. Of the latter, the project in Figure 232 is an outstanding French example.

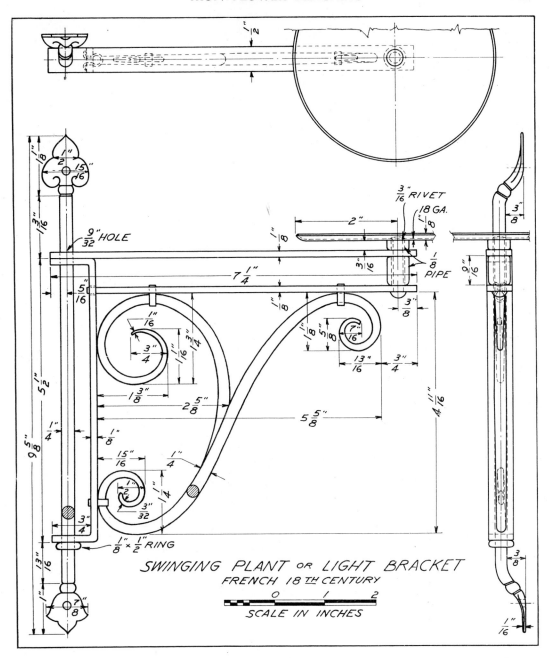

SWINGING PLANT or LIGHT BRACKET
FRENCH 18TH CENTURY

SCALE IN INCHES

Plate 55.

Procedure

1. Three bars are laid out, cut by a saw, and filed. See Filing, steps 1 and 2. They are drilled as described under Drilling, and one of them is shouldered for riveting. An-

other is bent at right angles at both ends by a vise and hammer.

2. The stock for the scrolls is heated red and drawn to a round taper. See Forging, steps 1, 2, and 3, d and i. The scrolls are

Bill of Material

Pieces	Material	Use	Thickness	Width	Length
1	Mild steel band	Upper arm	12 Ga.	½	7¼
1	Mild steel band	2nd arm	12 Ga.	½	6⅝
1	Mild steel band	Back frame	12 Ga.	½	7
1	Mild steel bar — round	Back	¼D.	¼	9½ (Forged to 9⅞)
1	Mild steel bar — round	Scroll	¼D.	¼	9 (Forged to 12⅞)
1	Mild steel bar — round	Inside scroll	¼D.	¼	6¼ (Forged to 8¼)
1	Sheet iron, box annealed, cold rolled, one pass	Plate	18 Ga. (B&S)	4	4
3	Sheet iron, box annealed, cold rolled, one pass	Scroll eyelets	18 Ga. (B&S)	⅛	1¼
1	Black iron pipe	Collar	⅛		3/16
1	Black iron pipe	Collar	⅛		9/16
1	Black iron rivet	Plate fastening	3/16		1¼
1	Black iron wire	Bearing ring	12 Ga.		1 3/16

bent as directed under Forging, step 8 or 9. The joining edges are fitted, filed bright, and soldered. See Soft Soldering, step 5, Example 6.

3. The pan is cut as described under Cutting, Thin Metal, shaped as directed under Low Raising, step 6, and drilled.

4. Two ⅛-in. pipe collars are made as follows: Their ends are drawn in as de-scribed under Forging, step 4, cut off as explained under Cutting, Pipe Cutting, and Cutting Tubing, and filed round on their cut edges.

5. The back rod is cut by a saw and flared at the top end. See Forging, step 3, *a*. It is filed to the pattern, and bent in a vise by a hammer to the angle shown in the drawing.

Fig. 232. An iron flower bracket.

6. All pieces not black are fired. See Finishing, Antique Iron.

7. The shouldered second upper bar is riveted to the backpiece. See Riveting.

8. The scroll is fastened to these by means of ⅛-in. bands, pinched tight in a vise over each curl opposite the holes, inserted, and bent over, as shown at *B*, Figure 196.

9. The contact surfaces of the top parallel bar and the angle are brightly filed, and the disk and collars are assembled by riveting.

10. The back bar is inserted, heated red hot below, forged, as described under Forging, step 3, *a*, and filed. See Filing, steps, 1, 2, and 3. It is bent in a vise by a hammer as was the other end. Holes are drilled into each leaf.

11. The top parallel bar is soldered at its point of bearing on the back bar. See Soft Soldering, step 5, Example 7.

12. The back bar is grooved by a file at the position of the lower ring. A wire is bent around a rod, cut, bent open, and pinched over the groove.

13. The bracket is finished. See Finishing, Antique Iron.

Plate 56. Cast Sundial

The next three plates are concerned with the casting and working of cast metal. Sundials, like the one shown in Figure 233, are ancient instruments, used at the present

Fig. 233. A cast sundial.

time mainly as garden ornaments. The shell motif comes to us from the Italian and Spanish Renaissance.

Procedure

1. A board provided with a rod set at the degree of latitude on which the observer stands (40 deg. at the 40th latitude) is hung or set, depending upon its ultimate position, with a compass and level, so that the sun may strike it all day. Marks are then made hourly on an arc centering at the foot of the rod, and lines are drawn through them radiating from the center.

2. The design including the numerals and lettering, built around the above graduations, is laid out on basswood board in reverse. These are carved by means of a sharp ⅛-in. parting chisel or gouge. The segments are rounded slightly into the edge and radiating lines.

3. The thickness of piece *B*, Figure 149, is next cut out of ¼-in. wood, nailed to piece *A*, and planed down to ⅛- or 3/16-in. thickness. It is then carved as shown at *C*, for adequate venting. The vents need be no more than hairlines, but they must lead upward. The pouring hole, *D*, is made large to provide for shrinkage and for the pressure at the extremities of the mold.

4. A cover piece is clamped to the piece just made, and lead, scrap pewter, type metal, solder, or a mixture of these ·is poured in at a temperature not much over its melting point.

5. After the casting is cool and the top and sideboards are removed, it is taken out, the mold is closed for the next casting, and the fins, vents, and sprue are removed from the cast.

6. It is then filed, see Filing, steps 1, 2, 3, and 5, and scraped, and the edges and design are burnished. See Finishing and Polishing. It is chased if necessary. See Chasing. The figures and lettering may be chased rather than carved.

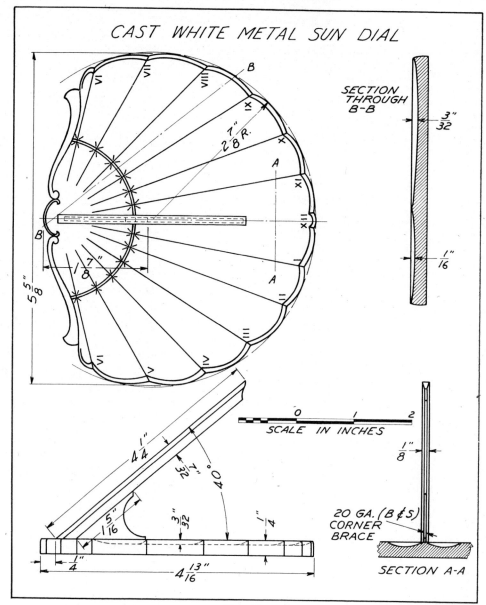

Plate 56.

Bill of Material

Pieces	Material	Use	Thickness	Width	Length
1	Brass bar — half hard	Stile	1/16	⅛	4¼
1	Brass bar — half hard	Stile rib	1/16	5/32	4 1/16
1	Brass sheet	Bracket	20 Ga. (B&S)	11/16	1¼
1	White metal, lead or other low-fusing alloy	Dial	About 2½-lb. casting		

7. The arm may be made of rod or casting, and soldered into the base, see Soft Solder-steps 1 to 4, and 5, Example 6, the flame being directed from above.

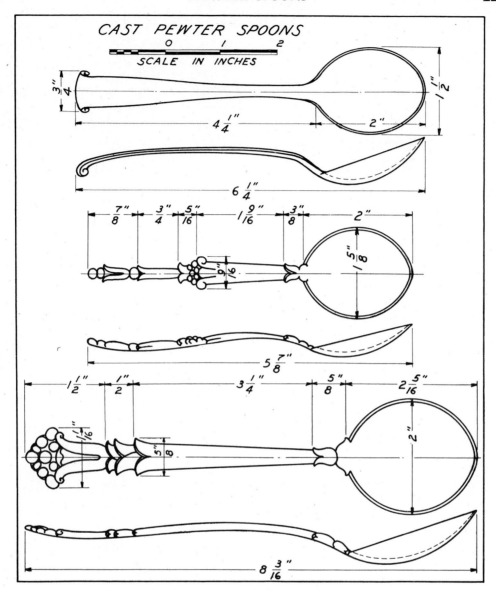

Plate 57.

Bill of Material

The three spoons are made of britannia metal scrap. A 2¾-oz. casting is used for the first; a 2¼-oz. casting for the second; and a 4¼-oz. casting for the third.

8. The lead or tin alloys may be treated in the same manner as pewter. See Finishing, Polishing, and Preserving Metals, step 1.

9. It is hung or set by means of screws.

Plate 57. Pewter Spoons

The spoons shown in Figure 234 are modern Scandinavian and classic in design, and are meant to provide experience in casting, carving, and chasing, burnishing, or planishing. The simple spoon should be made first.

Procedure

1. The design of a spoon is transferred

Fig. 234. Pewter spoons.

to a piece of ¼-in. basswood, or other non-resinous wood. It is cut out by a coping saw, filed to the line, and nailed to a back-board.

2. This is planed until the upper board is about 3/32 in. thick. The design at the top of the spoon may be carved into the lower board. The neck of the spoon should be carved deeper so that the casting may have adequate stiffness at that point.

3. The vents are carved into the side of the spoon mold leading up on each side, as shown at *B*, in the lower illustration, Figure 149. This is for the purpose of releasing gases imprisoned inside. A pouring gate is cut at the bowl end, as shown in Figure 149 and 234.

4. A flat cover piece is clamped over the above, and metal just over the temperature of fluidity is poured in.

5. The cooled metal is lifted out, trimmed of its fins and gate, and filed

smooth. See Filing, steps 1, 2, 3, and 5. Finally it is modeled, the lower handle being rounded and the upper oval.

6. Castings of the second and third spoons shown in the drawing are at this point fastened to a board with wood blocks and carved in detail. Wood-carving chisels are very satisfactory.

7. If the design requires further enrichment, the detail is chased. See Chasing, *D*, Figure 100. The spoon bowl is filed, planished, and formed. See Planishing and Low Raising, step 4.

8. The edges and large surfaces are burnished. See Finishing and Polishing.

9. The spoon is finished. See Finishing and Polishing.

Plate 58. Bronze Miniatures

The availability of bronze to ancient races made it one of their best mediums of expression. Many beautiful examples of their work are still extant, a coating of beautiful green patinas having served as protection against deep corrosion. The bronze urns in Figure 235 are of Grecian origin, while the center ornament dates from the Renaissance.

Procedure

1. The wood patterns are made of northern white pine, cherry, or mahogany, and if they are small and of fine detail, they may be made of walnut which is very firm and easy to carve. Core boxes are made to allow a ⅛-in. wall throughout. The patterns are sent to a foundry and cast in 85-5-5-5 alloy. Sandblasted castings are preferred.

2. On their return, fins and parting marks are filed smooth.

3. The flat surfaces are filed straight and square by a 6-in. handsmooth file. See Filing, steps 1, 2, 7, and 8.

4. The hole in the top is reamed or filed to a true center. The bottom is accurately center punched.

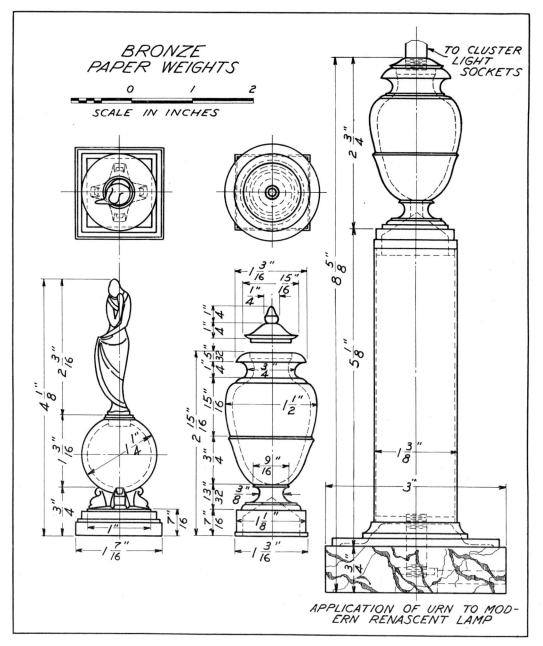

BRONZE
PAPER WEIGHTS

SCALE IN INCHES

TO CLUSTER
LIGHT
SOCKETS

APPLICATION OF URN TO MOD-
ERN RENASCENT LAMP

Plate 58.

Bill of Material

Both the paperweight and the urn are made of bronze 85–5–5–5 alloy 8-oz. castings

5. The work then is mounted in a revolving device. In the absence of an engine lathe, a bench or hand drill, mounted horizontally in a vise, a bench grinder, or a motor provided with tapered center fit into the end of the casting, is quite satisfactory. A dead center is secured against

the other end of the casting. For this, a center punch clamped to an angle block will do. The metal is turned at 300 revolutions per minute.

6. Lathe tools may not be used in this type of work. Lamp manufacturers scrape their castings by tools ground from files. This is followed by filing, grinding, and buffing. For this project, however, rough filing by half-round and round files, fol-

lowed by finishing with fine mill and round files, emery cloth, and tripoli, all while in the lathe, is recommended. See Finishing and Polishing. Files must be kept moving across the revolving bronze and frequently cleaned. The contour of the original design must be carefully adhered to for satisfactory results.

7. The bronze is finished. See Finishing, Polishing, and Preserving.

Fig. 235. Bronze miniatures.

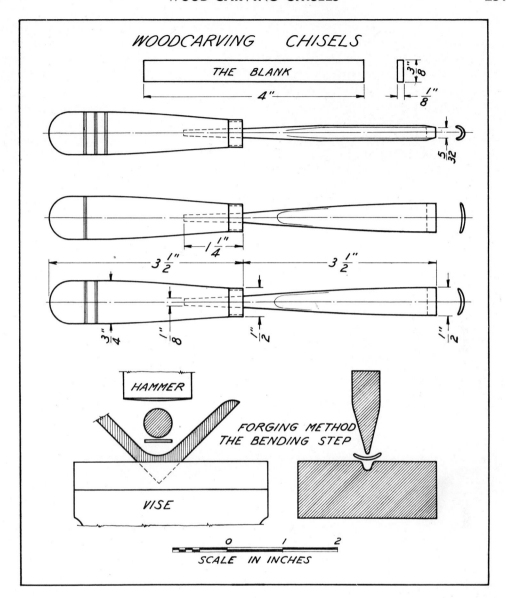

Plate 59.

Bill of Material

The chisels are made of ⅛ by ⅜ by 4-in. tool steel of a type recommended by the supply source.

Plate 59. Wood-Carving Chisels

Chisels may be divided into three general classes: the lining tool, the flat chisel for backgrounds, and the gouge for model-ing. Each has, of course, a wide range of widths. See Figure 236. The one to be made for this project is a flat chisel or a gouge, the forging of which may be simplified by the use of a jig, as shown in Figure 96. It can also be made by the use of a miniature drop forge built as a group project.

Procedure

1. Tool steel recommended by the manufacturer for chisels is purchased.

2. The piece of steel in convenient length is heated bright red, placed over an anvil, and drawn out. See Forging, steps 1, 2, and 3, f. Tool steel may not be hammered or bent below red heat. It is heated as often as necessary, but it is better not to heat it too often.

3. The blank is forged by following the directions under Forging, step 9, and Figure 96.

4. The chisel is now annealed as described under Annealing, step 2, aligned, and filed to shape. See Filing, steps 6 and 8. The inside is filed smooth. A bevel is ground on its end, and a tang is forged or filed. A standard carving chisel may be used as a model.

5. The tool is hardened and tempered.

6. It is then polished, handled, and sharpened.

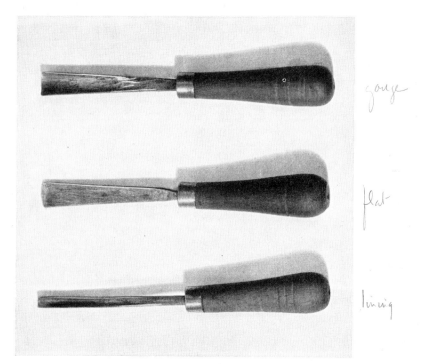

gouge

flat

lining

Fig. 236. Wood-carving chisels.

INDEX

*As mentioned in the introduction, the letters A, B, and C denote the level of experience necessary for successful execution.